Electric Circuit Theory

Electric Circuit Theory

J. M. Ivison
Department of Electronic and Electrical Engineering,
Loughborough University of Technology

VNR (UK) **Van Nostrand Reinhold (UK) Co. Ltd.**

Reprinted 1978, 1980, 1981, 1983, 1984

Published by Van Nostrand Reinhold (UK) Co. Ltd.
Molly Millars Lane, Wokingham, Berkshire, England

Library of Congress Cataloging in Publication Data

Ivison, J M
Electric circuit theory.

Includes index.
1. Electric circuits. I. Title

TK 454.188 621.319'S 76-45659
ISBN 0-442-30201-0
ISBN 0-442-30202-9 pbk.

Filmset in Ireland by Doyle Photosetting Ltd., Tullamore
Printed and bound in Hong Kong

Preface

This book is intended for use at the level of the first year of a degree course, or equivalent, in Electrical or Electronic Engineering; it should also find a place in the teaching of the electrical content of degree courses in other branches of engineering and in Higher National Diploma and Certificate Courses.

The material is suitable for inclusion in a 24-hour lecture course supported by an equal amount of tutorial instruction and a programme of laboratory work. Essential mathematics is covered only briefly, since it is usual for a mathematics course at an appropriate level to form part of the curriculum.

Normally students will read the relevant section of the text before the lecture which can be devoted to an explanation of the more difficult aspects, applications and practical demonstrations. The concise nature of this book should enable students to assimilate essential facts very rapidly.

Because of the significant variation in the material covered at school in A' level Physics and Mathematics or in ONC and OND courses, Chapters 1 and 2 aim to provide a common base for all students; this having been established, progress can be rapid.

A selection of worked examples and problems is provided; a number of these are drawn from fields such as control systems, transistor and integrated circuit electronics, electrical power and machines, which the student will normally meet later in his course. These applications can be introduced to the student before he attempts the associated problems and in many cases this approach encourages him to seek further knowledge of the topics.

† Dagger symbols in the margin are used to indicate some of the more important equations and relationships, so that the student can refer to them quickly.

I am grateful to Loughborough University of Technology for permission to use questions from past examination papers.

I wish to thank my wife, colleagues and former students who have helped, directly and indirectly, with this book and Mrs. J. M. Brown for typing the student notes that formed the basis of the manuscript.

Contents

CHAPTER ONE

Circuit Elements and Sources

1.1 INTRODUCTION

Electrical engineers are in general concerned with the design and production of systems for generating and distributing electrical signals, either directly as energy or in the form of information. To design the system it is necessary to understand the performance and limitations of the circuit elements that constitute the system and to describe them in terms of mathematical models. A sound knowledge of the appropriate analytical techniques is required so that the performance of the system can be predicted.

In general, we will be concerned with the performance of a circuit when a stimulus (or excitation, or input) is applied to it, resulting in an effect (or response or output) at some other point in the circuit. To familiarise students with the terminology and to give a good understanding of techniques, early sections of this book are concerned with circuits excited by direct current (d.c.) sources such as batteries or d.c. power supply units.

1.2 LINEAR CIRCUITS

Figure 1.1 shows a general electrical network, circuit or system having two terminals A and B.

Suppose a battery is connected between A and B and the current flowing into the network at A is measured. If the battery voltage is varied, the current will also vary and, if the resulting voltage/current characteristic is a straight line, as shown in figure 1.2, the circuit is said to be linear. This book deals almost exclusively with linear circuits.

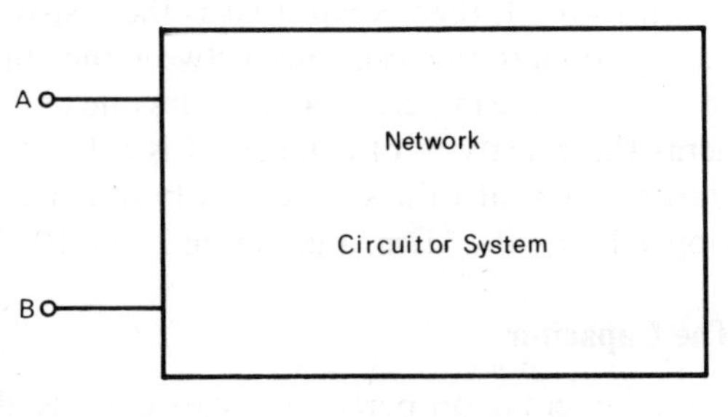

Fig. 1.1

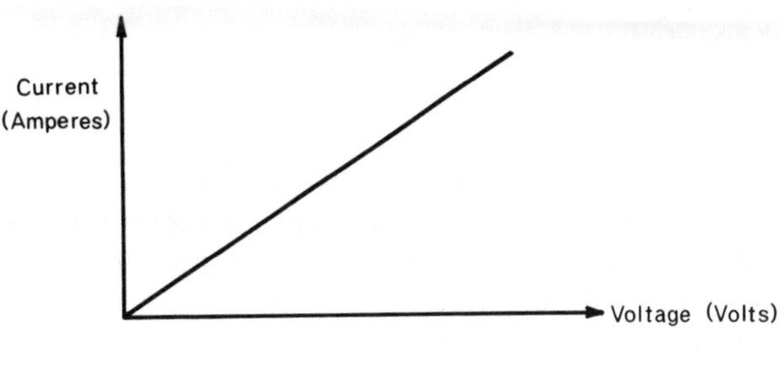

Fig. 1.2

The linear property of the circuit can be expressed in another way: *If an input $x_1(t)$ produces a response $y_1(t)$ and an input $x_2(t)$ produces a response $y_2(t)$; then an input $[x_1(t)+x_2(t)]$ produces a response $[y_1(t)+y_2(t)]$*. This is known as the PRINCIPLE OF SUPERPOSITION and a linear circuit is defined as one which obeys this principle.

In practice it may be found that a system is linear over only a limited range of input signal amplitudes, but at this stage ideal circuit elements, linear over the whole working range, will be considered.

1.3 SIGN CONVENTION FOR VOLTAGE AND CURRENT

If the battery connected to the circuit of figure 1.1 has a terminal voltage V and has its positive and negative terminals connected to A and B respectively, the convention is to represent the polarity of the battery by means of an arrow *with the arrowhead pointing towards the positive terminal* as shown in figure 1.3a.

It should be noted that there are two methods of representing the same current, as shown in figure 1.3b, or the same voltage as shown in figure 1.3c.

When the battery is connected to the network there is

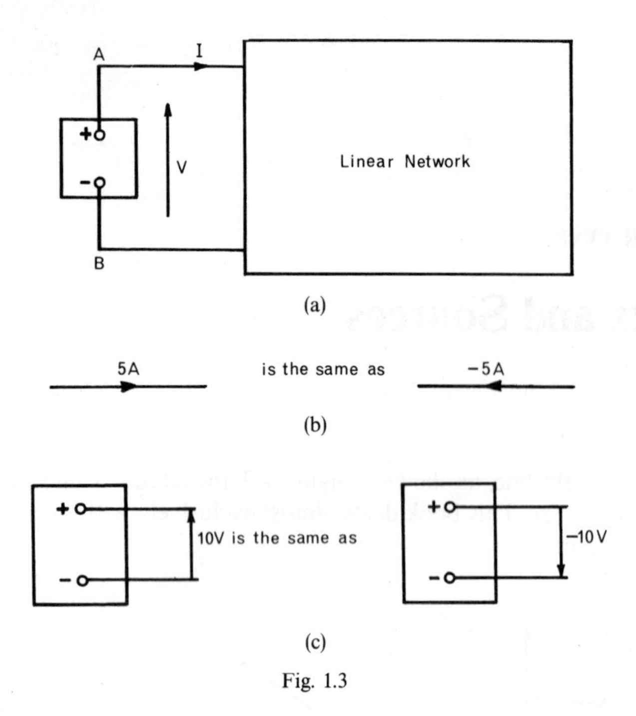

Fig. 1.3

a transfer of energy from the battery to the network; this is characterized by a flow of current I amperes into the network at A. Current is considered as a transfer of positive charge and has therefore a direction. The convention adopted is that *current flows into the network from the positive terminal of the battery, the arrowhead indicating the direction of flow*. A d.c. ammeter to measure the current and a d.c. voltmeter to measure the battery voltage can be connected as shown in figure 1.4.

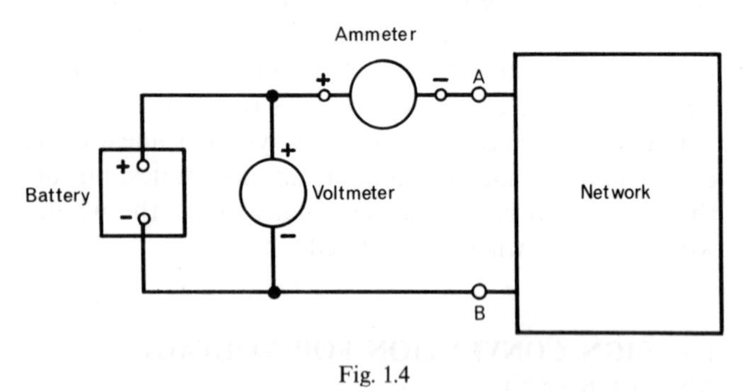

Fig. 1.4

1.4 THE DEFINITION OF CURRENT AND VOLTAGE

† Current in AMPERES is defined by the equation $I = \mathrm{d}Q/\mathrm{d}t$ where Q is the charge in COULOMBS (one coulomb is the charge of 6.2×10^{18} electrons) and t is in SECONDS. Thus a current of one ampere flows when the rate of transfer of charge is one coulomb per second.

The voltage of the battery is numerically equal to the energy required to transfer unit charge. The defining † equation for voltage, in VOLTS, is $V = \mathrm{d}W/\mathrm{d}Q$ where W is the energy in JOULES.

1.5 CIRCUIT ELEMENTS

The study of electric circuit theory is introduced by considering the voltage/current relationships of three basic circuit elements, the resistor, the capacitor and the inductor. It should be noted that we are in effect dealing with the mathematical models of idealized circuit elements, because, in practice, circuit components may consist of more than one element: for example a resistor may have inductance as well as resistance. At this stage however, attention will be focussed on ideal circuit elements.

(i) The Resistor

The fundamental property of a resistor is that it dissipates, but does not store, energy.

Figure 1.5 shows a resistor R through which a current I flows and across which there is a voltage, or potential difference, V.

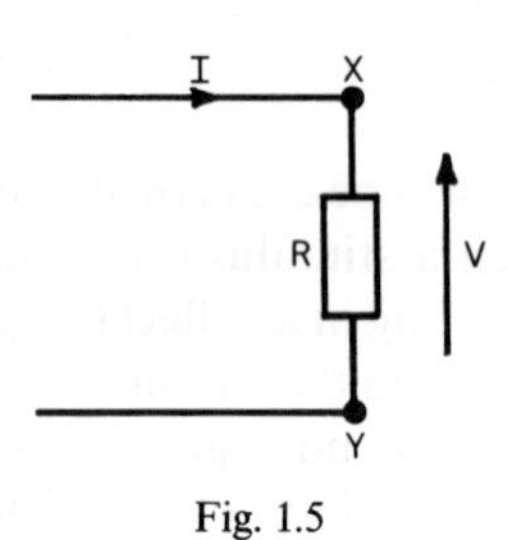

Fig. 1.5

The relationship between the current and the voltage † is $V = IR$.

If V is measured in VOLTS (V) and I in AMPERES (A), then R, the resistance of the resistor, is in OHMS (Ω). The † equation can be rearranged in the form $I = V/R = VG$ where $G(=1/R)$ is known as the *conductance* of the circuit element, measured in SIEMENS (S).

The resistance of a conductor of uniform cross section is given by $R = \rho l/a$ where l is its length in metres, a its cross sectional area in square metres and ρ is the *resistivity* in OHM METRES (Ωm). From the expression it may be seen that if $l = a = 1$, then $R = \rho$; that is the resistivity is numerically equal to the resistance between the opposite faces of a cube of the material having sides one unit long; in general the resistivity of a material is a function of temperature. Typical values of resistivity of conductors are; copper 1.56×10^{-8} Ωm, aluminium 2.45×10^{-8} Ωm.

(ii) The Capacitor

The fundamental property of a capacitor is that it stores energy when there is a potential difference, or voltage, between its terminals. It does not dissipate energy.

Figure 1.6 shows a capacitor C into which a current I flows and across which there is a voltage V.

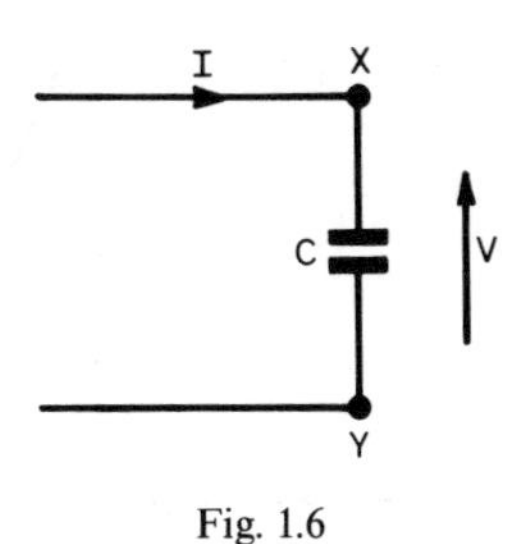

Fig. 1.6

The relationship between the current and the voltage is

† $$V=\frac{1}{C}\int_{-\infty}^{t} I\mathrm{d}t$$

If V, I and t are measured in volts, amperes and seconds respectively, the capacitance of the capacitor is in FARADS (F).

† The equation can be written in the form $I=C\mathrm{d}V/\mathrm{d}t$ and from this it is apparent that there is no current flowing through the capacitor if the voltage across it remains constant, *the capacitor therefore behaves as an open circuit to d.c.*

(iii) The Inductor

The fundamental property of an inductor is that it stores energy when current flows through it, but does not dissipate energy.

Figure 1.7 shows an inductor L into which a current I flows and across which there is a voltage V.

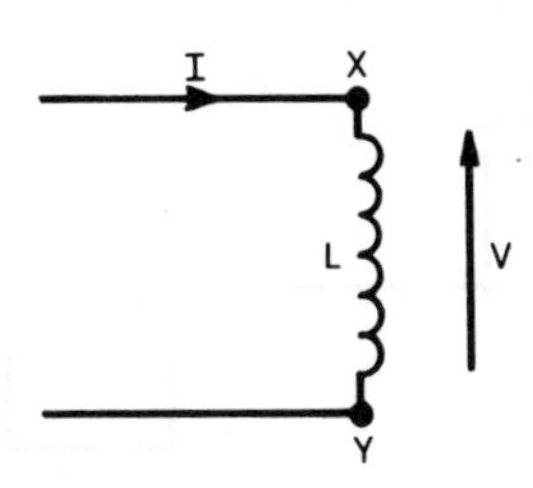

Fig. 1.7

The relationship between the current and the voltage is $V=L\mathrm{d}I/\mathrm{d}t$.

If V, I and t are measured in volts, amperes and seconds respectively, the inductance of the inductor is in HENRIES (H).

The defining equation can be written in the form

† $$I=\frac{1}{L}\int_{-\infty}^{t} V\mathrm{d}t$$

Since $V=L\mathrm{d}I/\mathrm{d}t$, there is no voltage across the inductor if the current through it remains constant; *the inductor therefore acts as a short circuit to d.c.*

For a linear inductor the inductance is independent of the current flowing.

It should be noted that, for all three circuit elements, the current enters the element at terminal X, which is therefore at a higher potential than terminal Y, the arrow associated with the voltage V accordingly points towards X.

(iv) Mutual Inductance

Mutual inductance differs from resistance, capacitance and inductance in that it is not a fundamental property of a two-terminal circuit element. However, since the operation of components such as transformers can be analyzed in terms of mutual inductance, it is introduced at the same time as the three basic circuit elements.

When two coils are placed near to each other so that the magnetic flux established by a changing current in one coil, known as the primary, induces a voltage in a second coil, known as the secondary, *mutual inductance* exists between the coils. Circuits with mutual inductance are said to be *inductively coupled.*

Figure 1.8 shows two coils L_1 and L_2 coupled by mutual inductance M. The current flowing in the primary coil L_1 is I_1 and the voltage induced in the secondary coil L_2 is V_2; the relationship between the induced secondary voltage and the primary current is

† $$V_2=M\frac{\mathrm{d}I_1}{\mathrm{d}t}$$

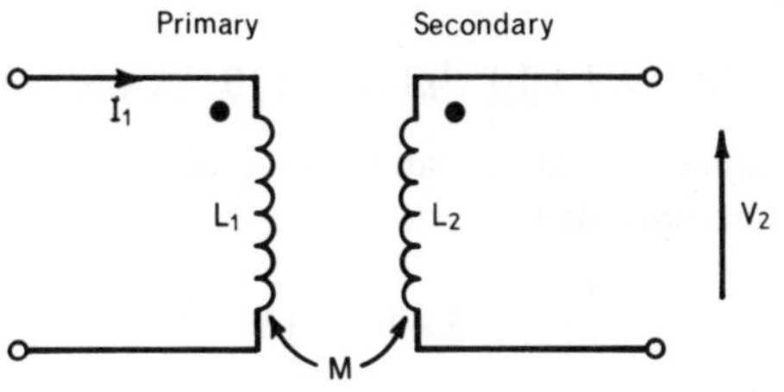

Fig. 1.8

If V_2, I_1 and t are measured in volts, amperes and seconds respectively, the mutual inductance is in HENRIES. The value of M depends on the proximity, shape and number of turns of both coils; it may also be considered positive or negative according to the relative direction of the windings of the coils. The convention adopted is that dots are placed on one end of each winding, as shown in figure 1.8, so that if a current enters at a dot in one coil, the voltage induced in the second coil will be positive at the dot on the second coil. Reversing the assumed direction of I_1 or V_2 or changing the position of one of the dots will change the sign of M.

Example

A current with the waveform shown in figure 1.9a flows through a circuit comprising a 5000 Ω resistor, a 2 μF capacitor and a 2 H inductor connected in series. Determine the voltage waveform across each of the three circuit elements.

Solution

The voltage across the resistor is given by $V=IR$ and has therefore the same form as the current; if the resistor has a resistance of 5000 Ω the maximum value of the voltage is

$$V_{R(\max)}=(20\times 10^{-3}\times 5000)=100\ \text{V}$$

as shown in figure 1.9b.

The voltage across the capacitor is given by

$$V_C=\frac{1}{C}\int_{-\infty}^{t} I\mathrm{d}t=\frac{1}{C}\int_{-\infty}^{0} I\mathrm{d}t+\frac{1}{C}\int_{0}^{t} I\mathrm{d}t$$

and if we assume that the capacitor is initially uncharged then

$$\frac{1}{C}\int_{-\infty}^{0} I\mathrm{d}t=0$$

and we can write

$$V_C=\frac{1}{C}\int_{0}^{t} I\mathrm{d}t$$

Now integration of current with respect to time is equivalent to evaluating the area enclosed by the current/time characteristic of figure 1.9a. If we take one square to represent

$$(5\times 10^{-3}\times 1\times 10^{-3})As=5\times 10^{-6}\ \text{Coulomb.}$$

and as capacitor has a capacitance of 2×10^{-6} F, one square corresponds to

$$\left(\frac{1}{2\times 10^{-6}}\times 5\times 10^{-6}\right)\text{V}=2.5\ \text{V}.$$

Using this scale factor and performing the graphical integration the capacitor voltage/time characteristic of figure 1.9c is obtained.

The form of this curve can also be obtained by considering the shape of the current/time characteristic; between $t=2$ ms and $t=4$ ms the current has the form $I=\mathrm{k}t$, therefore $\int I\mathrm{d}t$ has the form $\mathrm{k}t^2/2$ giving the square law characteristic shown in figure 1.9c for this time interval.

From $t=4$ ms to $t=8$ ms the current is constant, that is $I=\mathrm{B}$ where B is a constant, hence $\int I\mathrm{d}t=\mathrm{B}t$ and the capacitor voltage increases linearly with time during this time interval.

During the interval $t=8$ ms to $t=10$ ms the current has the form $I=(\mathrm{E}-\mathrm{D}t)$ where E and D are constants hence the capacitor voltage has the form $(\mathrm{E}t-\mathrm{D}t^2/2)$.

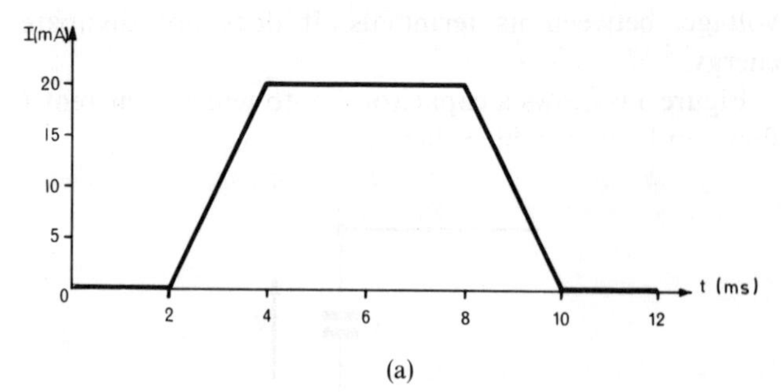

(a)

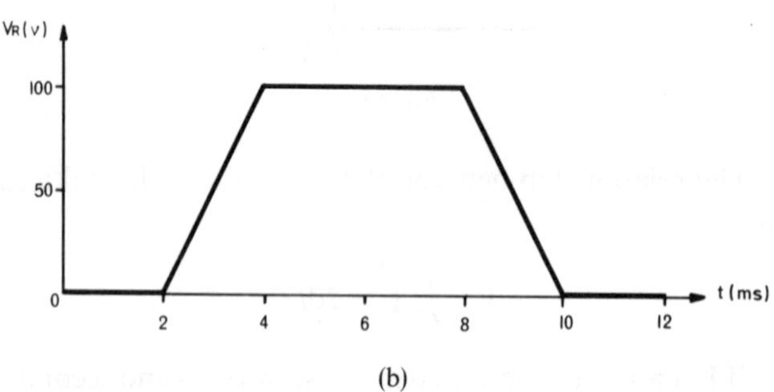

(b)

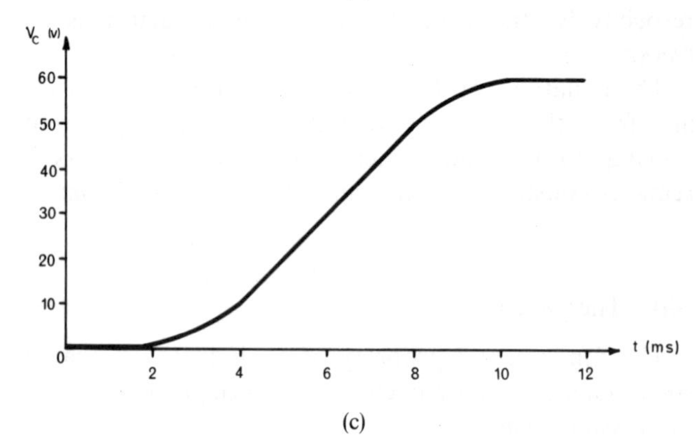

(c)

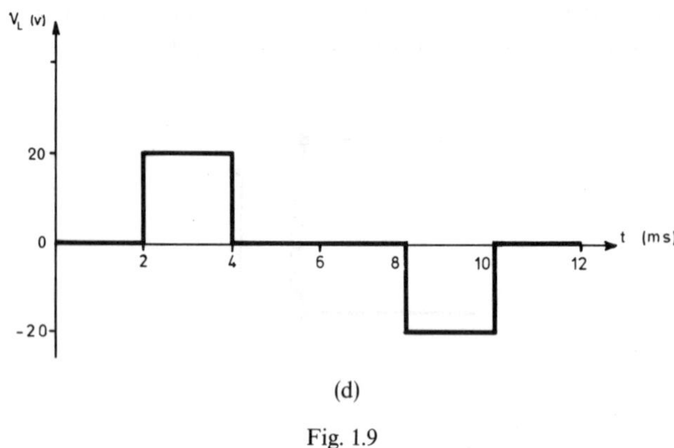

(d)

Fig. 1.9

It is a useful exercise to perform the integrations and check the results against those obtained by the graphical method:

(i) $t=2$ ms to $t=4$ ms; i.e. $t'=0$ to $t'=2$ ms $=0.002$ s where $t'=(t-2)$

Slope of I/t characteristic $=\dfrac{20\times 10^{-3}}{2\times 10^{-3}}=10\ \text{A s}^{-1}$

At $t=3$ ms, ($t'=1$ ms):

$$V_C=\frac{1}{C}\int_0^{0.001} I\text{d}t'=\frac{1}{2\times 10^{-6}}[5t'^2]_0^{0.001}$$

$$=\left[\frac{5\times 1\times 10^{-6}}{2\times 10^{-6}}\right]=2.5\ \text{V}$$

and at

$t=4$ ms, ($t'=2$ ms):

$$V_C=\frac{1}{C}\int_0^{0.002} I\text{d}t'=\frac{1}{2\times 10^{-6}}\int_0^{0.002} 10t'\text{d}t'$$

$$=\frac{1}{2\times 10^{-6}}\left[\frac{10t'^2}{2}\right]_0^{0.002}=\left[\frac{5\times 4\times 10^{-6}}{2\times 10^{-6}}\right]=10\text{V}$$

both of which agree with the graphical solution.

(ii) $t=4$ ms to $t=8$ ms or $t''=0$ to $t''=4$ ms where

$$t''=(t-4)$$

$$V_C=\frac{1}{C}\int_{-\infty}^{0} I\text{d}t''+\frac{1}{C}\int_0^{t''} I\text{d}t''$$

and since the capacitor voltage at $t=4$ ms or $t''=0$ is 10 V, we have

$$\frac{1}{C}\int_{-\infty}^{0} I\text{d}t''=10$$

$$\therefore V_C=10+\frac{1}{C}\int_0^{0.004} I\text{d}t''$$

and since

$$I=20\times 10^{-3}\text{A}$$

then at $t=8$ ms ($t''=4$ ms)

$$V_C=10+\frac{1}{2\times 10^{-6}}[20\times 10^{-3}t'']_0^{0.004}$$

$$=10+\frac{1}{2\times 10^{-6}}20\times 10^{-3}\times 0.004=50\ \text{V}$$

which agrees with the graphical solution.

(iii) $t=8$ ms to $t=10$ ms or $t'''=0$ to $t'''=2$ ms where

$$t'''=(t-8)$$

$$V_C=\frac{1}{C}\int_{-\infty}^{0} I\text{d}t'''+\frac{1}{C}\int_0^{t'''} I\text{d}t'''$$

and if we consider the voltage at $t=8$ ms to be the initial voltage we have, for $t=9$ ms ($t'''=1$ ms)

$$V_C=50+\frac{1}{C}\int_0^{0.001} I\text{d}t'''$$

Now the slope of the characteristic during the time interval $t=8$ ms to 10 ms is -10A s^{-1} and the initial value is $20\times 10^{-3}A$, hence $I=(20\times 10^{-3}-10t''')A$

$$\therefore V_C=50+\frac{1}{2\times 10^{-6}}\int_0^{0.001}(20\times 10^{-3}-10t''')\text{d}t'''$$

$$=50+\frac{1}{2\times 10^{-6}}[20\times 10^{-3}t'''-5t'''^2]_0^{0.001}$$

$$=50+\frac{1}{2\times 10^{-6}}[20\times 10^{-6}-5\times 10^{-6}]V$$

$$=(50+7.5)=57.5\ \text{V}$$

and at $t=10$ ms ($t'''=2$ ms)

$$V_C=50+\frac{1}{2\times 10^{-6}}[20\times 10^{-3}t'''-5t'''^2]_0^{0.002}$$

$$=50+\frac{1}{2\times 10^{-6}}[40-20]10^{-6}\ \text{V}$$

$$=(50+10)=60\ \text{V}$$

both of which agree with the graphical solution.

We now consider the voltage waveform across the inductor; this is given by $V_L=L\text{d}I/\text{d}t$. Differentiation of current with respect to time is equivalent to evaluating the slope of the current/time characteristic of Figure 1.9a.

From $t=0$ to $t=2$ ms the slope is zero hence $\text{d}I/\text{d}t=0$ and $V_L=L\text{d}I/\text{d}t=0$; from $t=2$ ms to $t=4$ ms the slope of the current/time characteristic is 10A s^{-1} so that, if the inductance of the inductor is 2 H, the voltage across the inductor $V_L=L\text{d}I/\text{d}t=2\times 10=20$ V.

From $t=4$ ms to $t=8$ ms and $t>10$ ms the slope is zero, giving $V_L=0$ during this period; from $t=8$ ms to $t=10$ ms the slope of the current/time characteristic is -10A s^{-1}, hence $V_L=-20$ V as shown in figure 1.9d.

If the three elements are connected in series the total voltage across the combination is given by

$$V=V_R+V_L+V_C=\left(IR+\frac{1}{C}\int_{-\infty}^{t} I\text{d}t+L\text{d}I/\text{d}t\right)$$

which is the sum of the waveforms of figures 1.9b, 1.9c and 1.9d.

1.6 POWER AND STORED ENERGY

If we examine the defining equations for current and voltage we see that the product of current and voltage is

$$VI=\frac{\text{d}W}{\text{d}Q}\cdot\frac{\text{d}Q}{\text{d}t}$$

which is the rate of change of energy, that is POWER. The power supplied to a network when a battery of terminal voltage V causes a current I to flow is $P=VI$ WATTS where V is in VOLTS and I is the current in AMPERES. It is apparent that 1 watt = 1 joule/second.

† The power dissipated in a resistor is $P=VI=I^2R=V^2/R$ watts.

For a capacitor, the energy stored in the electric field at time t is

$$W=\int_{-\infty}^{t} P\mathrm{d}t=\int_{-\infty}^{t} VI\mathrm{d}t=\int_{-\infty}^{t} VC\frac{\mathrm{d}V}{\mathrm{d}t}\cdot \mathrm{d}t$$

When the capacitor was manufactured, at $t=-\infty$, effectively the voltage across it was zero, and if the voltage across it at time t is V_1 we can write

† $$W=C\int_{0}^{V_1} V\mathrm{d}V=\tfrac{1}{2}CV_1^2 \text{ Joules}$$

Similarly the energy stored in the magnetic field of an inductor at time t, when the current flowing is I_1, is

$$W=\int_{-\infty}^{t} VI\mathrm{d}t=\int_{-\infty}^{t} L\frac{\mathrm{d}I}{\mathrm{d}t}\, I\mathrm{d}t$$

and assuming the current at $t=-\infty$ to be zero, we obtain

$$W=L\int_{0}^{I_1} I\mathrm{d}I,$$

or

† $$W=\tfrac{1}{2}LI_1^2 \text{ Joules}$$

1.7 SOURCES

To energize the two-terminal circuit elements considered in the previous section, sources of energy in the form of voltage and current generators are required. For the purposes of circuit analysis these sources are represented by two-terminal elements.

1.7.1 The Voltage Source

The battery connected to the network of figure 1.3 is a practical voltage source. We will however consider initially the model of an ideal voltage source, which is a two-terminal element capable of maintaining a constant voltage across its terminals regardless of the current that it supplies to the network to which it is connected. The circuit representation of the ideal voltage source, together with its voltage/current characteristic is shown in figure 1.10.

If a load in the form of a variable resistor is connected to a battery as a practical source, and the terminal voltage is measured for different values of load current as shown in figure 1.11a, the terminal voltage/load current characteristic may be obtained.

Figure 1.11b shows a characteristic such that the terminal voltage falls linearly as the current supplied by the source increases. How can this characteristic be represented by a circuit model? The characteristic is of the form $V=E-IR_S$ from the equation of a straight

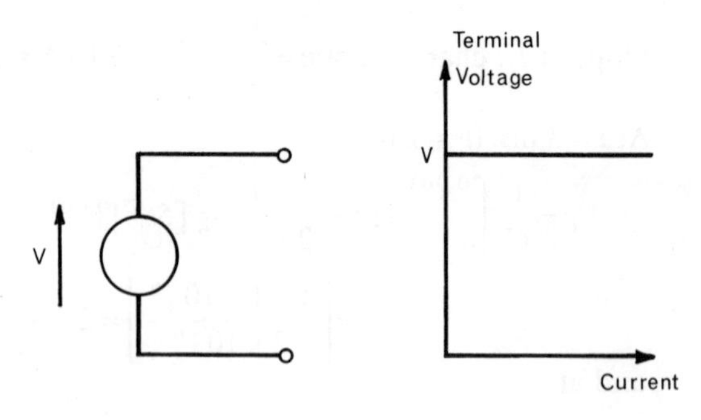

Fig. 1.10

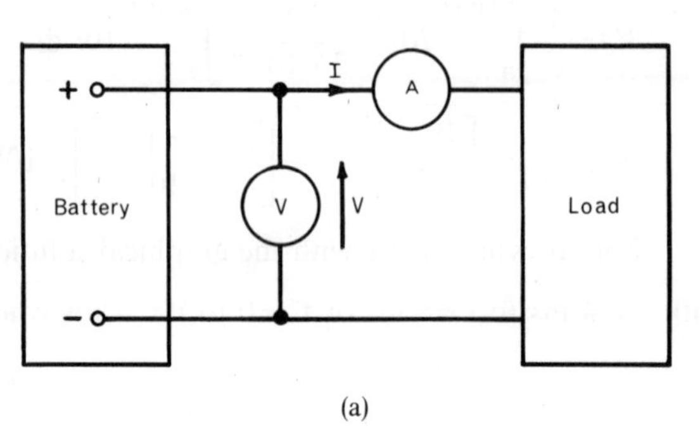

(a)

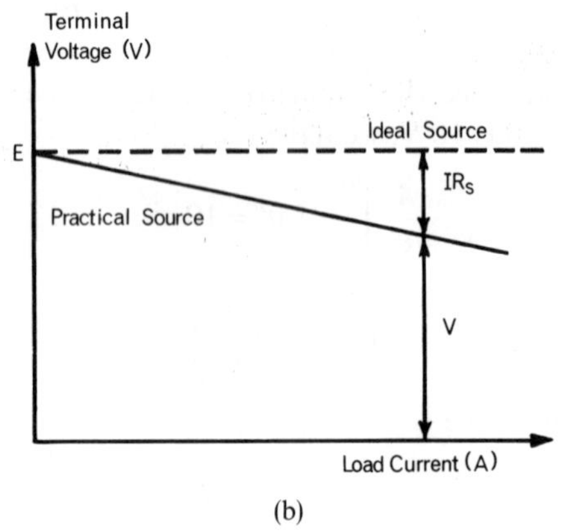

(b)

Fig. 1.11

line, ($y=c+mx$), where E is the terminal voltage when $I=0$ and $-R_S$ is the slope of the characteristic. Inspection of the voltage/current relationship $V=IR$ for a resistor shows that IR is the voltage across a resistance R when a current I flows through it, so that *we can represent this practical d.c. voltage source by an ideal constant voltage source E in* **series** *with a resistance* R_S. This is shown in figure 1.12; the terminal voltage is $V=E-IR_S$.
E is known as the *electromotive force* (or e.m.f.) and R_S the *source resistance* or *internal resistance* of the source, measured in volts and ohms respectively.

The directions of the currents and voltages shown on the equivalent circuit should be noted carefully.

From the characteristic it may be seen that the smaller the source resistance, the smaller the change in terminal voltage for a given change in load current since $\delta V=$

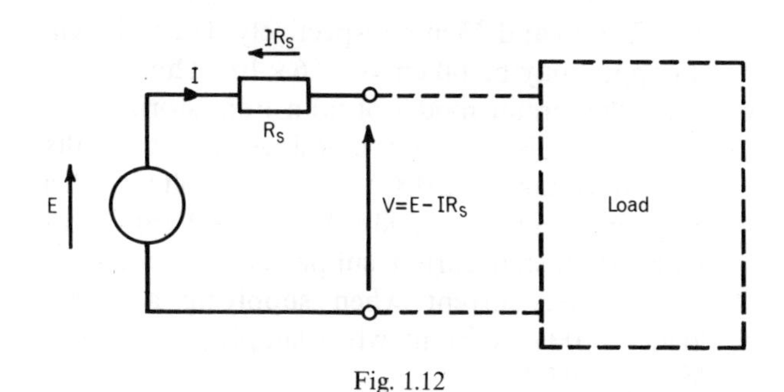

Fig. 1.12

$-\delta I.R_S$. *An ideal voltage source has zero source resistance* and typical values of source resistance for practical sources are 0.03 Ω for a 12 V lead-acid battery, and 0.01 Ω for a regulated transistor low voltage d.c. supply.

The ratio: (no-load terminal voltage—full load terminal voltage) to (no-load voltage) is known as the *regulation* of the source.

1.7.2 The Current Source

In some applications a constant current source is required. Ideally this consists of a two-terminal element capable of maintaining a constant current through an external load, regardless of the value of that load. The circuit representation of the ideal current source and its current/voltage characteristic are shown in figures 1.13a and 1.13b respectively.

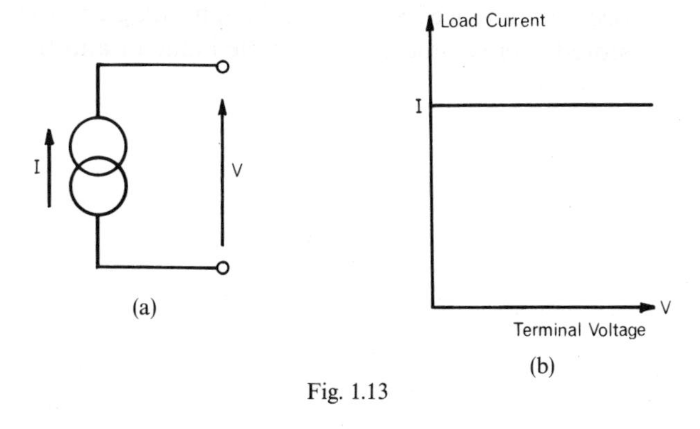

Fig. 1.13

If a variable load resistor is connected to a practical constant current source, which may be a transistorized unit, as shown in figure 1.14a, and the terminal voltage and load current are measured for different values of load resistor, the characteristic of 1.14b is obtained.

It is seen from figure 1.14b that the characteristic of the practical current source is of the form $I_L = I - VG_S$ ($y = c + mx$) where I is the current supplied by the source when its terminals are short circuited, that is when $R_L = 0$. Hence $V = 0$, and $-G_S$ is the slope of the characteristic. Now VG_S represents the current through a conductance G_S or a resistance $R_S = 1/G_S$, when the voltage across it is V_i; therefore *we can represent a practical d.c. current*

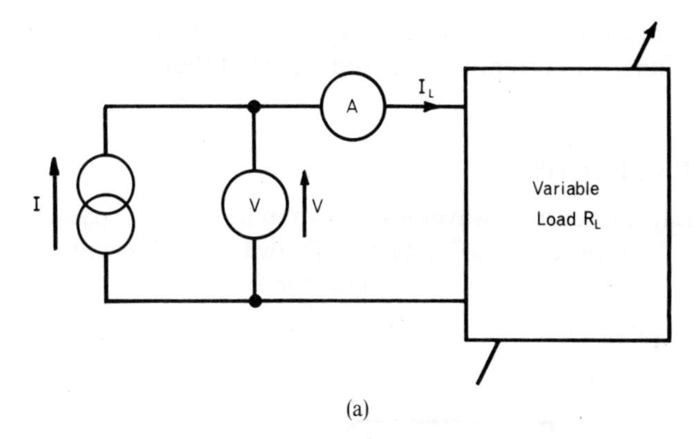

(a)

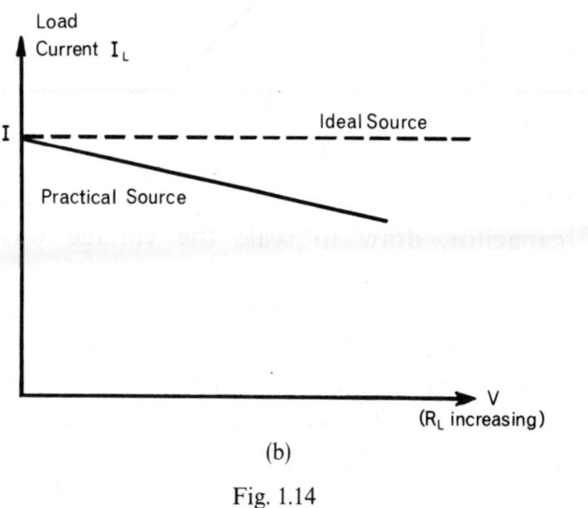

(b)

Fig. 1.14

source by an ideal d.c. current source in **parallel** *with a resistance* R_S as shown in figure 1.15.

It may be seen from figure 1.15 that the generated current I of the ideal source divides at X, a current $V/R_S = VG_S$ flows through the internal resistance of the practical source and the remainder $I_L = (I - V/R_S)$ flows into the external load.

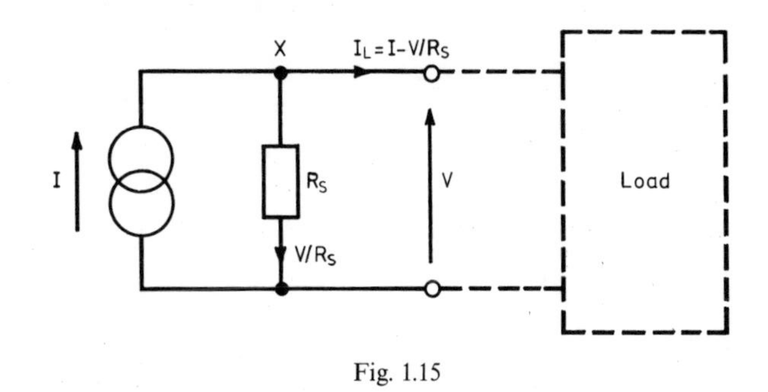

Fig. 1.15

From the characteristic it may be seen that the smaller G_S the smaller the change in load current for a given change in terminal voltage since $\delta I_L = -\delta V.G_S = -\delta V/R_S$. *An ideal current source has infinite source resistance.*

The sources that have been described are known as *independent* sources or generators, because their parameters do not depend on the external circuits to which they are connected; we will deal later with *dependent* or *controlled sources* in which the output is a function of the voltage or current in some other part of the circuit.

PROBLEMS

1.1. The current waveform shown in figure Q1 is passed through a 10 μF capacitor. Draw to scale the voltage waveform across the capacitor.

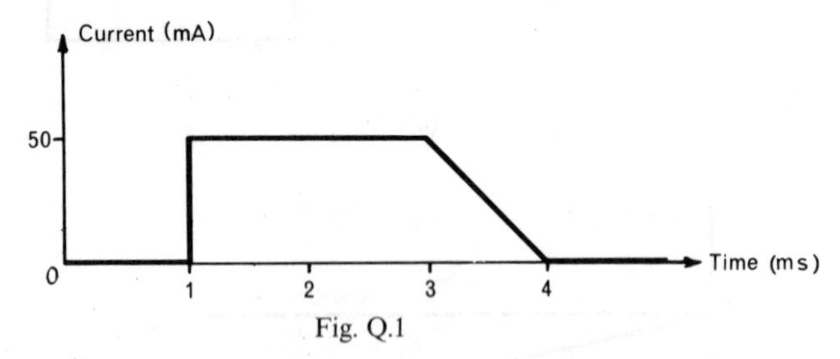

Fig. Q.1

1.2. If a 1 kΩ resistor is connected in series with the capacitor, draw to scale the voltage waveform ($v_c + v_R$) across both components.

1.3. A current $i = 10 \cos 100\pi t$ mA is passed through a 10 H inductor; obtain an expression for the voltage across the terminals of the inductor. Sketch the voltage and current waveforms and comment on their phase relationship.

1.4. The current waveform shown in figure Q1 is passed through (a) a 10 H inductor and (b) a 10μF capacitor. Plot a curve of stored energy/time for each component.

1.5. Calculate the resistance of a 10 metre length of copper tubing having external and internal diameters 25 mm and 23 mm respectively. The resistivity of copper may be taken as 1.56×10^{-8}Ωm.

1.6. Draw the circuit model of (a) a transistorized low voltage supply giving the following test results; no-load voltage = 12.000 V, terminal voltage when supplying a current of 200 mA = 11.980 V (b) a transistorized constant current supply giving the following test results; current when supplying a 1000 Ω load = 0.100 A, current when supplying a 10000Ω load = 0.095 A.

1.7. A time-varying current defined by $i = 5t^2$ mA, where t is in seconds, flows through a 1 kΩ resistor for 3 seconds. Determine the energy dissipated in the resistor.

1.8. A voltage $v = 100 \sin 10^4 t$ V is applied to an inductor $L = 0.1$ H and a capacitor $C = 0.1$ μF as shown in figure Q.8. Derive expressions for the currents i_L and

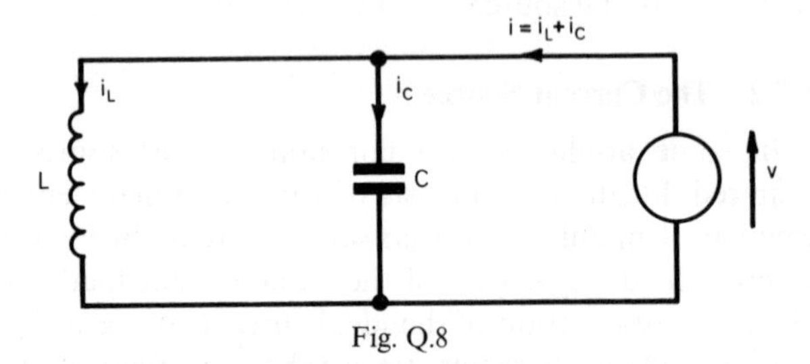

Fig. Q.8

i_C; hence show that no steady current is supplied by the voltage source. Why does this condition not occur in practice? Sketch, on the same diagram, the stored energy/time graphs for the inductor and the capacitor.

CHAPTER TWO

Some Circuit Theorems and their Application to D.C. Circuits

2.1 INTRODUCTION

To become familiar with the techniques of circuit analysis, while avoiding undue complexity, at this stage we confine the study to circuits containing resistors and independent current and/or voltage sources only.

In principle we require only three laws, namely Ohm's Law and the two laws of Kirchhoff to analyze d.c. circuits. These laws are stated below.

2.2 OHM'S LAW

The voltage across a linear resistor is proportional to the current flowing through it. The constant of proportionality is called the resistance. The law is described by the † equation $V = IR$. It is important to observe the sign convention as shown in figure 1.5.

2.3 KIRCHHOFF'S CURRENT LAW

The algebraic sum of the currents entering a junction (or node) in an electric circuit is zero. The law is described † by the equation $\Sigma I = 0$.

Consider the junction (or node) shown in figure 2.1; the algebraic sum of the currents entering the junction is $I_1 - I_2 - I_3 + I_4 - I_5 - I_6 = 0$.

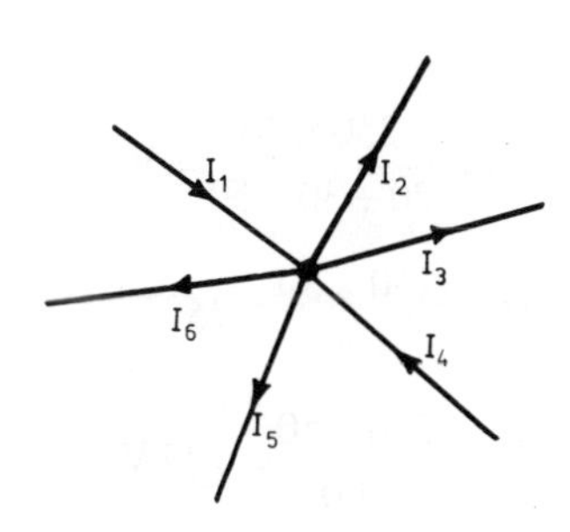

Fig. 2.1

2.4 KIRCHHOFF'S VOLTAGE LAW

In any closed loop of an electric circuit the algebraic sum of all the voltages in that loop is zero. The law is described by the equation $\Sigma V = 0$.

In the closed loop shown in figure 2.2 are voltage sources and resistors; the algebraic sum of the voltages in the loop is $V_1 - V_2 - V_3 - V_4 + V_5 = 0$.

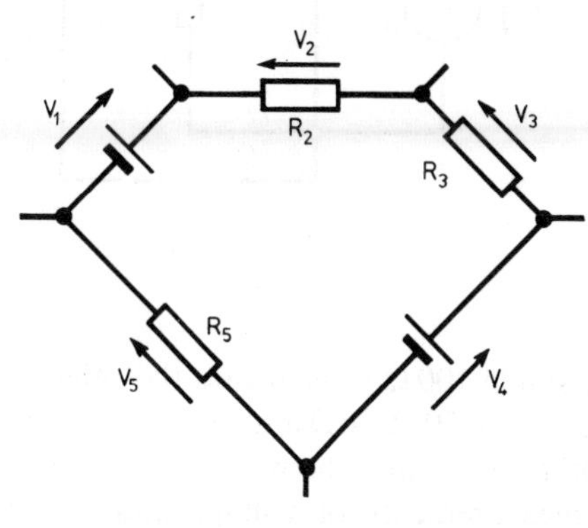

Fig. 2.2

It is important that careful attention is paid to the polarity of the voltages in the loop.

2.5 SOME APPLICATIONS OF THE BASIC CIRCUIT LAWS

These laws will now be applied to derive some useful relationships.

2.5.1 Resistors In Series

In figure 2.3a three resistors R_1, R_2 and R_3 are connected in series to a voltage source V. The resultant current I is obtained by the application of Kirchhoff's Voltage Law and Ohm's Law.

$$V = (V_1 + V_2 + V_3) = I(R_1 + R_2 + R_3) \qquad (2.1)$$

In figure 2.3b the resistor R has a value such that, when it is connected to the source V, a similar current I flows. Applying Ohm's Law gives

$$V = IR \qquad (2.2)$$

and from equations 2.1 and 2.2 we see that

† $$R = R_1 + R_2 + R_3 \qquad (2.3)$$

Thus if there are two identical 'black boxes', one con-

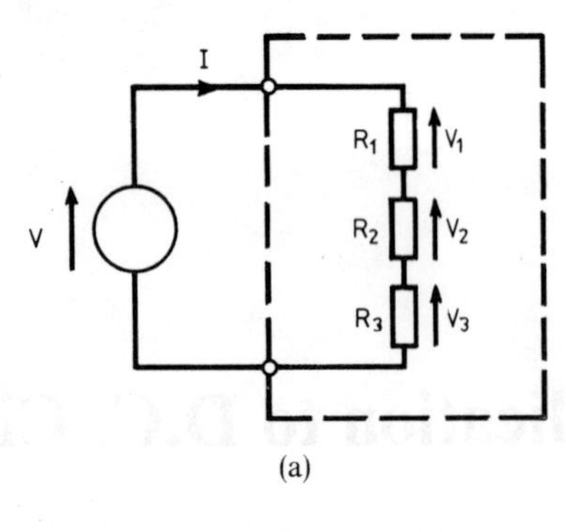

(a)

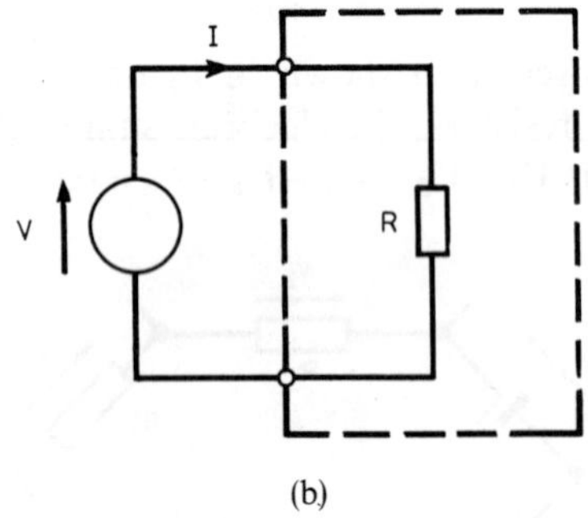

(b)

Fig. 2.3

taining a single 100 Ω resistor and the other containing three resistors of 20 Ω, 30 Ω and 50 Ω connected in series, one cannot distinguish between the 'black boxes' by making measurements of voltage and current at the terminals of the boxes.

2.5.2 Resistors in Parallel

In figure 2.4a three resistors R_1, R_2 and R_3 are connected in parallel to a voltage source V, the resultant current I is obtained by the application of Kirchhoff's Current Law and Ohm's Law.

$$I=(I_1+I_2+I_3)=V(1/R_1+1/R_2+1/R_3) \quad (2.4)$$

In figure 2.4b a similar current I flows when the voltage source V is applied to the single resistor R, thus

$$I=V/R \quad (2.5)$$

From equations 2.4 and 2.5 we see that

† $$1/R=1/R_1+1/R_2+1/R_3 \quad (2.6)$$

In terms of conductance, which is the reciprocal of resistance, equations 2.4, 2.5 and 2.6 become

$$I=V(G_1+G_2+G_3) \quad (2.7)$$

$$I=VG \quad (2.8)$$

and

$$G=(G_1+G_2+G_3) \quad (2.9)$$

respectively.

† It is seen that equations 2.7, 2.8 and 2.9 are of the same form as equations 2.1, 2.2 and 2.3 but with current and voltage interchanged, and conductance replacing resistance as one goes from a series to a parallel circuit, or from Kirchhoff's Voltage Law to Kirchhoff's Current Law. These *dual* relationships will become more apparent at a later stage.

Example

If three resistors of 500 Ω, 330 Ω and 200 Ω are connected in parallel, what is the value of the equivalent single resistor?

Solution

$G=G_1+G_2+G_3=(1/500+1/330+1/200)$
$=(0.002+0.003+0.005)=0.01$ S.
$\therefore R=1/G=100\ \Omega$.

For a number of resistors in parallel it is, in general, more convenient to work in terms of conductance rather than resistance.

2.5.3 Division of Voltage Across Series Resistors

Consider the circuit of figure 2.3a. By Ohm's Law $V_1=IR_1$, $V_2=IR_2$, $V_3=IR_3$ and by Kirchhoff's Voltage Law $V=V_1+V_2+V_3$, giving $V=I(R_1+R_2+R_3)$

$$\therefore I=\frac{V}{(R_1+R_2+R_3)}$$

and

$$\left.\begin{aligned} V_1=IR_1=\frac{VR_1}{R_1+R_2+R_3}=\frac{VR_1}{\Sigma R} \\ \text{Similarly} \quad V_2=\frac{VR_2}{\Sigma R} \text{ and } V_3=\frac{VR_3}{\Sigma R}\end{aligned}\right\} \quad (2.10)$$

Thus if $V=250$ V, $R_1=20\ \Omega$, $R_2=30\ \Omega$ and $R_3=50\ \Omega$

then

$$V_1=\frac{250\times 20}{20+30+50}=50\text{ V}$$

$$V_2=\frac{250\times 30}{100}=75\text{ V}$$

$$V_3=\frac{250\times 50}{100}=125\text{ V}$$

2.5.4 Division of Current Between Parallel Resistors

Consider the circuit of figure 2.4a. In this case it is required to determine how the current I divides between the resistors R_1, R_2 and R_3. By Ohm's Law $I_1=V/R_1=VG_1$, $I_2=V/R_2=VG_2$, $I_3=V/R_3=VG_3$ and by Kirch-

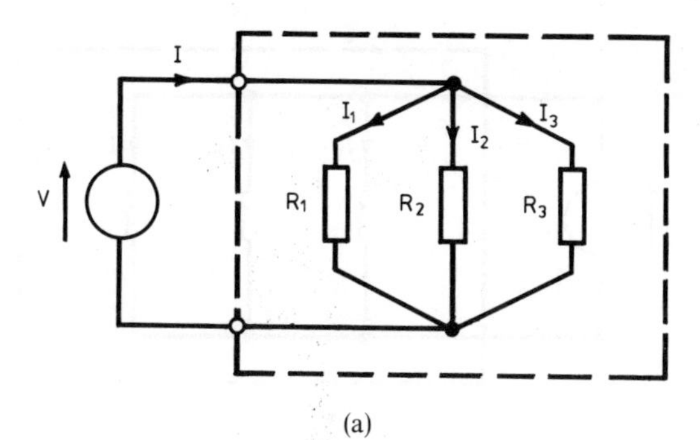

(a)

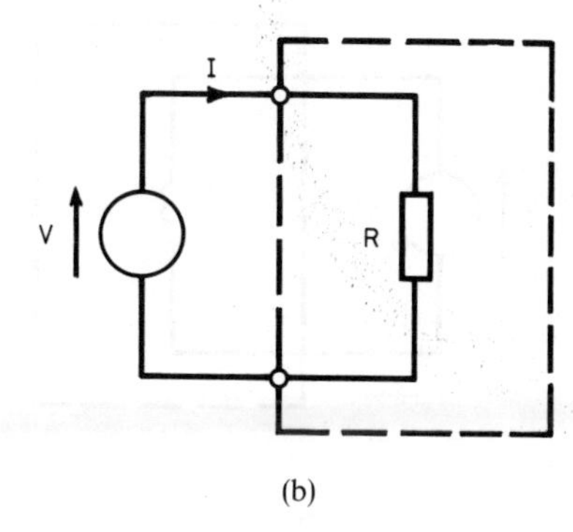

(b)

Fig. 2.4

hoff's Current Law $I=I_1+I_2+I_3$, giving $I=V(G_1+G_2+G_3)$ or

$$V=\frac{I}{(G_1+G_2+G_3)}$$

and

$$I_1=VG_1=\frac{IG_1}{(G_1+G_2+G_3)}=\frac{IG_1}{\Sigma G}$$

similarly

$$I_2=\frac{IG_2}{\Sigma G} \text{ and } I_3=\frac{IG_3}{\Sigma G} \qquad (2.11)$$

Thus if $I=10$ mA, $R_1=500\ \Omega$, $R_2=330\ \Omega$ and $R_3=200\ \Omega$

$$G_1=\frac{1}{500}=0.002\text{ S},\ G_2=\frac{1}{330}=0.003\text{ S},\ G_3=\frac{1}{200}=0.005\text{ S}$$

Hence

$$\Sigma G=0.01\text{ S and } I_1=\frac{10\times 0.002}{0.01}=2\text{ mA}$$

$$I_2=\frac{10\times 0.003}{0.01}=3\text{ mA and } I_3=\frac{10\times 0.005}{0.01}=5\text{ mA}$$

A comparison of equations 2.10 and 2.11 illustrates again the dual relationships referred to earlier.

When there are only two resistors R_1 and R_2 in parallel, as shown in figure 2.5, it is more convenient to work directly in terms of resistance.

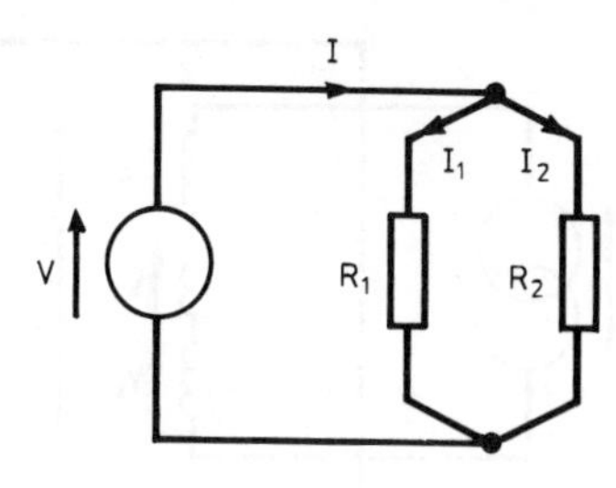

Fig. 2.5

Applying Kirchhoff's Current Law, $I=I_1+I_2$, and by Ohm's Law $I_1=V/R_1$, $I_2=V/R_2$

Therefore

$$I=V\left(\frac{1}{R_1}+\frac{1}{R_2}\right)=\frac{V(R_1+R_2)}{R_1R_2}$$

giving

$$V=\frac{IR_1R_2}{(R_1+R_2)}$$

Hence

$$I_1=V/R_1=\frac{IR_2}{R_1+R_2} \qquad (2.12)$$

and

$$I_2=V/R_2=\frac{IR_1}{R_1+R_2} \qquad (2.13)$$

It is useful to observe that in this case the value of the equivalent resistor R is given by

$$\frac{1}{R}=\frac{1}{R_1}+\frac{1}{R_2}=\frac{R_1+R_2}{R_1R_2}$$

Whence

† $$R=\frac{R_1R_2}{R_1+R_2}=\frac{\text{Product of } R_1 \text{ and } R_2}{\text{Sum of } R_1 \text{ and } R_2} \qquad (2.14)$$

2.5.5 Inductors in Series

In figure 2.6a three inductors L_1, L_2 and L_3 are connected in series to a current cource I; the resultant voltage V is obtained by the application of Kirchhoff's Voltage Law and the voltage/current relationship for an inductor. Assuming that there is no coupling between the inductors we have

$$V=V_1+V_2+V_3=L_1\frac{dI}{dt}+L_2\frac{dI}{dt}+L_3\frac{dI}{dt}$$

$$=(L_1+L_2+L_3)\frac{dI}{dt} \qquad (2.15)$$

In figure 2.6b the inductor L has a value such that, when it is connected to the source I, a similar voltage V is

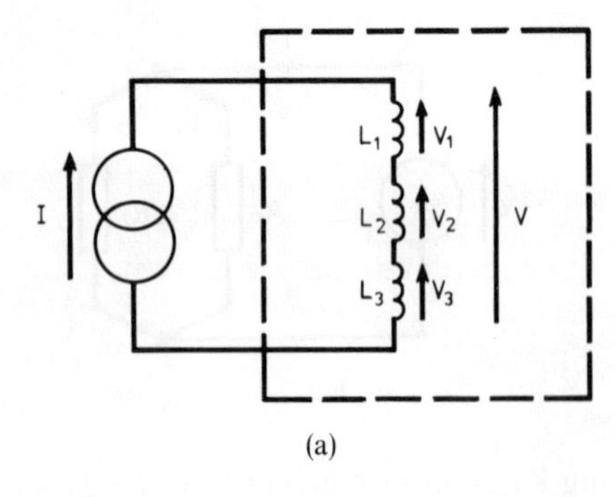

(a)

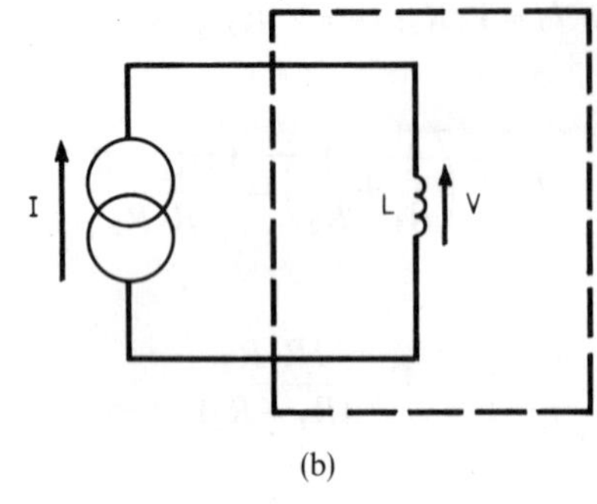

(b)

Fig. 2.6

produced; it follows that

$$V=L\frac{\mathrm{d}I}{\mathrm{d}t} \tag{2.16}$$

From equations 2.15 and 2.16 above we see that

† $$L=L_1+L_2+L_3 \tag{2.17}$$

2.5.6 Inductors in Parallel

In figure 2.7a three inductors L_1, L_2 and L_3 are connected in parallel to a voltage source V; the resulting current I is

$$I=I_1+I_2+I_3=\frac{1}{L_1}\int V\mathrm{d}t+\frac{1}{L_2}\int V\mathrm{d}t+\frac{1}{L_3}\int V\mathrm{d}t$$

$$=\left(\frac{1}{L_1}+\frac{1}{L_2}+\frac{1}{L_3}\right)\int V\mathrm{d}t \tag{2.18}$$

In figure 2.7b the inductor L has a value such that when it is connected to the source V a similar current I flows; it follows that

$$I=\frac{1}{L}\int V\mathrm{d}t \tag{2.19}$$

From equations 2.18 and 2.19 we see that

† $$\frac{1}{L}=\frac{1}{L_1}+\frac{1}{L_2}+\frac{1}{L_3} \tag{2.20}$$

2.5.7 Capacitors in Series

In figure 2.8a three capacitors C_1, C_2 and C_3 are

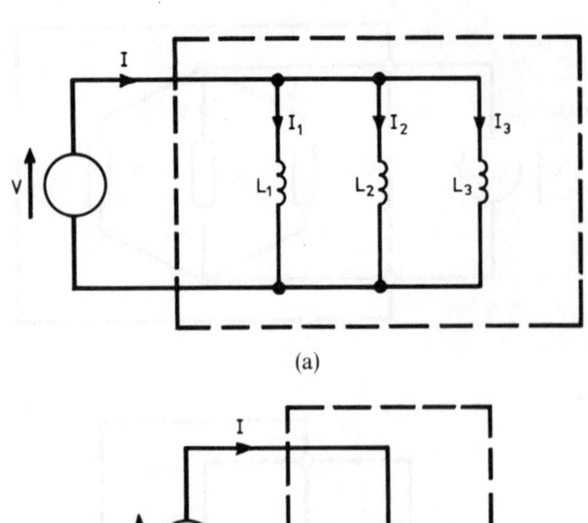

(a)

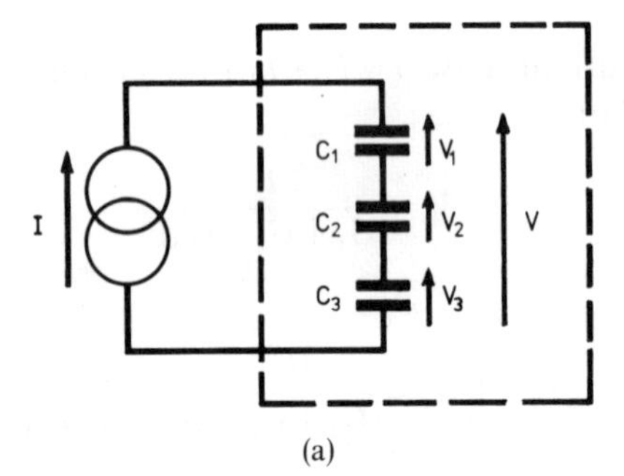

(b)

Fig. 2.7

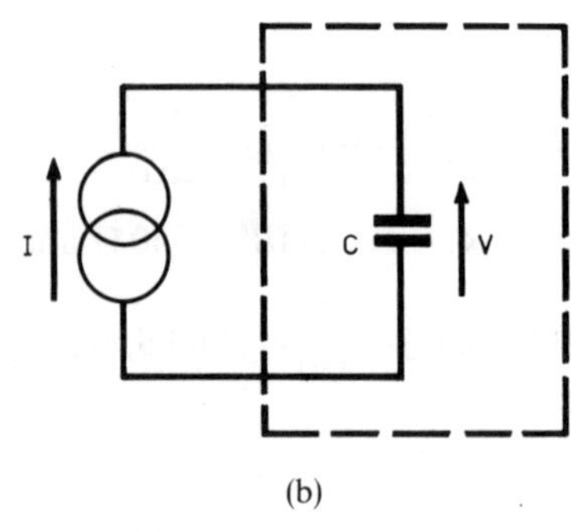

(a)

I C V

(b)

Fig. 2.8

connected in series to a current source I; the resultant voltage V is

$$V=V_1+V_2+V_3=\frac{1}{C_1}\int I\mathrm{d}t+\frac{1}{C_2}\int I\mathrm{d}t+\frac{1}{C_3}\int I\mathrm{d}t$$

$$=\left(\frac{1}{C_1}+\frac{1}{C_2}+\frac{1}{C_3}\right)\int I\mathrm{d}t \tag{2.21}$$

In figure 2.8b the capacitor C has a value such that when it is connected to the source I a similar voltage V is produced; it follows that

$$V=\frac{1}{C}\int I\mathrm{d}t \tag{2.22}$$

From equations 2.21 and 2.22 we see that

† $$\frac{1}{C}=\frac{1}{C_1}+\frac{1}{C_2}+\frac{1}{C_3} \tag{2.23}$$

2.5.8 Capacitors in Parallel

In figure 2.9a three capacitors C_1, C_2 and C_3 are connected in parallel to a voltage source V; the resulting current I is

$$I=I_1+I_2+I_3=C_1\frac{\mathrm{d}V}{\mathrm{d}t}+C_2\frac{\mathrm{d}V}{\mathrm{d}t}+C_3\frac{\mathrm{d}V}{\mathrm{d}t}$$

$$=(C_1+C_2+C_3)\frac{\mathrm{d}V}{\mathrm{d}t} \tag{2.24}$$

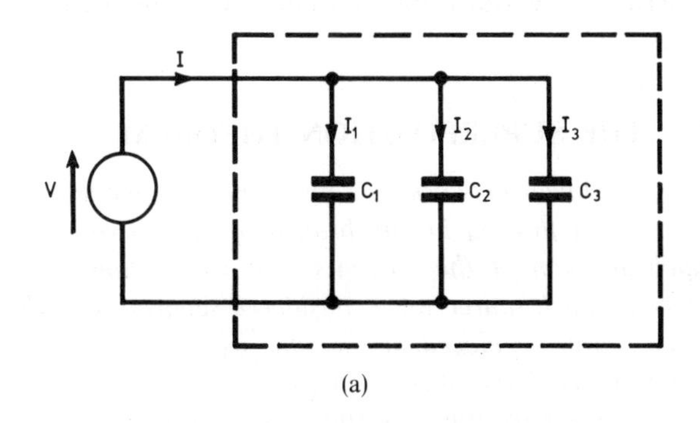

(a)

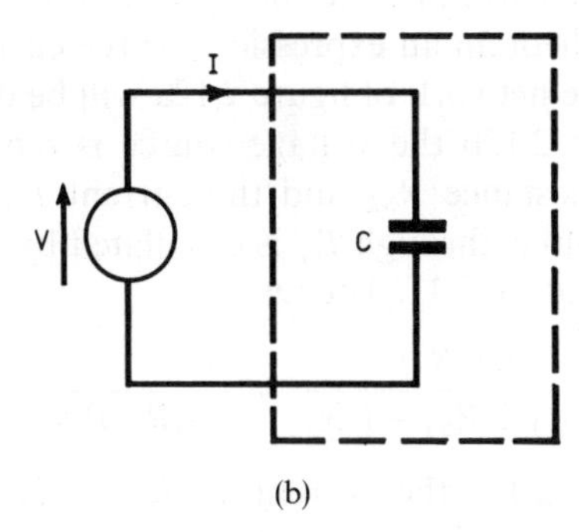

(b)

Fig. 2.9

In figure 2.9b the capacitor C has a value such that when it is connected to the source V, a similar current I flows; it follows that

$$I=C\frac{\mathrm{d}V}{\mathrm{d}t} \tag{2.25}$$

From equations 2.24 and 2.25 we see that

$$C=C_1+C_2+C_3 \tag{2.26}$$

2.6 ANALYSIS OF A SIMPLE CIRCUIT

Formal methods of circuit analysis will be discussed in chapter 3. For the present, attention will be confined to simple circuits and the method of solution will be to assign a current to each *branch* of the network, a branch being a path containing an element joining two junctions (or nodes). A set of equations, containing these currents, is then obtained by applying Kirchhoff's Voltage Law around the independent loops of the network and Kirchhoff's Current Law at the nodes. This method, leads to more equations and is less systematic than the methods to be described later, but is easier to grasp at this stage and leads to a satisfactory solution for simple circuits.

In the circuit of figure 2.10 given that $V=30$ V, $R_1=100\,\Omega$, $R_2=200\,\Omega$, $R_3=300\,\Omega$, $R_4=600\,\Omega$, we will determine the current supplied by the source and the current flowing in each resistor.

Currents I_1-I_5 are assigned as shown and the resulting voltage drops across the resistors calculated by applying Ohm's Law.

Applying Kirchhoff's Current Law at nodes A and B gives

$$I_5-I_2-I_1=0 \tag{2.27}$$

$$I_1-I_3-I_4=0 \tag{2.28}$$

and applying Kirchhoff's Voltage Law to the loops gives

Loop HAFG $\quad V-I_2R_2=0$

and inserting numerical values

$$30-200I_2=0 \tag{2.29}$$

Loop ABEF $\quad I_1R_1+I_3R_3-I_2R_2=0$

and with numerical values

$$100\,I_1+300\,I_3-200\,I_2=0 \tag{2.30}$$

Loop BCDE $\quad I_3R_3-I_4R_4=0$

and with numerical values

$$300\,I_3-600\,I_4=0 \tag{2.31}$$

Thus we have five equations and five unknowns I_1-I_5. It is usual for sets of simultaneous equations to be solved by the use of determinants as described in Appendix 1, however the equations 2.27–2.31 are simple and can be readily solved without the use of determinants, giving

$I_1=100$ mA, $I_2=150$ mA, $I_3=67$ mA, $I_4=33$ mA, $I_5=250$ mA.

This method of solution has been employed to illustrate the direct use of the Kirchhoff Laws. Other methods of solution are possible; for example let us apply some of the relationships we have already derived: resistors R_3 and R_4 are connected in parallel and can, therefore be replaced by a single resistor $R' = R_3R_4/(R_3+R_4)$ (see equation 2.14). Inserting numerical values gives $R' = 200\ \Omega$, and the circuit of figure 2.10 can therefore be redrawn as shown in figure 2.11.

By direct application of Ohm's Law

$$I_2 = \frac{V}{R_2} = \frac{30}{200}\ \text{A} = 150\ \text{mA}$$

$$I_1 = \frac{V}{R_1+R'} = \frac{30}{300} = 0.1\ \text{A} = 100\ \text{mA}$$

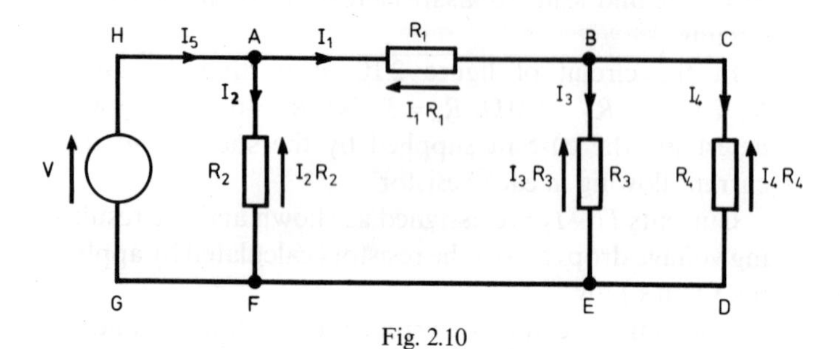

Fig. 2.10

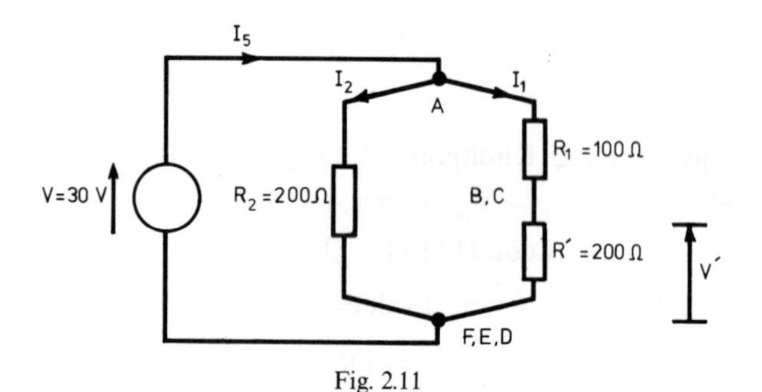

Fig. 2.11

Applying Kirchhoff's Current Law at the upper node gives

$$I_5 = I_1 + I_2 = 250\ \text{mA}.$$

If we now apply equation 2.10 to the right hand branch, the voltage across R' is

$$V' = \frac{VR'}{R_1+R'} = \frac{30\times 200}{300} = 20\ \text{V}$$

Referring to figure 2.10 and applying Ohm's Law to branches BE and CD

$$I_3 = \frac{V'}{R_3} = \frac{20}{300} = 0.067\ \text{A} = 67\ \text{mA}$$

and

$$I_4 = \frac{V'}{R_4} = \frac{20}{600} = 0.033\ \text{A} = 33\ \text{mA}.$$

These values agree with those obtained by the first method.

If only the current supplied by the source is required it is possible to reduce the network of figure 2.11 to a single resistor R equal to R_2 in parallel with $(R'+R_1)$

Thus

$$R = \frac{(R'+R_1)R_2}{R'+R_1+R_2} = \frac{300\times 200}{500} = 120\ \Omega$$

Hence

$$I_5 = \frac{V}{R} = \frac{30}{120} = 0.25\ \text{A} = 250\ \text{mA}$$

We shall be dealing with networks containing one or more voltage or current sources in addition to resistors; these networks are known as *active* networks. Networks that do not contain sources are known as *passive* networks. An active network having only two terminals is known as an *active two-terminal network* or an *active one-port network*.

One frequently has to find the current flowing in a branch of a linear network containing more than one generator; the following theorem can be applied in such cases.

2.7 THE SUPERPOSITION THEOREM

In any linear network containing more than one source, the current flowing in any branch of the network is the algebraic sum of the currents that would flow in that branch if each source were considered separately, with all other sources replaced at the time by resistors equal in value to their internal resistances.

In order to illustrate the application of the Superposition Theorem an expression for the current flowing in R_1 of the network of figure 2.12a will be derived.

In figure 2.12b the voltage source is replaced by its internal resistance R_{S2} and the current I_1, due to the current source, through R_1 is calculated by the application of equation 2.11. The result is

$$I_1 = \frac{I(1/R_1)}{1/R_1+1/R_{S1}+1/R_{S2}} = \frac{I}{1+(R_1/R_{S1})+(R_1/R_{S2})}$$

In figure 2.12c the current source is replaced by its internal resistance R_{S1} and the current I_2 (due to the voltage source) through R_1 is calculated by the application of equations of the form of equations 2.10, 2.13 and 2.14. The result is

$$I_2 = \frac{V}{R_{S2}+\{R_1R_{S1}/(R_1+R_{S1})\}}\cdot\frac{R_{S1}}{R_1+R_{S1}}$$

$$= \frac{VR_{S1}}{R_1R_{S1}+R_{S1}R_{S2}+R_{S2}R_1}$$

The Superposition Theorem is now applied, giving the total current through R_1 as $I_0 = I_1 + I_2$.

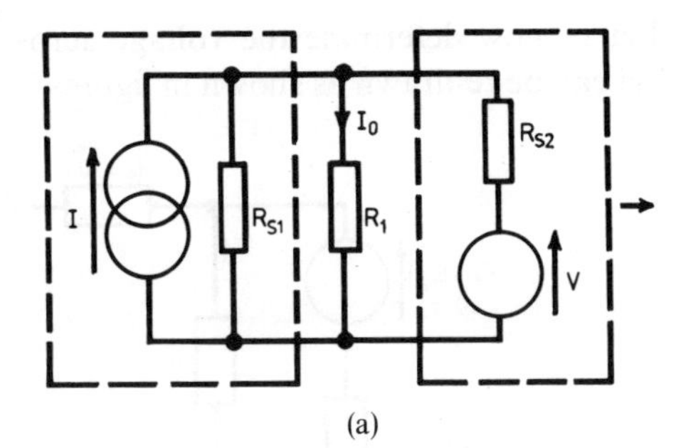

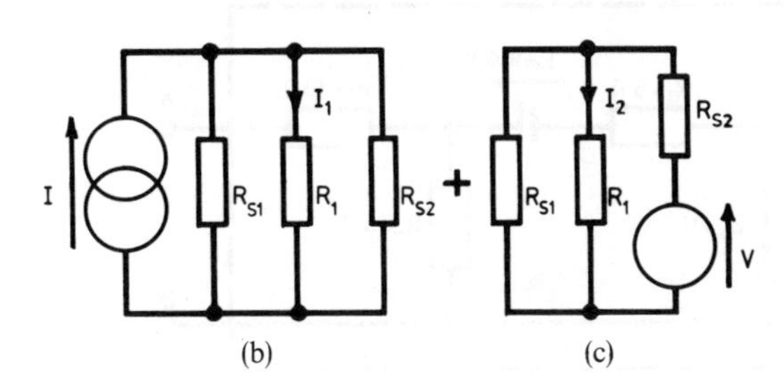

Fig. 2.12

It is important to note that the Superposition Theorem cannot be used to calculate the power dissipated in a resistor by determining the power dissipated due to each source in turn and then adding. This may be shown by reference to figure 2.13.

By the Superposition Theorem, the total current through R is $I_0=(I_1+I_2)$ where I_1 and I_2 are the currents through R due to V_1 and V_2 respectively.

The power dissipated in R is $I_0{}^2R=(I_1+I_2)^2R=I_1{}^2R+I_2{}^2R+2I_1I_2R$. But if we calculate the power due to V_1, with V_2 replaced by its source resistance as in figure 2.13b, and add it to the power due to V_2, with V_1 replaced by its source resistance as in figure 2.13c, we obtain $I_1{}^2R+I_2{}^2R=(I_1{}^2+I_2{}^2)R$ which is not the same as the true power $(I_1+I_2)^2R$.

The network of figure 2.13a represents also two d.c. generators, or batteries, connected in parallel to a common load R. The Superposition Theorem can be applied to determine the voltage V across the load. The voltage across R due to V_1 alone is, from figure 2.13b,

$$\frac{V_1R'}{R_{S1}+R'}$$

where

$$R'=\frac{RR_{S2}}{R+R_{S2}}$$

and the voltage across R due to V_2 alone is, from figure 2.13c

$$\frac{V_2R''}{R_{S2}+R''}$$

where

$$R''=\frac{RR_{S1}}{R+R_{S1}}$$

Applying the Superposition Theorem gives

$$V=\left[\frac{V_1R'}{R_{S1}+R'}+\frac{V_2R''}{R_{S2}+R''}\right]$$

$$=\left[\frac{V_1/R_{S1}+V_2/R_{S2}}{1/R+1/R_{S1}+1/R_{S2}}\right]$$

Two theorems which enable complicated active two terminal linear networks to be simplified will now be introduced.

2.8 THEVENIN'S THEOREM

Any two-terminal linear network of generators and resistors can be replaced by a **single voltage source in series with a resistor.** *The e.m.f. of the source is equal to the open-circuit voltage at the terminals of the network; the value of the resistor is equal to the resistance measured between the terminals of the network when all generators are replaced by their internal resistances.*

Let us first consider Thevenin's Theorem from a practical viewpoint. Figure 2.14a represents a two-terminal network consisting of two voltage sources and three linear resistors; figure 2.14b is the Thevenin equivalent circuit.

E_1 and E_2 are the open-circuit voltages of two batteries whose internal resistances may be determined practically

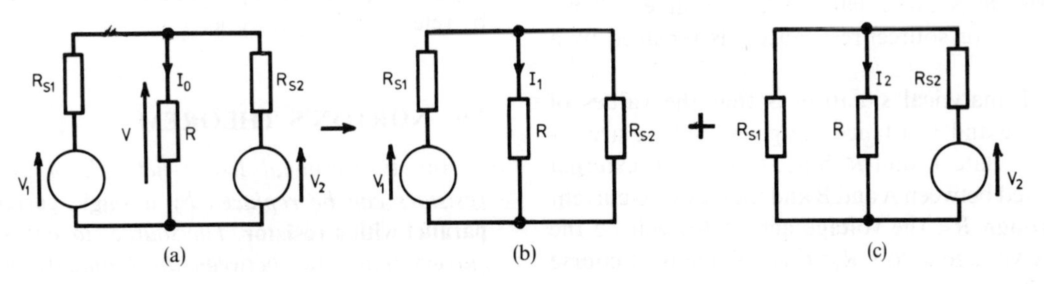

Fig. 2.13

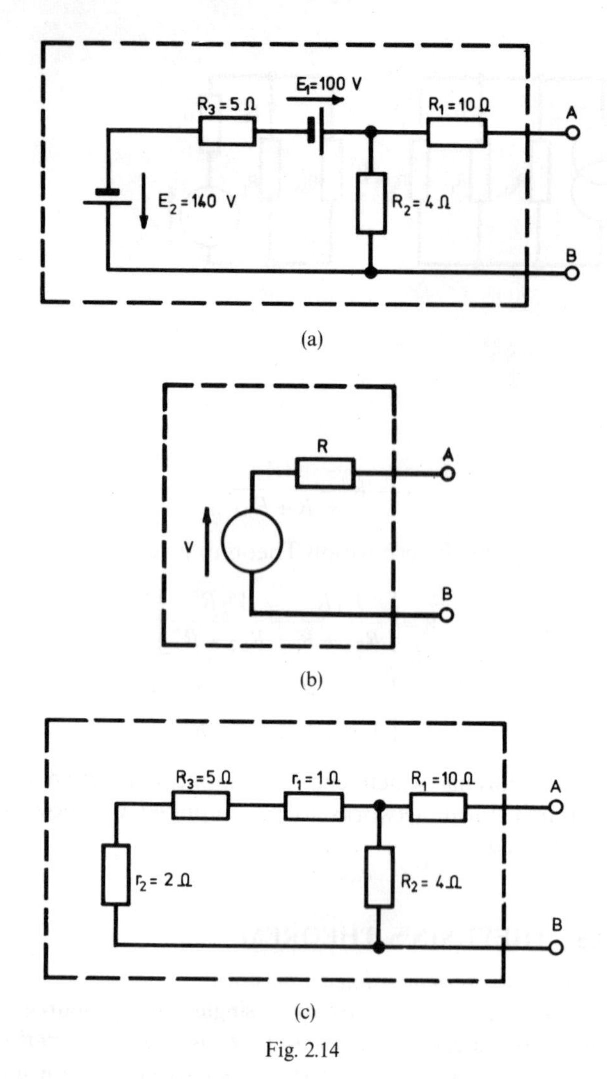

(a)

(b)

(c)

Fig. 2.14

as shown by figure 1.11; let these internal resistances be 1 Ω and 2 Ω respectively. To obtain the value of V in figure 2.14b a d.c. voltmeter is connected across AB. Assuming the voltmeter resistance is very high, the voltmeter may be considered to act as an open circuit between terminals A and B, hence the voltmeter reading is equal to V. To evaluate R, the batteries are removed from the network and replaced by a 1 Ω and a 2 Ω resistor respectively as shown in figure 2.14c.

An ohmmeter connected between A and B will indicate R ohms since the sources have been replaced by their internal resistances. Note that a voltage source of e.m.f. E and internal (or source) resistance r is replaced by a resistance r.

The usual analytical situation is that the values of source voltage and resistance are given and we are required to calculate V and R. Since there is no external load connected between A and B and therefore no current flowing through R_1, the voltage across AB will be the same as the voltage across R_2; this voltage is of course V of figure 2.14b.

Let us now determine the voltage across R_2. Figure 2.14a can be re-drawn as shown in figures 2.15a and b.

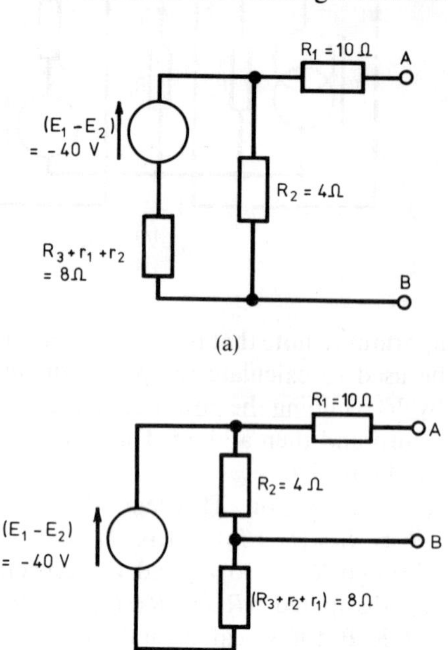

(a)

(b)

Fig. 2.15

Hence the voltage across R_2 is

$$\frac{(E_1 - E_2)R_2}{R_2 + (R_3 + r_1 + r_2)}$$

(ref. equation 2.10)

$$= \frac{-40 \times 4}{12} = -13.3 \text{ V}$$

and this is the value of V to be inserted in figure 2.14b.

From figure 2.14c the resistance measured between A and B when the sources are replaced by their internal resistances is

$$R = R_1 + \frac{R_2(R_3 + r_1 + r_2)}{R_2 + R_3 + r_1 + r_2} = 10 + \frac{4 \times 8}{12} = 12.7\ \Omega$$

Thus the linear two-terminal network of figure 2.14a can be replaced by a voltage source of e.m.f. $V = -13.3$ V in series with a resistance of 12.7 Ω as far as measurements at the terminals AB are concerned. The significance of the − sign in the expression for the voltage is apparent by referring to figure 1.3c.

2.9 NORTON'S THEOREM

Any two-terminal linear network of generators and resistors can be replaced by a **single current source in parallel with a resistor**. *The source current is equal to the current that flows between the terminals when they are short-circuited; the value of the resistor is equal to the* *resistance measured between the terminals when all generators are replaced by their internal resistances.*

If we refer again to the linear active two-terminal network of figure 2.14a we can determine the parameters I and R of its Norton equivalent circuit which is shown in figure 2.16.

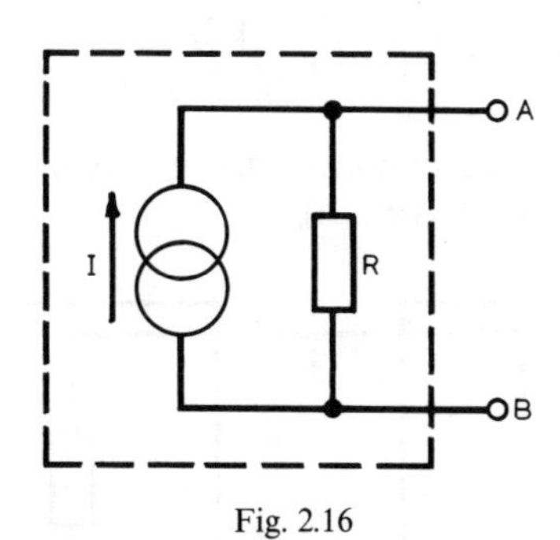

Fig. 2.16

To determine practically the value of I in figure 2.16 a d.c. ammeter is connected between A and B of figure 2.14a. Assuming the ammeter resistance is very low, the ammeter may be considered to act as a short circuit between the terminals, hence the ammeter reading is equal to I. R is evaluated in the same way as for the Thevenin equivalent circuit.

Let us calculate the ammeter reading; if we connect a short-circuit between A and B of figure 2.15a the circuit reduces successively to those of figures 2.17a and 2.17b.

Applying Ohm's Law to figure 2.17b; the current supplied by the source is

$$I' = (E_1 - E_2) \bigg/ \left[R_3 + r_1 + r_2 + \frac{R_1 R_2}{R_1 + R_2} \right]$$

$$= -40 \bigg/ \left[8 + \frac{40}{14} \right] = \frac{-70}{19} \text{ A}$$

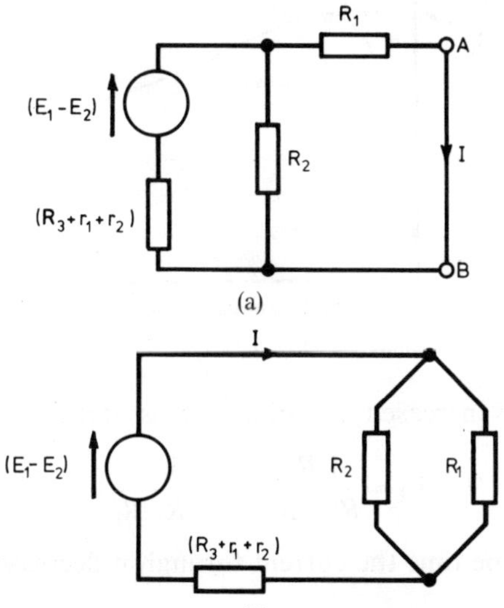

(a)

(b)

Fig. 2.17

Applying equation 2.12 we obtain

$$I = \frac{I' R_2}{R_1 + R_2} = \frac{-70}{19} \cdot \frac{4}{14} = \frac{-20}{19} = -1.05 \text{ A.}$$

Thus in figure 2.16

$$I = -1.05 \text{ A}, R = 12.7 \, \Omega.$$

It is appropriate at this point to consider the significance of the phrase in Thevenin's and Norton's Theorems, 'when all generators are replaced by their internal resistances'. When the voltage source of figure 2.18a is replaced by its internal resistance, figure 2.18b results and when the current source of figure 2.18c is replaced by its internal resistance, figure 2.18d results.

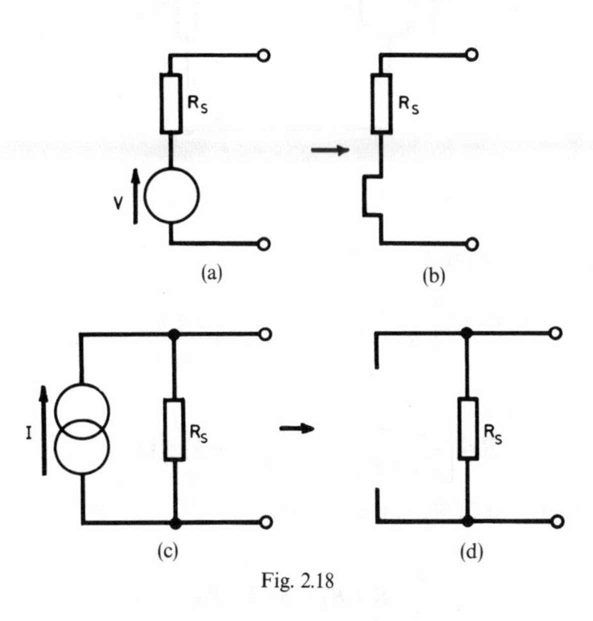

Fig. 2.18

Thus if we consider the 'practical' sources of 2.18a and 2.18c as 'ideal' sources to which are added source, or internal, resistances it is apparent that to replace a practical voltage source by its internal resistance, we replace the 'ideal' generator V by a short circuit. To replace a practical current source by its internal resistance, we replace the 'ideal' generator I by an open circuit. For this reason it is often said that *a 'dead' ideal voltage source is a short circuit and a 'dead' ideal current source is an open circuit.*

Thevenin's Theorem is sometimes applied to networks which do not, at first sight, appear to be two-terminal networks; for example it may be used to calculate the current in branch CD of the circuit of figure 2.19a. The internal resistance of the voltage source is assumed to be zero.

Suppose R_5 is removed so that there is now a two-terminal network with C and D as the terminals; applying Thevenin's Theorem it is found that in the equivalent

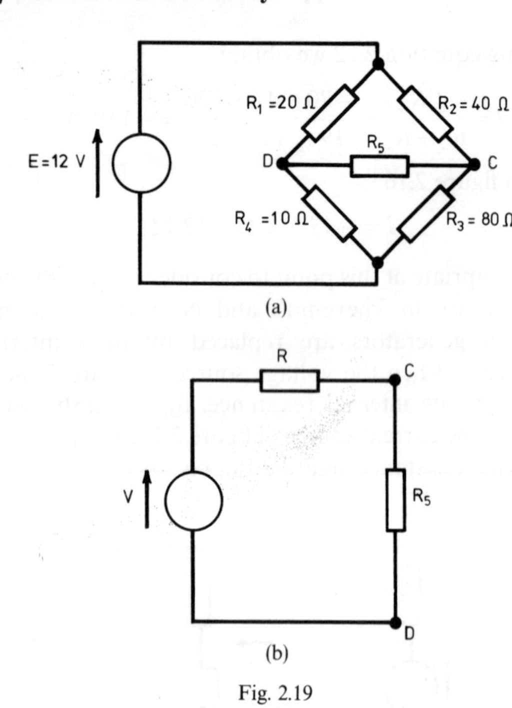

(a)

(b)

Fig. 2.19

circuit shown in figure 2.19b

$$V=E\left[\frac{R_3}{R_2+R_3}-\frac{R_4}{R_1+R_4}\right]=4\text{ V}$$

and

$$R=\left[\frac{R_1R_4}{R_1+R_4}+\frac{R_2R_3}{R_2+R_3}\right]=33.3\,\Omega$$

The current in R_5 is therefore

$$I=\frac{V}{R+R_5}=\frac{4}{33.3+R_5}$$

and can easily be determined for any value of R_5. For example if $R_5=50\,\Omega$, $I=0.048$ A $=48$ mA. The problem can also be solved by direct application of Kirchhoff's Laws; the student should do this and compare the results obtained by the two methods.

2.10 THE MAXIMUM POWER TRANSFER THEOREM

In many branches of electrical and electronic engineering one requires to transfer power from a source to a load; at this stage attention will be confined to a source supplying a resistance load. The following theorem states the condition for maximum power transfer.

A source of internal resistance R_S supplies maximum power to a resistance load R_L when $R_L=R_S$; that is, when the source and load resistances are equal. The value of this maximum power is known as the *available power* and the condition for maximum power transfer is known as the *matched condition.*

The theorem may be proved by writing down an expression for the power P supplied to a load resistance R_L. If R_L is varied, the power will be a maximum when $dP/dR_L=0$.

Applying Ohm's Law to the circuit of figure 2.20. $I=V/(R_S+R_L)$ and the power dissipated in R_L is

$$P=I^2R_L=\frac{V^2R_L}{(R_S+R_L)^2}$$

If R_L is varied, the condition for maximum power dissipation in R_L is $dP/dR_L=0$.

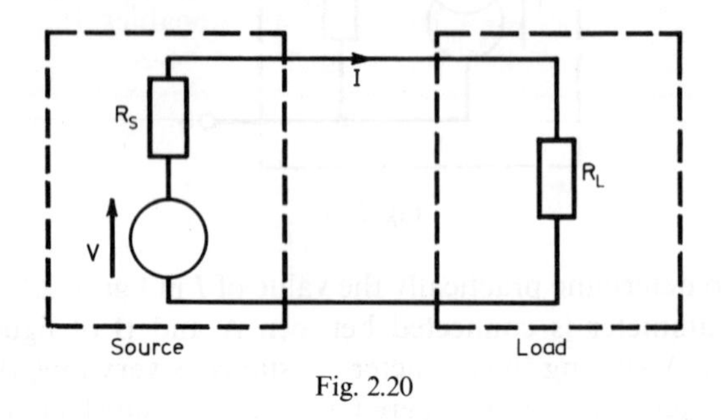

Fig. 2.20

That is

$$\frac{(R_S+R_L)^2-R_L2(R_S+R_L)}{(R_S+R_L)^4}=0$$

† giving $R_L=R_S$ which is the matched condition.

When $R_L=R_S$, the voltage across the load is $V/2$ and the available power is

$$\left(\frac{V}{2}\right)^2\bigg/R_L=\frac{V^2}{4R_L}=\frac{V^2}{4R_S}$$

If the power in the load is measured for different values of R_L a curve of the form shown in figure 2.21 is obtained.

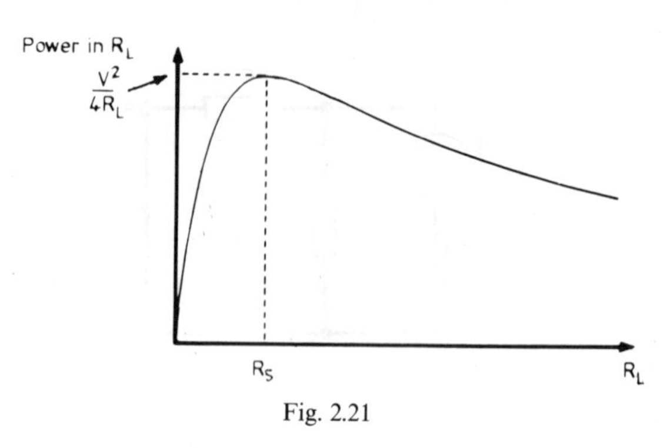

Fig. 2.21

As R_L is increased the voltage across it increases, since

$$V_L=\frac{VR_L}{R_S+R_L}=\frac{V}{1+R_S/R_L};$$

At the same time the current through it decreases, since

$$I=\frac{V}{R_S+R_L}.$$

2.11 THE STAR-DELTA (T-Π) TRANSFORMATION

When introducing Thevenin's and Norton's Theorems it was stated that the networks being considered had one pair of terminals; in practice there are many networks having three terminals although for the purpose of analysis they are often drawn as four-terminal or *two-port* networks, two of the terminals being connected to the same point. In their simplest form these networks contain three resistors which may be in the form of a T (or star) or a Π (or delta) as shown in figures 2.22a and 2.22b. The following transformation enables the two configurations to be interchanged.

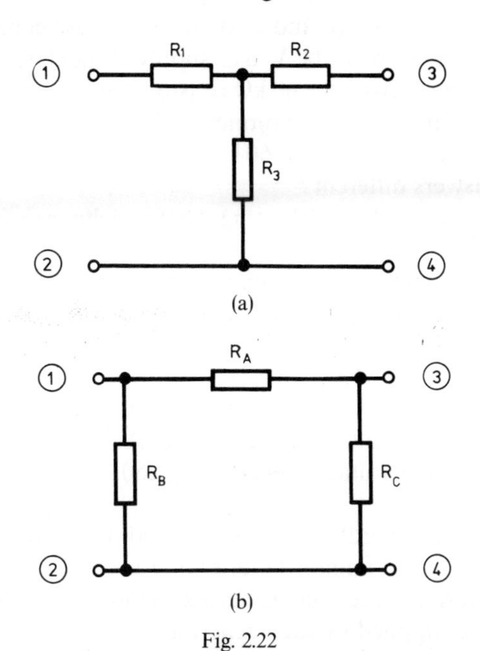

Fig. 2.22

It is required to express R_1, R_2 and R_3 in terms of R_A, R_B and R_C so that the two networks are equivalent where terminal measurements are concerned. The procedure is to determine the resistance, or conductance, between corresponding pairs of terminals, under prescribed conditions, and equate them.

The input resistance at port①②with port③④open is

$$R_1+R_3=\frac{R_B(R_A+R_C)}{R_A+R_B+R_C} \qquad (2.32)$$

The input resistance at port③④with port①② open is

$$R_2+R_3=\frac{R_C(R_A+R_B)}{R_A+R_B+R_C} \qquad (2.33)$$

The input resistance between terminals ① and ③ with ports①② and③④ open is

$$R_1+R_2=\frac{R_A(R_B+R_C)}{R_A+R_B+R_C} \qquad (2.34)$$

From equations 2.32, 2.33, 2.34

$$\left.\begin{aligned} R_1&=\frac{R_AR_B}{R_A+R_B+R_C}\\ R_2&=\frac{R_CR_A}{R_A+R_B+R_C}\\ R_3&=\frac{R_BR_C}{R_A+R_B+R_C}\end{aligned}\right\} \qquad (2.35)$$

To perform the inverse transformation from star to delta it is convenient to work in terms of conductances. Putting $G_A=1/R_A$, $G_1=1/R_1$ etc. and adopting a similar procedure to that used above we obtain the following.

The input conductance at port①②with port③④short-circuited is

$$G_A+G_B=\frac{G_1(G_2+G_3)}{G_1+G_2+G_3} \qquad (2.36)$$

The input conductance at port③④with port①②short-circuited is

$$G_C+G_A=\frac{G_2(G_3+G_1)}{G_1+G_2+G_3} \qquad (2.37)$$

The input conductance at port①② with terminals①③ short-circuited is

$$G_B+G_C=\frac{G_3(G_1+G_2)}{G_1+G_2+G_3} \qquad (2.38)$$

From equations 2.36, 2.37, 2.38

$$\left.\begin{aligned} G_A&=\frac{G_1G_2}{G_1+G_2+G_3} \text{ giving } R_A=\frac{R_1R_2+R_2R_3+R_3R_1}{R_3}=\frac{\Sigma R_1R_2}{R_3}\\ G_B&=\frac{G_3G_1}{G_1+G_2+G_3} \text{ giving } R_B=\frac{\Sigma R_1R_2}{R_2}\\ G_C&=\frac{G_2G_3}{G_1+G_2+G_3} \text{ giving } R_C=\frac{\Sigma R_1R_2}{R_1}\end{aligned}\right\} \qquad (2.39)$$

It will have been observed that conductances in series are treated in the same way as resistances in parallel and vice-versa.

PROBLEMS

2.1. Using Kirchhoff's Laws determine the resistance between terminals A and B of the network shown in figure Q.1.

2.2. Determine, using (i) Kirchhoff's Laws and (ii) the Principle of Superposition, the current flowing in R in the circuit of Fig. Q.2.

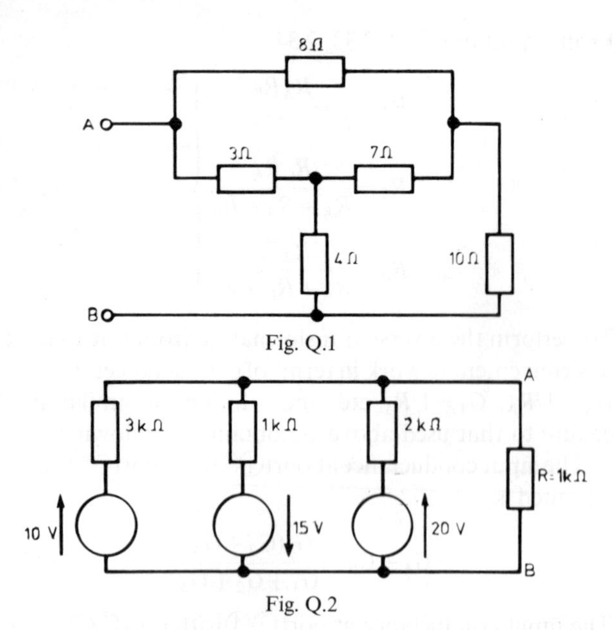

Fig. Q.1

Fig. Q.2

2.3. Determine the Thevenin and Norton equivalent circuits of the network shown in figure Q.3.

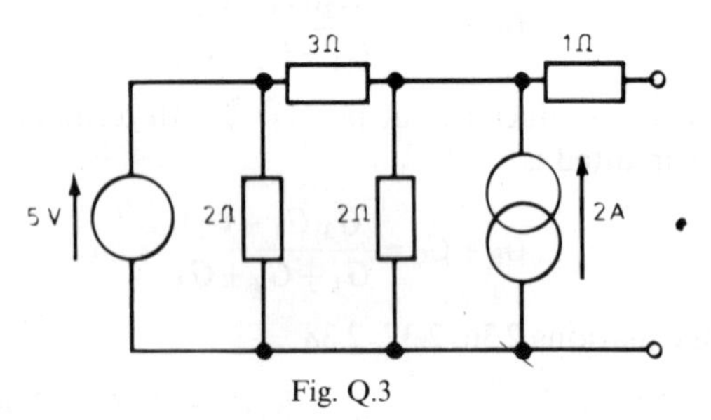

Fig. Q.3

2.4. Use Thevenin's Theorem to reduce the circuit of figure Q.4. to a single voltage generator in series with a resistor.

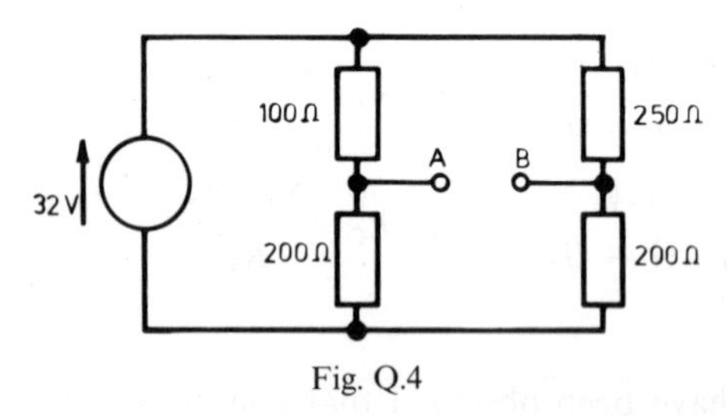

Fig. Q.4

Plot a curve showing the variation of the power dissipated in a resistor R_L connected across AB as R_L is varied between 0 and 500 Ω.

2.5. Derive the Thevenin and Norton equivalent circuits of the network shown in figure Q.5. Hence, determine the current that would flow in a 1 kΩ resistor connected across AB.

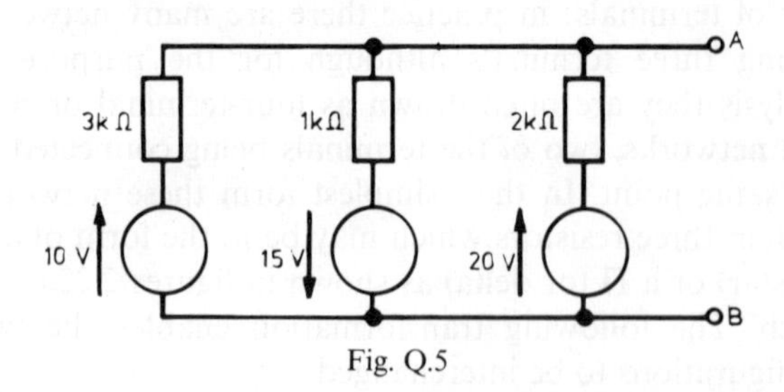

Fig. Q.5

2.6. A 10 kΩ resistor and a 60 kΩ resistor are connected in series to a 100 V d.c. supply. Calculate (i) the voltage across the 60 kΩ resistor and (ii) the reading of a moving coil voltmeter of resistance 100 kΩ connected across the 60 kΩ resistor. Why are the two answers different?

2.7. Repeat problem 2.1. using the star-delta transformation.

2.8. Measurements of terminal voltage and load current on two d.c. generators gave the following results:

Load current	0	25	50	A
Terminal voltage: generator A	250	240	230	V
Terminal voltage: generator B	250	215	180	V

If the generators are connected in parallel and supply a common load, taking a current of 50 A, determine the voltage across the load and the current supplied by each generator.

2.9. A two-wire distributor 200 m long is fed at one end from a nominal 240 V supply. It is loaded as follows

Distance from feed point	50	80	120	200	m
Current loading	40	50	30	60	A

(a) Determine the voltage at each load point if the cross sectional area of each copper conductor is 1.3×10^{-4} m^2 and the resistivity of copper is 1.56×10^{-8} Ωm.

(b) Determine the voltage at each load point when the distributor is fed simultaneously at both ends from the 240 V supply.

CHAPTER THREE

Methods of Circuit Analysis

3.1 INTRODUCTION

In the worked example of section 2.6 the current through, and the voltage drop across each resistor was determined by assigning a current to each branch of the network and applying Kirchhoff's Laws. A solution was also obtained by the method of successive simplification of the network. Whilst these methods are satisfactory for relatively simple networks, when dealing with complicated circuits it is important to work with the minimum number of variables to obtain the simplest method of solution. In the following sections the methods of mesh and nodal analysis are introduced; in general these result in fewer equations than the branch current method.

3.2 NETWORK TOPOLOGY

To select the most appropriate method of analyzing a network it is necessary to examine the way in which the elements and sources in the network are interconnected; one is not concerned with the values of the elements nor indeed with the type of element.

The study of the interconnections is known as *network topology* and some of the relevant terms will now be defined.

A *graph* is a diagram showing the interconnection of the elements, in which the elements are replaced by lines. In a network containing ideal sources the voltage sources are replaced by short-circuits and the current sources are replaced by open-circuits before the graph is drawn.

Figure 3.1b shows the graph of the network of figure 3.1a.

A *node* is the junction of two or more elements; in figure 3.1b points 1 2 3 and 4 are nodes.

A *branch* is the path between two nodes and a *loop* is a set of branches forming a closed path.

A *mesh* is a loop which does not contain any closed loops within it; thus in figure 3.1b the closed path 1 2 3 4 is a *loop* but not a *mesh.*

A *tree* is a collection of branches which connects all the nodes but does not contain any loops; branches of the graph not included in the tree are known as *link branches.* There may be several possible trees for a given graph as shown in figures 3.1c, d and e; the link branches are shown by the broken lines.

When sections of a network do not have a direct connection between them but are coupled by mutual inductance they are said to be *separate parts* of the network. *Only those networks having a single part will be considered at this stage.*

The problem of analyzing the network of figure 3.1a is to establish the minimum number of variables that will describe completely the behaviour of the network and then to write down and solve *the minimum number of independent equations for the network.* In this context the term independent means that each equation contains some information not found in the other equations.

3.3 SOME METHODS OF NETWORK ANALYSIS

3.3.1 Branch Current Analysis

In the branch current method of analysis, a current is assigned to each of the b branches of the network. Kirchhoff's Voltage Law is applied round each closed loop and Kirchhoff's Current Law is applied at $(n-1)$ nodes where n is the total number of nodes in the network; the equation for the nth node is not an independent equation. Since there are b branch currents there are therefore b equations to solve.

In the network of figure 3.1a there are six branches ($b=6$), the branch currents are $I_1 - I_6$ and the equations are

$$V_1 - I_1R_1 - I_2R_2 + I_4R_4 = 0 \text{ for loop①②④}$$

$$V_2 - I_6R_6 + I_5R_5 + I_4R_4 = 0 \text{ for loop②③④}$$

$$I_2R_2 + I_5R_5 - I_3R_3 = 0 \text{ for loop①②③}$$

$$I_1 - I_2 - I_3 = 0 \text{ for node ①}$$

$$I_2 + I_4 - I_5 = 0 \text{ for node ②}$$

$$I_3 + I_5 + I_6 = 0 \text{ for node ③}$$

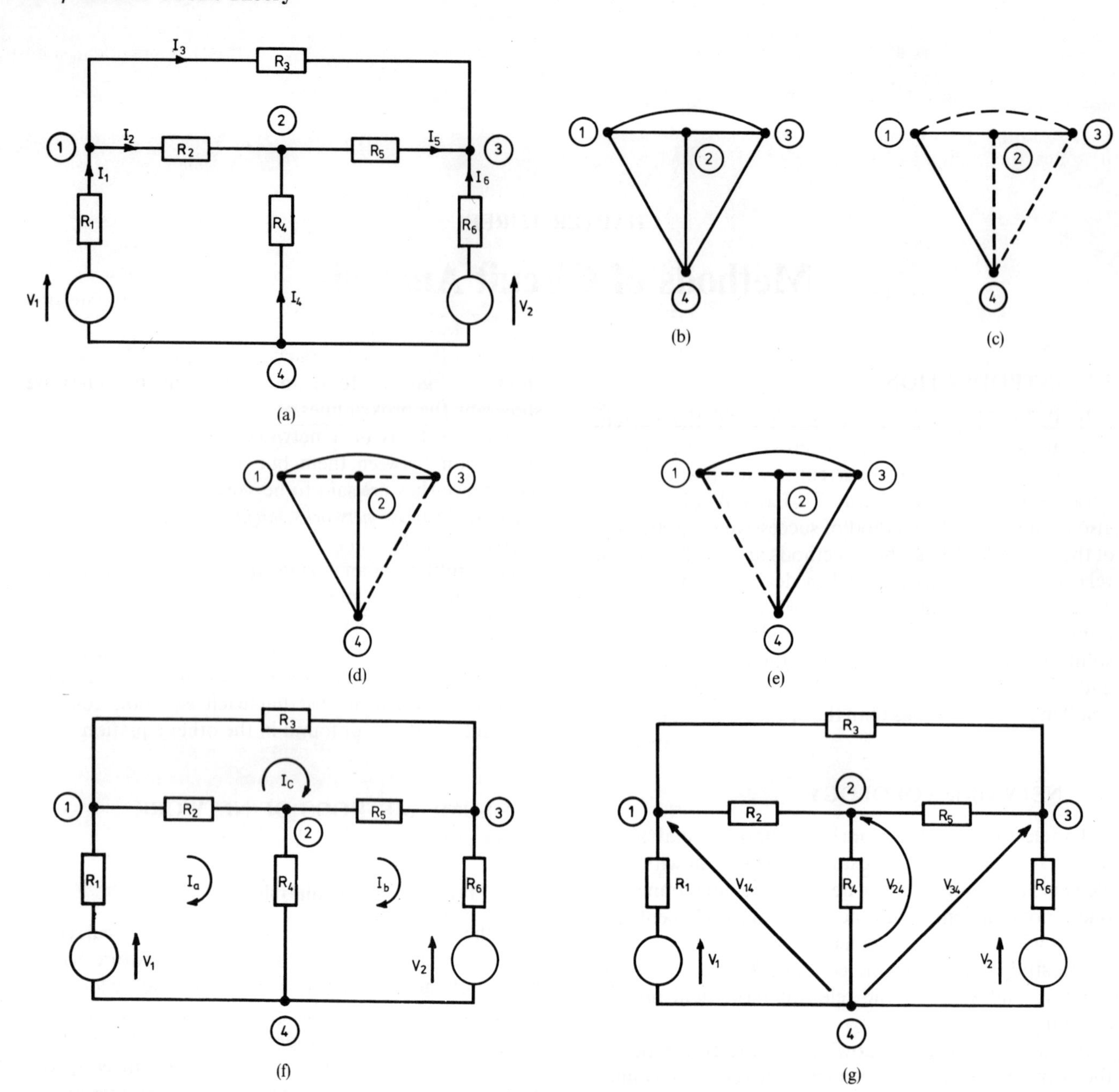

Fig. 3.1

The equations may be re-arranged as follows

$$I_1R_1 + I_2R_2 \qquad -I_4R_4 \qquad = V_1 \qquad (3.1)$$

$$-I_4R_4 - I_5R_5 + I_6R_6 = V_2 \qquad (3.2)$$

$$I_2R_2 - I_3R_3 \qquad + I_5R_5 \qquad = 0 \qquad (3.3)$$

$$I_1 \quad -I_2 \quad -I_3 \qquad = 0 \qquad (3.4)$$

$$I_2 \qquad + I_4 \quad -I_5 \qquad = 0 \qquad (3.5)$$

$$I_3 \qquad + I_5 \quad + I_6 \quad = 0 \qquad (3.6)$$

Solution for the branch currents $I_1 - I_6$ is most conveniently performed using determinants as shown in Appendix 1.

3.3.2 Loop or Mesh Analysis

In mesh analysis it is necessary to introduce the concept of a current circulating in a loop or mesh, although such a current is not a reality. For example, I_a, I_b and I_c in figure 3.1f are loop currents of the network of figure 3.1a but they are not necessarily the currents flowing in the circuit elements. Considering the clockwise direction as positive, the currents in R_2, R_4 and R_5 are respectively $(I_a - I_c)$, $(I_a - I_b)$ and $(I_b - I_c)$.

It is required to determine the minimum number of independent loop currents that will describe the network completely.

If the graph of the network has a total of b branches and n nodes then, the tree will have $(n-1)$ branches and $(b-n+1)$ link branches, since the first branch connects *two* nodes and each subsequent branch connects *one* additional node.

It can be seen from figures 3.1c, d and e that as each link branch is added to the tree an additional closed loop is formed so that the number of closed loops is equal to the number of link branches; moreover the loops are independent, each additional loop containing a new element. In general we can state that

In any single part network the number of independent loops is one greater than the difference between the number of branches and the number of nodes

† *or* $l=(b-n+1)$

[For a network having p separate parts $l=(b-n+p)$]

The procedure for applying mesh analysis is to assign the loop currents and then apply Kirchhoff's Voltage Law to each loop, so that for a single part network $l=(b-n+1)$ independent equations are obtained. It may, in practice, be convenient to convert all current generators to equivalent voltage generators.

The equations for figure 3.1f are

$$I_a R_1+(I_a-I_c)R_2+(I_a-I_b)R_4=V_1 \text{ for loop①②④}$$

$$I_c R_3+(I_c-I_a)R_2+(I_c-I_b)R_5=0 \text{ for loop①②③}$$

$$I_b R_6+(I_b-I_c)R_5+(I_b-I_a)R_4=-V_2 \text{ for loop ②③④}$$

These equations may be re-arranged in the form

$$I_a(R_1+R_2+R_4)-I_b R_4 \quad -I_c R_2 \quad =V_1 \qquad (3.7)$$

$$-I_a R_4 \quad +I_b(R_4+R_5+R_6)-I_c R_5 \quad =-V_2 \qquad (3.8)$$

$$-I_a R_2 \quad -I_b R_5 \quad +I_c(R_2+R_3+R_5)=0 \qquad (3.9)$$

Solution for the loop currents I_a, I_b and I_c may conveniently be performed using determinants.

3.3.3 Nodal Analysis

It is shown in 3.3.2 that the tree of a network of n nodes contains $(n-1)$ branches and since each branch joins two nodes there are $(n-1)$ independent node voltages; the voltage at the nth node may be obtained from the $(n-1)$ equations and is not independent. It is often convenient to select one node as the reference and pair all the remaining nodes with it, giving $(n-1)$ independent *node-pair* voltages.

In general we can state that

In any single part network the number of independent nodal equations is one less than the number of nodes in the network.

When applying nodal analysis one node is selected as a reference and each remaining node is assigned a voltage with respect to the reference; in figure 3.1g which has four nodes 4 is the reference node and V_{14}, V_{24} and V_{34} are the three node-pair voltages. Kirchhoff's Current Law is now applied at each node except the reference node. In practice it may be convenient to convert all voltage sources to current sources, although this has not been done for the network of figure 3.1a.

The equations for the network of figure 3.1g are

$$\frac{(V_{14}-V_1)}{R_1}+\frac{(V_{14}-V_{24})}{R_2}+\frac{(V_{14}-V_{34})}{R_3}=0 \text{ at node①}$$

$$\frac{(V_{24}-V_{14})}{R_2}+\frac{(V_{24}-V_{34})}{R_5}+\frac{V_{24}}{R_4}=0 \text{ at node②}$$

$$\frac{(V_{34}-V_2)}{R_6}+\frac{(V_{34}-V_{24})}{R_5}+\frac{(V_{34}-V_{14})}{R_3}=0 \text{ at node③}$$

After re-arranging, and using conductances instead of resistances, the equations become

$$V_{14}(G_1+G_2+G_3)-V_{24}G_2 \quad -V_{34}G_3=V_1G_1 \qquad (3.10)$$

$$-V_{14}G_2 \quad +V_{24}(G_2+G_4+G_5)-V_{34}G_5=0 \qquad (3.11)$$

$$-V_{14}G_3 \quad -V_{24}G_5 \quad +V_{34}(G_3+G_5+G_6)=V_2G_6 \qquad (3.12)$$

The equations may be solved for V_{14}, V_{24} and V_{34} in the usual manner.

3.4 CHOICE OF METHOD OF ANALYSIS

The method of analysis chosen will usually be the one requiring the solution of the least number of equations.

The branch current method requires b equations, mesh analysis requires $l=(b-n+1)$ equations and nodal analysis requires $(n-1)$ equations. Before commencing the analysis it is therefore necessary to count the number branches b and the number of nodes n contained in the network. The number of link branches l can then be determined and if $(n-1)<l$ the nodal analysis method may be chosen; if $(n-1)=l$ either the nodal or mesh method may be chosen.

PROBLEMS

3.1. For the circuit of figure Q.1 determine the ratio Vi/Vo using
(i) Mesh analysis
(ii) Nodal analysis
(iii) Thevenin's Theorem
Resistance values are in ohms.

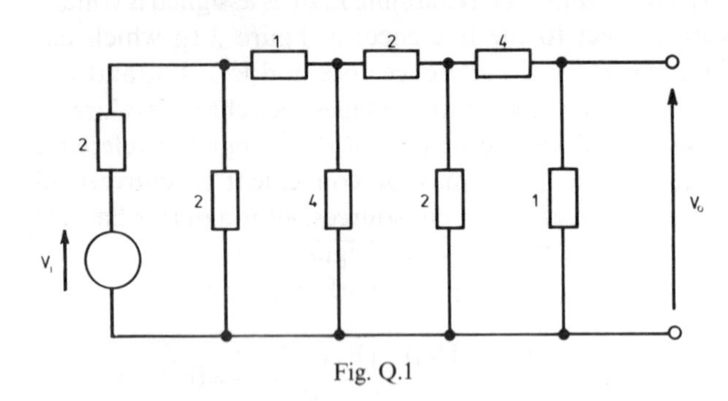

Fig. Q.1

3.2. Using either mesh or nodal analysis write down the equations and state the procedure to determine the current in the 6-ohm resistor of figure Q.2. (Study the topology of the network to determine the simplest method.) Resistance values are in ohms.

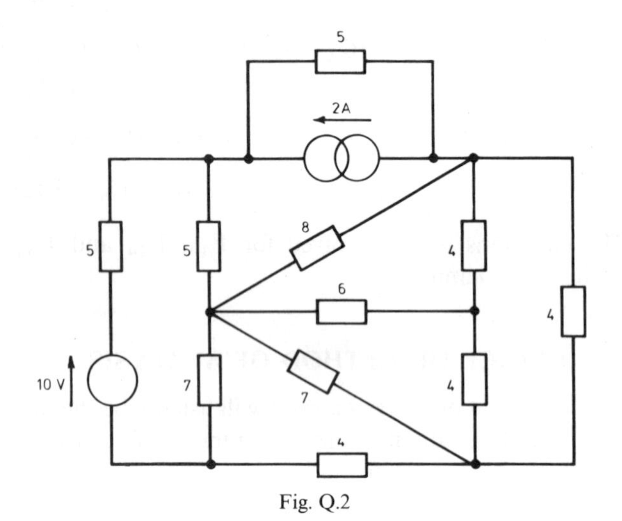

Fig. Q.2

3.3. Calculate the current in the 4-ohm resistor in the circuit of figure Q.3 using
(i) Mesh analysis
(ii) Nodal analysis
(iii) Norton's Theorem
Resistance values are in ohms.

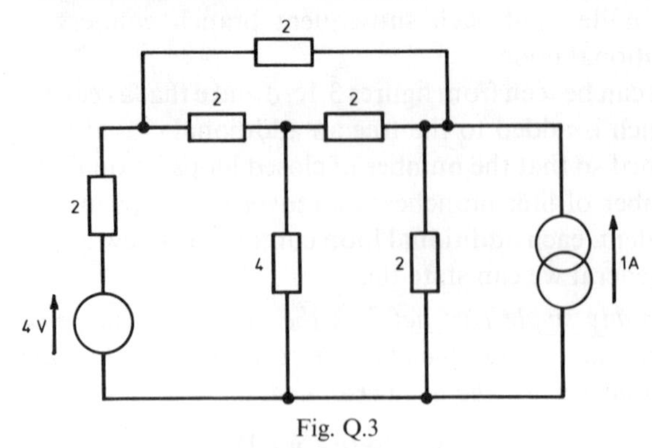

Fig. Q.3

3.4. In the circuit of figure Q.4. calculate the currents I_1, I_2 and I_3. Resistance values are in ohms.

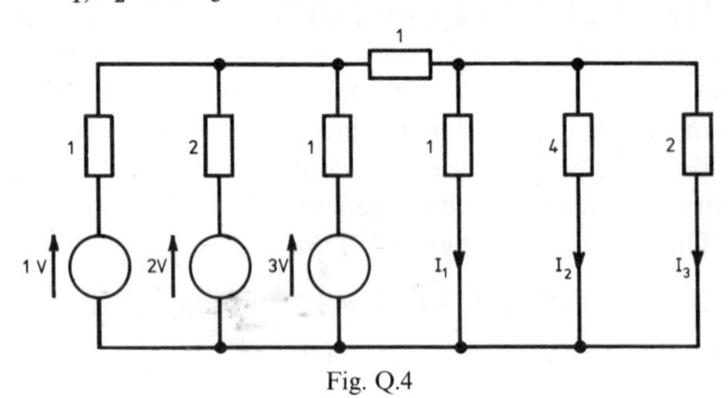

Fig. Q.4

3.5. For the circuit shown in figure Q.5., determine the ratio of the readings of the ammeter *A* when the switch SW is open and when it is closed.

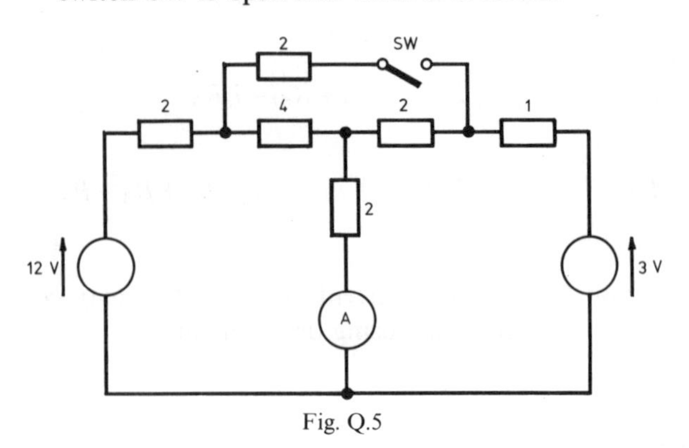

Fig. Q.5

CHAPTER FOUR

The Transient Response of Simple Circuits

4.1 INTRODUCTION

In the analysis of the circuits in the previous chapter it has been assumed that the voltages and currents are constant quantities and do not vary with time; the circuits are said to be in the *steady state*. We will now study the response of some circuits when the excitation or stimulus is changed; this is known as the *transient* performance of the circuit.

4.2 THE CR CIRCUIT

The network of figure 4.1a consists of a resistor R and a capacitor C as shown in figure 4.1b. The excitation is a voltage source V, applied to the network when the switch SW is closed. It is required to determine the variation of voltage, as a function of time, across the capacitor C.

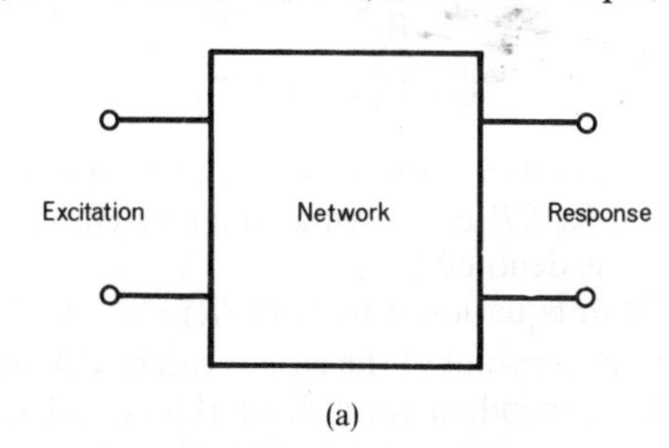

(a)

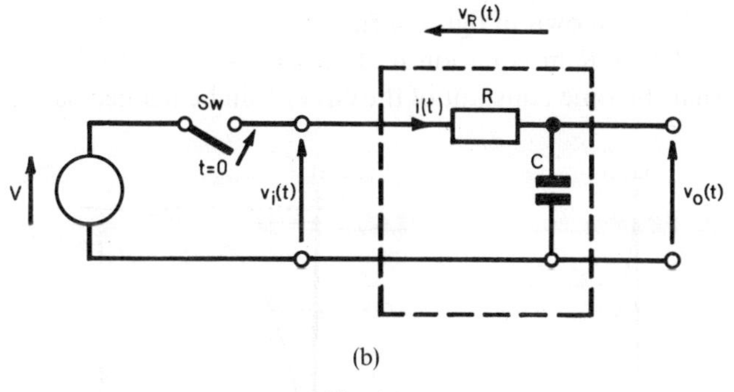

(b)

Fig. 4.1

For convenience, the instant at which the switch is closed is designated $t=0$; it is assumed that the capacitor initially has a charge Q_0, resulting in a capacitor voltage $V_0=Q_0/C$ at $t=0$. V_0 is such that the upper plate of the capacitor is positive with respect to the lower plate. The form of the excitation is shown in figure 4.2; it is known as a *step function* of amplitude V and is defined by

$$v_i(t)=0 \text{ when } t<0$$
$$=V \text{ when } t\geqslant 0$$

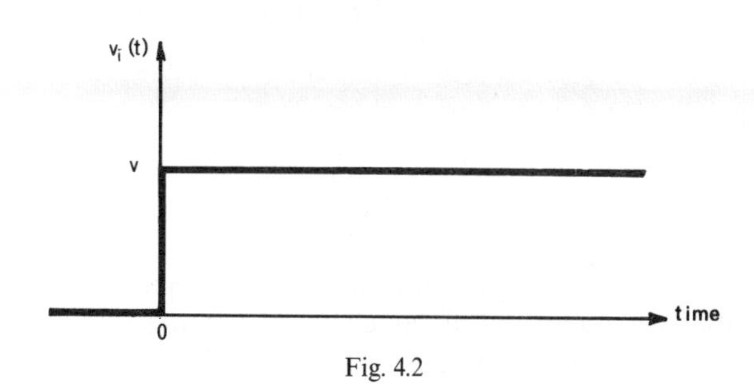

Fig. 4.2

Applying Kirchhoff's Voltage Law to the circuit for $t>0$ gives

$$V-v_R-v_0=0$$

that is

$$V=v_R+v_0$$

$$=iR+\frac{1}{C}\int i\mathrm{d}t \quad (4.1)$$

This is a *first order linear differential equation* which may be solved by differentiating both sides, separating the variables, integrating with respect to time and using the boundary conditions to determine the constant of integration.

Thus from equation 4.1 we obtain

$$0=R\frac{\mathrm{d}i}{\mathrm{d}t}+\frac{i}{C} \quad (4.2)$$

Separating the variables gives

$$-\frac{\mathrm{d}t}{CR}=\frac{\mathrm{d}i}{i} \quad (4.3)$$

and integrating both sides of equation 4.3 between the same limits

$$-\frac{t}{CR}+A=\log_e i \quad (4.4)$$

where A is the constant of integration.

In order to evaluate A, consider the initial conditions; immediately after the switch is closed, denoted by $t=0^+$, the voltage across the resistor is $(V-V_0)$, resulting in an initial current $I_0=(V-V_0)/R$. Putting $t=0$ and $i=I_0=(V-V_0)/R$ in equation 4.4 gives

$$A=\log_e I_0=\log_e \frac{(V-V_0)}{R}$$

and substituting for A in equation 4.4

$$-\frac{t}{CR}=\log_e i-\log_e I_0$$

Hence

$$e^{-t/CR}=i/I_0$$

or

† $$i=I_0\,e^{-t/CR}=\frac{(V-V_0)}{R}\,e^{-t/CR} \qquad (4.5)$$

or

† $$i=\frac{V}{R}\,e^{-t/CR}-\frac{V_0}{R}\,e^{-t/CR} \qquad (4.6)$$

It is seen that the current in the circuit decreases exponentially from an initial value $(V-V_0)/R$ at $t=0$ to zero at $t=\infty$ as shown in figure 4.3

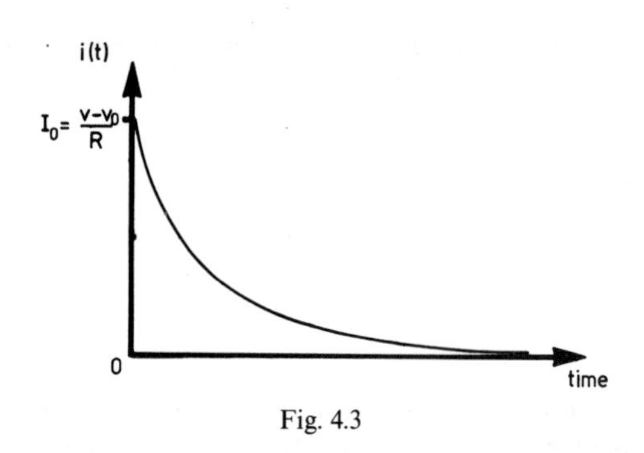

Fig. 4.3

The voltage across the capacitor after the switch is closed is given by

$$v_0=\frac{1}{C}\int i\mathrm{d}t$$

$$=\frac{(V-V_0)}{CR}\int e^{-t/CR}\,\mathrm{d}t$$

$$=\frac{(V-V_0)}{CR}\left[-CR\,e^{-t/CR}+B\right] \qquad (4.7)$$

where B is the constant of integration. Its value is determined by noting that at $t=0$, $v_0=V_0$. Inserting these boundary conditions in equation 4.7 gives

$$V_0=\frac{(V-V_0)}{CR}\left[-CR+B\right]$$

from which

$$B=\frac{VCR}{(V-V_0)}$$

Substituting for B in equation 4.7

† $$v_0=-(V-V_0)\,e^{-t/CR}+V$$

$$=V\left[1-e^{-t/CR}\right]+V_0\,e^{-t/CR} \qquad (4.8)$$

$$=V_0+(V-V_0)\left[1-e^{-t/CR}\right] \qquad (4.9)$$

It is seen that the voltage across the capacitor increases exponentially from an initial value V_0 at $t=0$ to V at $t=\infty$ as shown in figure 4.4.

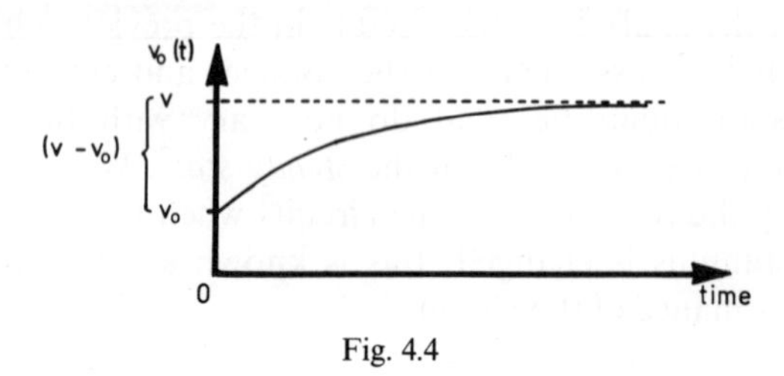

Fig. 4.4

If, as is often the case, the capacitor is initially uncharged, $V_0=0$, and one of the terms disappears, so the expressions for the current and the capacitor voltage are:

† $$i=\frac{V}{R}\,e^{-t/CR} \qquad (4.10)$$

$$v_0=V\left[1-e^{-t/CR}\right] \qquad (4.11)$$

These expressions are shown graphically in figure 4.5.

The product CR is known as the *time constant* of the circuit, and is denoted by τ.

If $t=CR$ in equation 4.10 $i=(V/R)\,e^{-1}=0.37\,V/R$ so that the time constant of the circuit can be defined as the time for the dependent variable (in this case the current) to decrease to approximately 37 per cent of its initial value as shown in figure 4.5a.

If $t=CR$ in equation 4.11 $v_0=V(1-e^{-1})=0.63\,V$ so that the time constant of the circuit can be defined as the

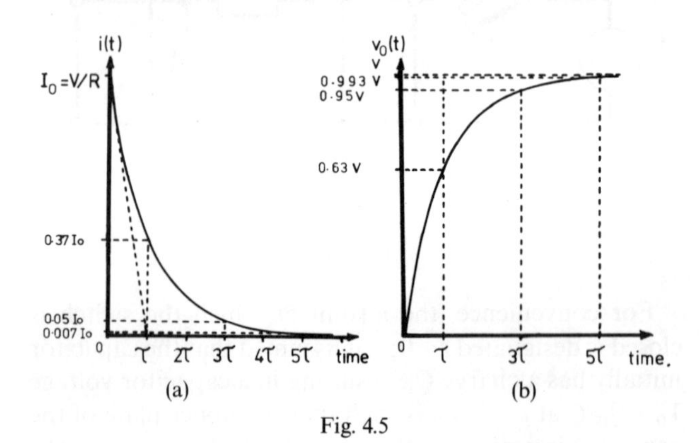

Fig. 4.5

time for the dependent variable (in this case the capacitor voltage) to increase to approximately 63 per cent of its final value as shown in figure 4.5b.

In each case the values of the dependent variable at $t=3\tau$ and $t=5\tau$ are shown as they provide useful rule of thumb information for the engineer wishing to estimate the response of a circuit.

The student should take particular care when applying these definitions to circuits in which there are initial voltages, for example, in figure 4.4 the time constant is the time taken for the capacitor voltage to reach $[V_0+0.63(V-V_0)]$ and *not* the time taken to reach $0.63\,V$.

The time constant of a circuit is also related to the slope of the characteristic, for example from equation 4.10, the slope is

$$\frac{di}{dt}=-\frac{V}{R}\cdot\frac{1}{CR}\,e^{-t/CR}$$

and the initial slope is

$$\left(\frac{di}{dt}\right)_{t=0}=-\frac{V}{R}\frac{1}{CR}=-\frac{I_0}{CR}\text{ amperes per second} \qquad (4.12)$$

so that if the current continued to fall at its initial rate, it would reach zero at $t=CR=\tau$. In figure 4.5a a line is drawn tangential to the initial portion of the characteristic and is seen to meet the time axis at $t=\tau$.

Similarly from equation 4.11

$$\frac{dv_0}{dt}=\frac{V}{CR}\,e^{-t/CR}$$

and the initial slope is

$$\left(\frac{dv_0}{dt}\right)_{t=0}=\frac{V}{CR}\text{ volts per second.} \qquad (4.13)$$

Thus if the capacitor voltage continued to rise at its initial rate it would reach the terminal value V at $t=CR=\tau$.

Consider now a charged capacitor which is discharged through a resistor as shown in figure 4.6a.

The current in the circuit subsequent to the closing of the switch at $t=0$ is

$$i=\frac{v}{R}=-\frac{Cdv}{dt}$$

or

$$\frac{Cdv}{dt}+\frac{v}{R}=0 \qquad (4.14)$$

giving

$$\frac{-t}{CR}+B=\log_e v \qquad (4.15)$$

At $t=0$, $v=V_0$

Therefore $B=\log_e V_0$

Substituting for B in equation (4.15) gives

$$\frac{t}{CR}=\log_e v-\log_e V_0$$

Hence

† $$v=V_0\,e^{-t/CR} \qquad (4.16)$$

but

$$i=v/R$$

Therefore

† $$i=\frac{V_0}{R}\,e^{-t/CR} \qquad (4.17)$$

where V_0/R is the current at $t=0^+$.

The current and voltage waveforms are shown in figure 4.6b and figure 4.6c respectively.

Inspection of equations 4.6 and 4.8 shows that the right-hand side consists of two exponential terms, one of which depends on the excitation V but is independent of the initial voltage V_0; the second term is independent of the excitation but depends on the initial condition of the circuit. Consideration of equation 4.6 shows that the first term on the right hand side is that which would be obtained by applying a voltage V to an *uncharged* capacitor C in series with a resistor R; the second term can be considered as resulting from the connection of a capacitor C, charged initially to V_0, to a resistor R.

Because the circuit consists of linear elements, the Superposition Theorem can be applied for $t>0$ as shown in figure 4.7.

From equations 4.10 and 4.17 the total current

$$i=i_1+i_2=\frac{V}{R}\,e^{-t/CR}-\frac{V_0}{R}\,e^{t/CR}$$

(Compare the direction of the current in figures 4.7c and 4.6a.) The voltage across the capacitor in figure 4.7a is, from equations 4.11 and 4.16

$$v=v_1+v_2=V(1-e^{-t/CR})+V_0\,e^{-t/CR} \qquad (4.18)$$

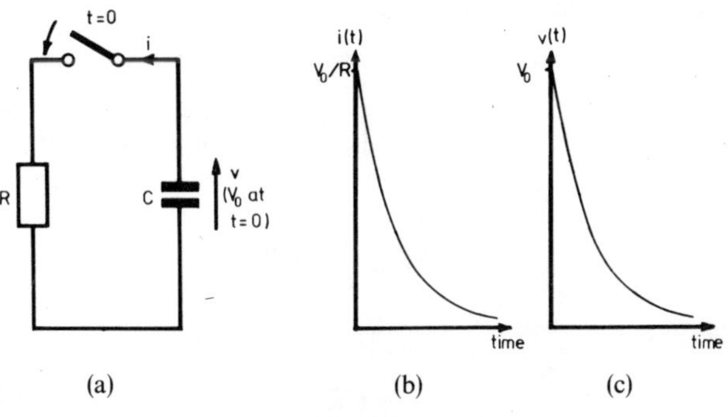

Fig. 4.6

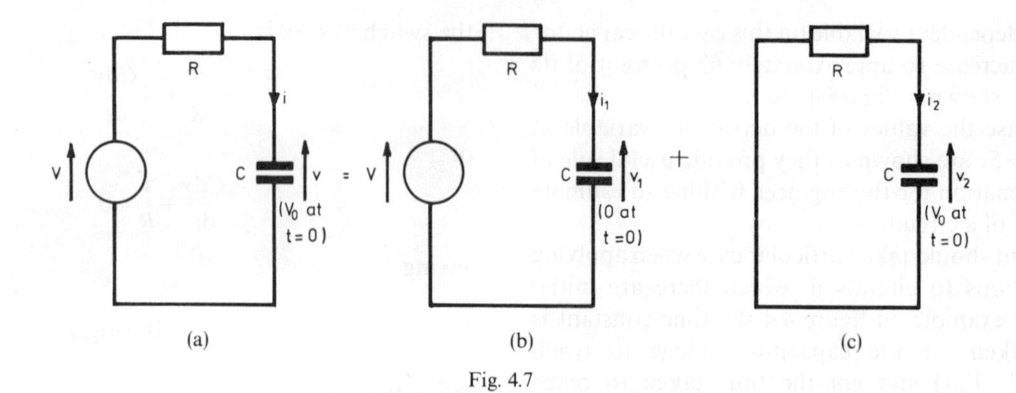

Fig. 4.7

We can now determine the response of a simple CR circuit to a rectangular pulse. The pulse, of width t_1 and amplitude V can be generated by the circuit of figure 4.8a.

At $t=0$ the switch is turned from 1 to 2 where it remains until $t=t_1$ when it is turned to position 3. The voltage v_i applied to the CR circuit is shown in figure 4.8b. Applying equation 4.11, it is seen that between $t=0$ and $t=t_1$ the voltage across the capacitor rises exponentially from zero at $t=0$ to $V'=V(1-e^{-t_1/CR})$ at $t=t_1$.

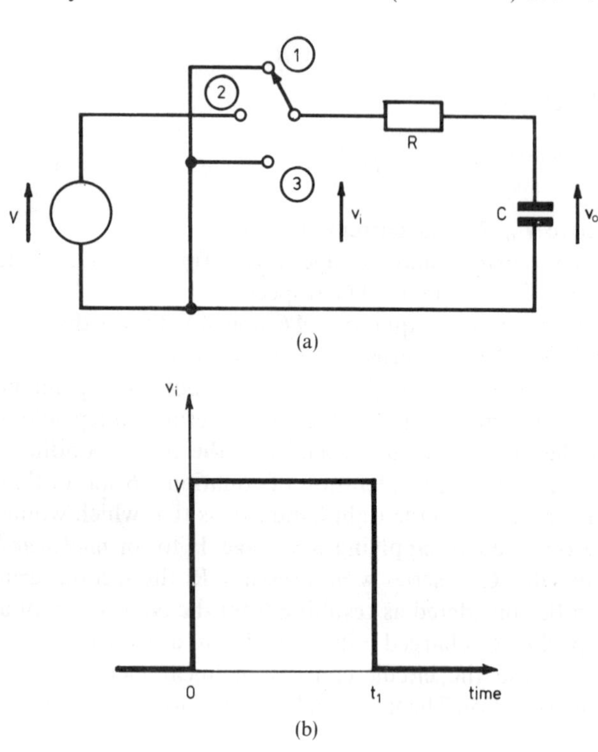

Fig. 4.8

For $t>t_1$ equation 4.16 applies and the voltage decays exponentially to zero from a value $V'=V(1-e^{-t_1/CR})$; that is

$$v_0=V'\,e^{-t'/CR}$$

the new time origin being $t=t_1$; that is $t'=(t-t_1)$.

The waveform of the voltage across the capacitor is shown in figure 4.9.

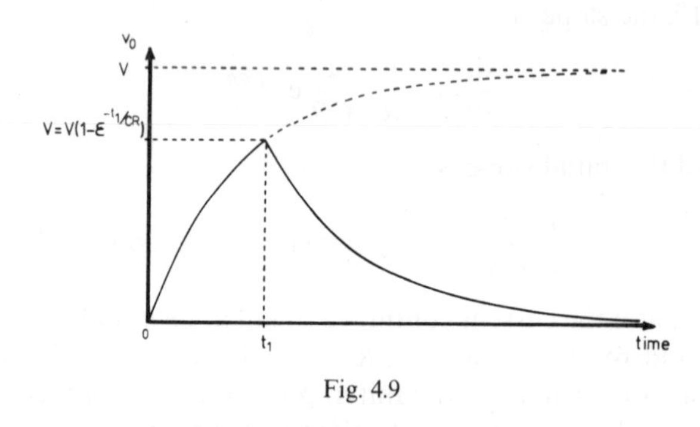

Fig. 4.9

4.3 DIFFERENTIATING AND INTEGRATING CIRCUITS

Using CR circuits it is possible to obtain approximations to the mathematical operations of differentiation and integration with respect to time as shown below.

4.3.1 Differentiation with Respect to Time

The circuit equations for figure 4.10a are

$$v_i=v_0+\frac{1}{C}\int_0^t i\mathrm{d}t$$

$$v_0=iR$$

and if, for any particular set of conditions, C and R are chosen so that $v_0 \ll v_i$

then

$$v_i \doteqdot \frac{1}{C}\int_0^t i\mathrm{d}t$$

$$=\frac{1}{CR}\int_0^t v_0\mathrm{d}t$$

or

† $$v_0 \doteqdot CR\,\frac{\mathrm{d}v_i}{\mathrm{d}t} \qquad (4.19)$$

4.3.2 Integration with Respect to Time

The circuit equations for figure 4.10b are

$$v_i = v_0 + iR$$

$$v_0 = \frac{1}{C}\int_0^t i\,dt$$

and if, for any particular set of conditions, C and R are chosen to that $v_0 \ll v_i$

then

$$v_i \doteq iR$$

$$= CR\frac{dv_0}{dt}$$

or

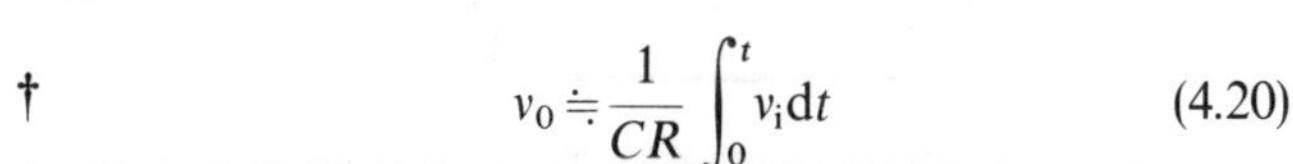

† $$v_0 \doteq \frac{1}{CR}\int_0^t v_i\,dt \qquad (4.20)$$

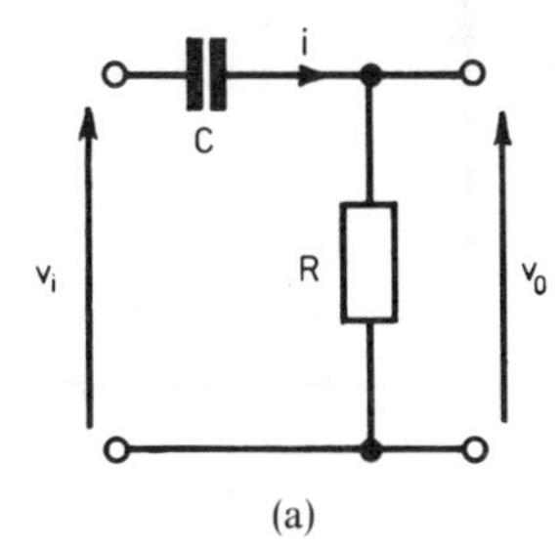

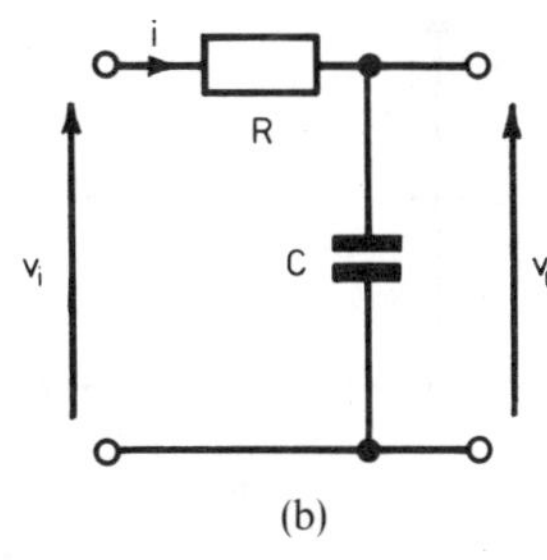

Fig. 4.10

Thus if v_i is a square wave, as shown in figure 4.11a, the differentiated and integrated outputs are as shown in figures 4.11b and 4.11c respectively, and the appropriate waveforms from the integrating and differentiating circuits will approximate to these.

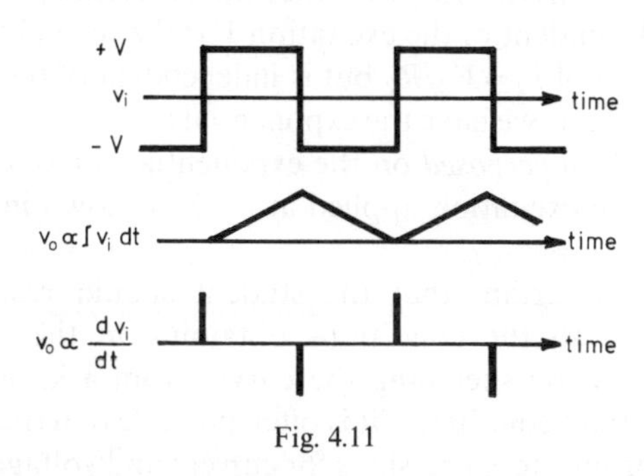

Fig. 4.11

The ability to perform these mathematical operations, particularly integration, is the basis of the analogue computer, but to obtain increased accuracy, the CR circuits are used in conjunction with high-gain electronic amplifiers.

4.4 THE LR CIRCUIT

The growth and decay of current in an inductive circuit will now be examined briefly using techniques similar to those used for the CR circuit.

Figure 4.12a shows a circuit consisting of a resistor R in series with an inductor L; a voltage V is applied at $t=0$.

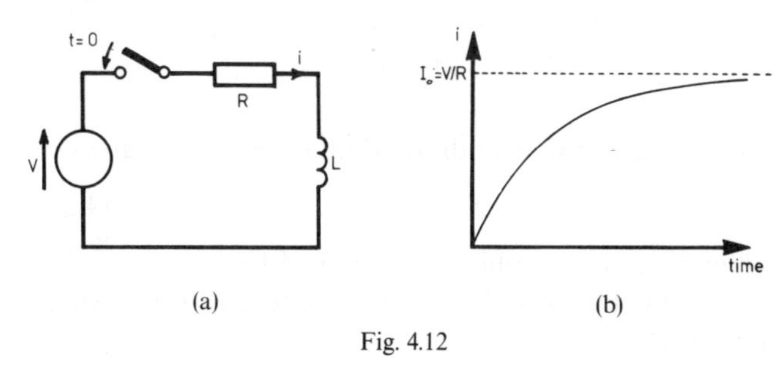

Fig. 4.12

The circuit equation for $t>0$ is

$$V - iR - L\frac{di}{dt} = 0 \qquad (4.21)$$

Re-arranging the terms and multiplying both sides by $e^{Rt/L}$ gives

$$\left[e^{Rt/L}\frac{di}{dt} + \frac{R}{L}e^{Rt/L}i\right] = \frac{V}{L}e^{Rt/L} \qquad (4.22)$$

That is

$$\frac{d}{dt}[i\,e^{Rt/L}] = \frac{V}{L}e^{Rt/L} \qquad (4.23)$$

Integrating both sides of the equation

$$i\,e^{Rt/L} = \frac{V}{L}\frac{L}{R}e^{Rt/L} + A \qquad (4.24)$$

where A is the constant of integration.

To evaluate A insert the initial condition that at $t=0$, $i=0$, giving $A = -V/R$. Putting this value of A in equation 4.24 and re-arranging the terms gives

† $$i = \frac{V}{R}[1 - e^{-Rt/L}] \qquad (4.25)$$

which is shown graphically in figure 4.12b.

We now consider a series circuit consisting of a resistor R and an inductor L, carrying a current, suddenly short-circuited. The problem is illustrated by figure 4.13a in which the switch moves from position 1 to position 2 at time $t=0$.

The circuit equation for $t>0$ is

$$iR + L\frac{di}{dt} = 0 \qquad (4.26)$$

This equation is of the same form as (4.2). Solving and

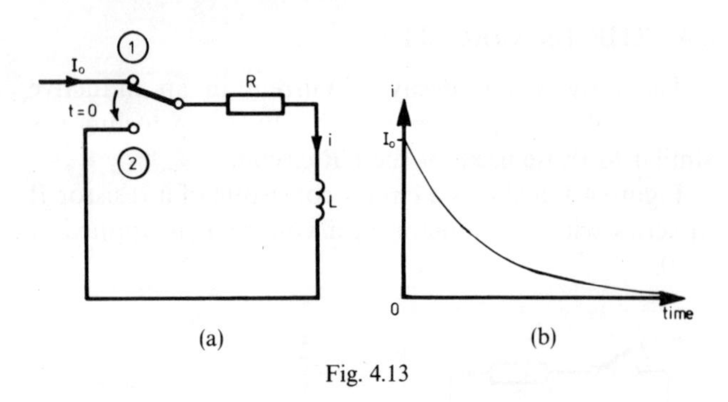

Fig. 4.13

inserting the initial condition that at $t=0$, $i=I_0$ gives

† $$i=I_0\,\mathrm{e}^{-Rt/L} \tag{4.27}$$

which is shown graphically in figure 4.13b.

It should be noted that for this circuit the *time constant* † is $\tau=L/R$.

The case where the resistance of a current-carrying series *LR* circuit is suddenly changed is now considered. This type of problem is encountered for example with some d.c. motor starters, which progressively reduce the armature circuit resistance as the motor speed increases to its normal value.

In the circuit of figure 4.14a the switch is initially in position 1 so that, under steady state conditions, the current flowing through the inductor L is $I_1=V_1/R_1$. The switch is then moved to position 2; the instant of switching is designated $t=0$.

For $t>0$ the problem is described by figure 4.12b. The circuit equation is

$$V_2-iR_2-L\frac{\mathrm{d}i}{\mathrm{d}t}=0 \tag{4.28}$$

Solving this equation and inserting the boundary condition $i=I_1=V_1/R_1$ at $t=0$, gives

$$i=\frac{V_2}{R_2}+\left(\frac{V_1}{R_1}-\frac{V_2}{R_2}\right)\mathrm{e}^{-R_2t/L} \tag{4.29}$$

$$=I_2+(I_1-I_2)\,\mathrm{e}^{-R_2t/L} \tag{4.30}$$

$$=I_1+(I_2-I_1)[1-\mathrm{e}^{-R_2t/L}] \tag{4.31}$$

The result is shown in figure 4.14c $[I_1>I_2]$ and figure 4.14d $[I_2>I_1]$.

It is useful at this stage to examine equation 4.30 in more detail; the expression indicates a steady current I_2 on which is *superposed* an exponential term whose amplitude is equal to the *difference* between the initial and final steady state currents. This applies to figure 4.14c and 4.14d; in the latter case $I_2>I_1$ and equation 4.30 can be written in the form

$$i=I_2-(I_2-I_1)\,\mathrm{e}^{-R_2t/L} \tag{4.32}$$

Alternatively the expression for the current can be

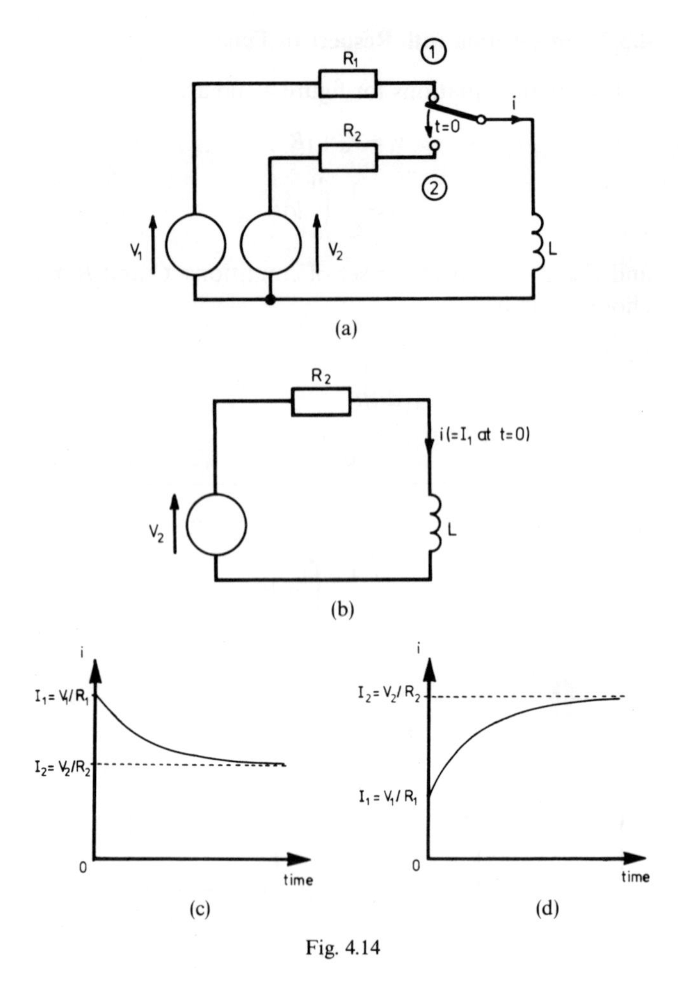

Fig. 4.14

expressed as the sum of two exponential terms

$$i=i_1+i_2=I_1\,\mathrm{e}^{-R_2t/L}+I_2[1-\mathrm{e}^{-R_2t/L}] \tag{4.33}$$

The first term is a function of the initial current $I_1=V_1/R_1$ but independent of the excitation V_2; the second term is a function of $I_2=V_2/R_2$ but is independent of the initial current. Thus we have the exponential decay of the initial current I_1 *superposed* on the exponential rise of current due to the excitation applied at $t=0$ as shown in figure 4.15.

It is important that the student should relate the equations to the conditions obtaining in the circuit; conversely, by sketching the curves from a knowledge of the circuit conditions, it is often possible to write down the appropriate expressions for current and voltage without actually solving the differential equations.

An examination of the solutions of the first order linear differential equations for the *RC* and *RL* circuits shows that *the steady state performance is given by the particular integral and the transient performance is given by the complementary function.* This is a general result.

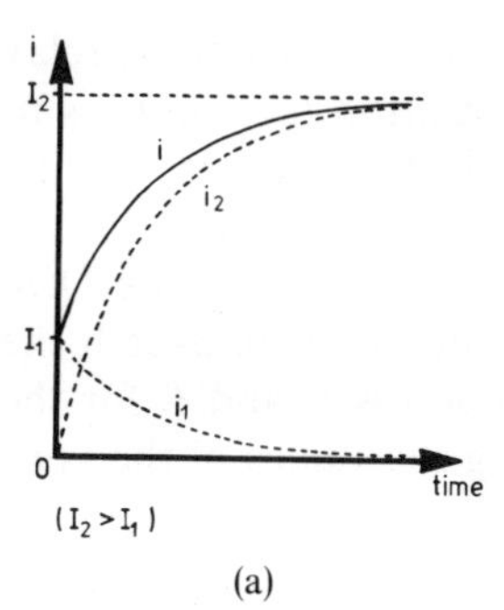

(a)

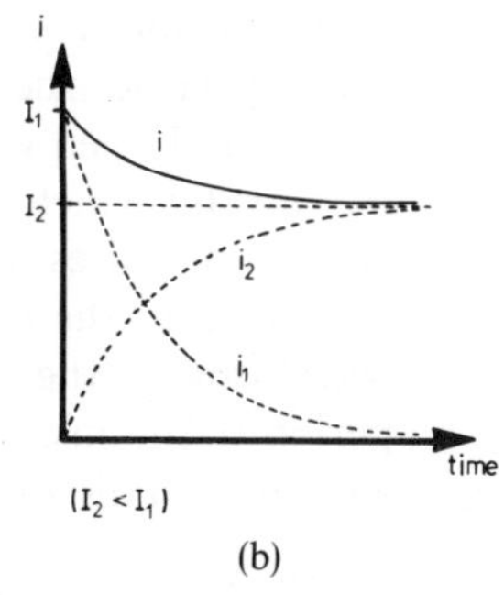

(b)

Fig. 4.15

4.5 THE LCR CIRCUIT

When Kirchhoff's Voltage Law is applied to a series *LCR* circuit, as shown in figure 4.16, a second order linear differential equation is obtained.

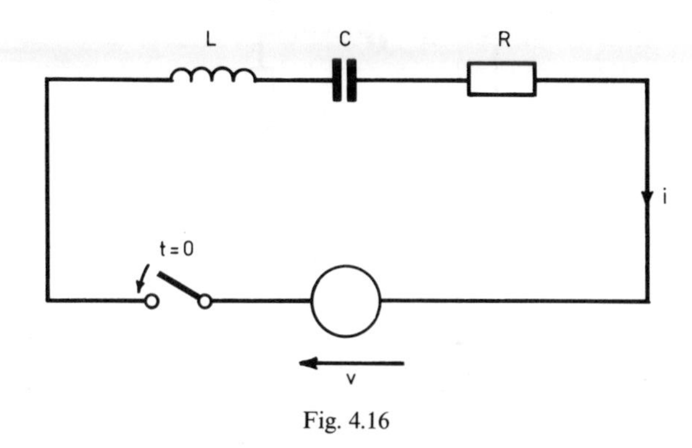

Fig. 4.16

The circuit equation for $t > 0$ is

$$V - L\frac{di}{dt} - \frac{1}{C}\int_0^t i\mathrm{d}t - iR = 0 \qquad (4.34)$$

Solution of this equation shows that the complementary function has one of three different forms depending on the relative values of the circuit constants L, C and R; the particular integral is zero when V is a steady voltage. The equation is not solved at this point because a powerful operational method of solving linear differential equations, known as the Laplace Transformation, will now be introduced.

PROBLEMS

4.1. A 10 μF capacitor is connected in series with a 100 kΩ resistor as shown in figure Q.1. The capacitor is charged initially so that terminal A is 70 V negative with respect to terminal B.

Derive an expression for the capacitor voltage v_c as a function of time, subsequent to the closing of the switch SW which connects the 100 V d.c. supply to the circuit.

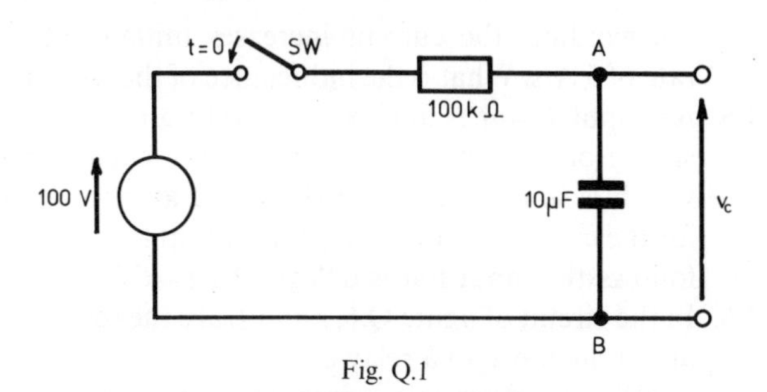

Fig. Q.1

Sketch the waveform of the capacitor voltage.

Determine the time at which the capacitor voltage is zero.

What is the initial rate of rise of the capacitor voltage?

4.2. The 100 μF capacitor C, in figure Q.2 is charged from the 1 kV d.c. supply, which has a maximum current rating of 40 mA. The resistor R_2 limits the current so that the power supply is not overloaded.

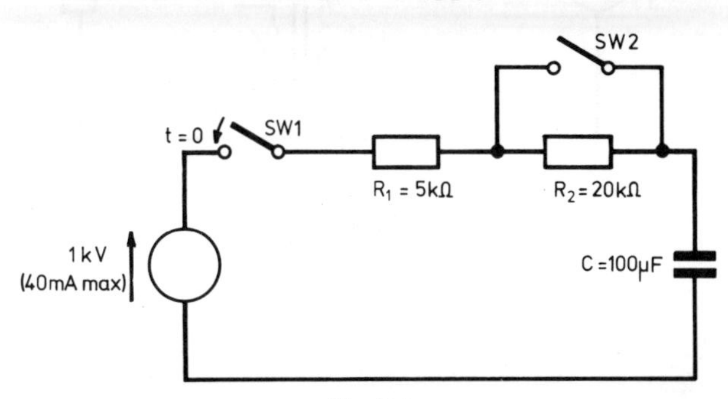

Fig. Q.2

If SW1 is closed at $t = 0$, determine the time at which SW2 must be closed so that the capacitor charges to 980 V as quickly as possible. Under these conditions how long does the capacitor take to charge to 980 V? Sketch the waveform of the capacitor voltage.

4.3. In the circuit of figure Q.3, obtain an expression for the current i subsequent to the closing of the switch SW. Sketch the waveform of the current.

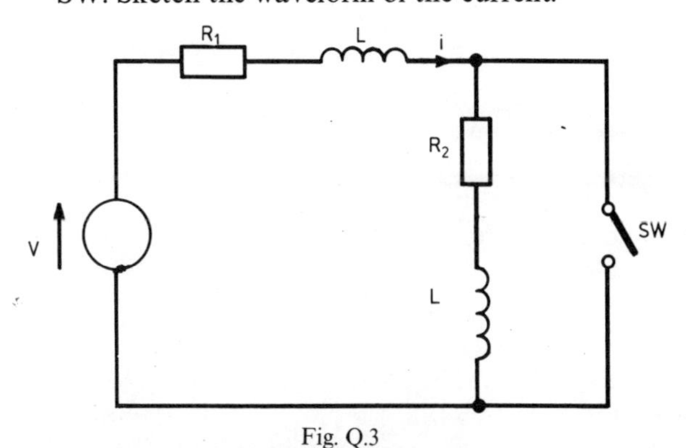

Fig. Q.3

4.4. The field winding of a d.c. machine has a resistance of 50 Ω. When a d.c. voltage of 100 V is applied to the winding, the current increases initially at the rate of 5 A/s. What is the inductance of the winding?

4.5. An input $v_i = \alpha t$ is applied at $t=0$ to a circuit consisting of a resistor R in series with a capacitor C which is initially uncharged. Derive an expression for the capacitor voltage and show that for $t \gg CR$ it follows the input but is delayed by $t=CR$.

4.6. In the circuit of figure Q.6, r and L are the resistance and inductance of a relay coil.

SW is an electronic switch which goes from A to B at $t=0$ and from B to C at $t=20$ ms. If the relay contacts close when the current in the coil rises to 70 mA and open when it falls to 50 mA, determine the time for which the contacts are closed.

4.7. A train of pulses of the form shown in figure Q.7a is applied to the circuit of figure Q.7b. Sketch the waveforms of the voltages across C and R for the period 0–100 ms, indicating the values of the voltages at each discontinuity.

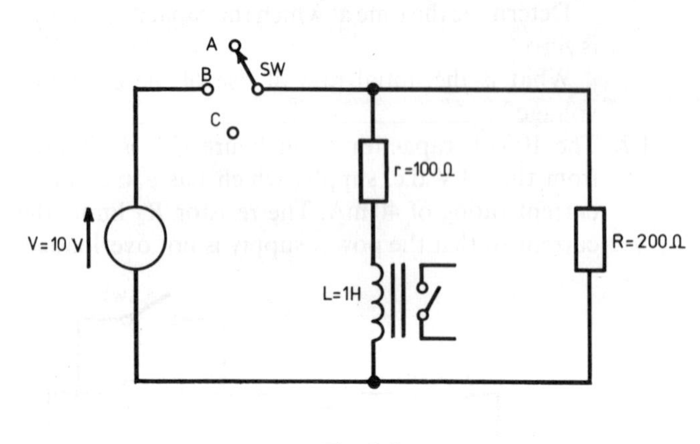

Fig. Q.6

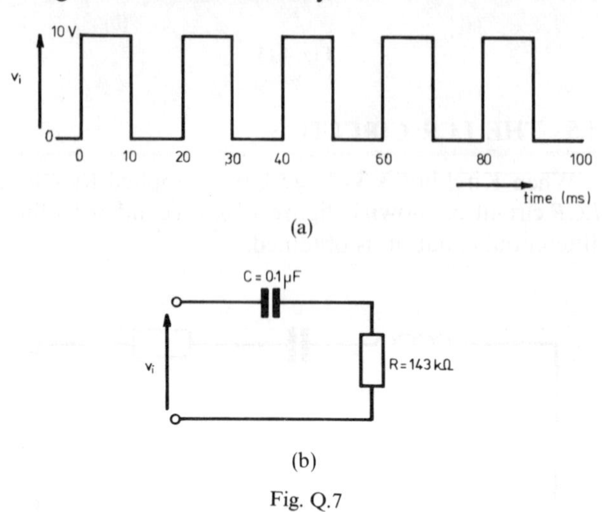

Fig. Q.7

CHAPTER FIVE

The Application of the Laplace Transform to Electric Circuits

5.1 INTRODUCTION

The use of mathematical transformations to simplify the solution of problems is familiar to all students, though probably not recognized as such. The operation of multiplication may be simplified by transforming the numbers into logarithms, adding the logarithms and finally taking the inverse transform (or 'detransforming') to obtain the antilogarithm, which is the numerical solution of the problem.

When studying the behaviour of electric circuits excited by complex signals, solving the differential equations can become tedious and difficult, particularly when initial conditions have to be considered. However, the labour involved can be greatly reduced by the use of the Laplace transform. The differential equation is transformed to an algebraic equation, which is then manipulated by standard algebraic techniques into one or more standard forms. The resulting expression is then detransformed to obtain the function of time which is the solution of the original differential equation. The analogy between Logarithmic transforms and Laplace transforms is shown in Table 5.1.

To obtain the Laplace transform of a function $f(t)$, defined for $t>0$, multiply the function by e^{-st} and integrate from zero to infinity with respect to time. At this stage 's' has no significance other than that it is an auxiliary variable introduced to simplify the solving of the differential equations, but it must have a value such that the integral is convergent.

Table 5.2 on page 41 gives the Laplace transforms of a number of frequently used functions of time and this table is used in a manner analogous to the use of tables of logarithms. It is however instructive to perform the integration for some of these functions.

(i) $f(t)=V$, where V is a constant. This is the step function applied at $t=0$.

The Laplace transform of $f(t)$ is denoted by $\mathscr{L}\,f(t)$, $\bar{f}$ or $F(s)$. In this case

$$F(s)=\int_0^\infty Ve^{-st}\,dt=-\frac{V}{s}\left[e^{-st}\right]_0^\infty=\frac{V}{s}$$

(ii) The time derivative of a function $f(t)$ is $df(t)/dt$ and the Laplace transform is

$$F_1(s)=\int_0^\infty e^{-st}\left[\frac{d}{dt}f(t)\right]dt$$

Integration by parts gives

$$F_1(s)=\left[e^{-st}f(t)\right]_0^\infty+s\int_0^\infty e^{-st}f(t)\,dt$$

$$=-f(0)+sF(s)$$

or $F_1(s)=sF(s)-f(0)$ where $f(0)$ is the value of $f(t)$ at $t=0$.

This result is particularly important in the solution of problems in electric circuit theory, since for an inductor $v=L(di/dt)$ and, from the above derivation, we obtain $v(s)=L[sI(s)-I_0]$ where I_0 is the current in the inductor at $t=0$ and $I(s)$ is the s-domain current. It is convenient to write the expression as $\bar{v}=Ls\bar{i}-LI_0$, $\bar{v}$ and $\bar{i}$ representing the transformed voltage and current respectively. †

(iii) The time integral of the function $f(t)$ is

$$\int_{-\infty}^{t} f(t)\,dt$$

TABLE 5.1

Required operation = Multiplication (number domain)	→	Transform numbers to logarithms (logarithm domain)	→	Add logarithms	→	Detransform sum of logarithms (antilog) (number domain)
Required operation = Solution of differential equation (time domain)	→	Laplace transform differential equation to algebraic equation (s-domain)	→	Manipulate algebraic equation into standard form	→	Detransform processed algebraic equation (time domain)

and the Laplace transform is

$$F_2(s)=\int_0^{\infty} e^{-st}\left[\int_{-\infty}^{t} f(t)\,dt\right]dt$$

Integration by parts gives

$$F_2(s)=\left[-e^{-st}\frac{\int_{-\infty}^{t} f(t)\,dt}{s}\right]_0^{\infty}+\frac{1}{s}\int_0^{\infty} e^{-st}f(t)\,dt$$

$$=\frac{1}{s}F(s)+\left[\frac{1}{s}\int_{-\infty}^{t} f(t)\,dt\right]_{t=0} \qquad (5.1)$$

If the lower limit of the integration is zero, that is if

$$F_2(s)=\int_0^{\infty} e^{-st}\left[\int_0^{t} f(t)\,dt\right]dt,$$

the second term on the right hand side of equation 5.1 vanishes and we obtain

$$\mathscr{L}\left[\int_0^{t} f(t)\,dt\right]=\frac{1}{s}F(s) \qquad (5.2)$$

Consider equations 5.1 and 5.2 as they apply to the voltage across a capacitor

$$v=\frac{1}{C}\int_{-\infty}^{t} i\,dt \qquad (5.3)$$

$$=\frac{1}{C}\int_{-\infty}^{0} i\,dt+\frac{1}{C}\int_0^{t} i\,dt$$

$$=V_0+\frac{1}{C}\int_0^{t} i\,dt \qquad (5.4)$$

If the result expressed in equation 5.1 is applied to equation 5.3

$$F_2(s)=\bar{v}=\frac{\bar{i}}{Cs}+\left[\frac{\int_{-\infty}^{t} i\,dt}{Cs}\right]_{t=0}$$

$$=\frac{\bar{i}}{Cs}+\frac{V_0}{s} \quad \text{since} \quad \frac{1}{C}\int_{-\infty}^{t} i\,dt\Big|_{t=0}=V_0$$

Alternatively if the result expressed in equation 5.2 is applied to the second term on the right hand side of equation 5.4

† $$F_2(s)=\bar{v}=\frac{V_0}{s}+\frac{\bar{i}}{Cs} \qquad (5.5)$$

which is the same as the previous result. Thus when using the Laplace transform method, the initial voltage across the capacitor is automatically taken into account.

(iv) We will now show that if F(s) is the Laplace transform of f(t), then $e^{-sT}F(s)$ is the Laplace transform of f(t) delayed by time T, where $t>0$.

The function f(t) is shown in figure 5.1a and the delayed function is shown in figure 5.1b.

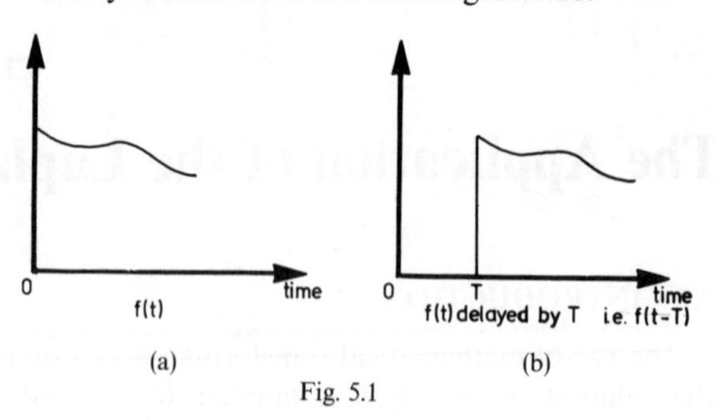

(a) (b)

Fig. 5.1

Mathematically we can write the first function f(t) . H(t) and the second function f($t-T$) . H($t-T$) where $H(t)=0,\ t<0$
$=1\ \ t\geqslant 0$

$$\mathscr{L}f(t-T)=\int_0^{\infty} e^{-st}f(t-T)\,.\,H(t-T)\,dt$$

$$=\int_0^{T} e^{-st}f(t-T)\,.\,H(t-T)\,dt$$

$$+\int_T^{\infty} e^{-st}f(t-T)\,.\,H(t-T)\,dt$$

$$=0+\int_T^{\infty} e^{-st}\,f(t-T)\,dt$$

since $H(t-T)=0;\ 0<t<T;$
$=1;\ t>T$

Put $(t-T)=\tau$, that is $t=(\tau+T)$, therefore $dt=d\tau$ since T is a constant. The integral may now be evaluated and is

$$\int_0^{\infty} f(\tau)\,.\,e^{-s(\tau+T)}\,d\tau$$

Note that the lower limit of the integral has been changed; $t=T$ giving $\tau=0$.

Therefore

$$\mathscr{L}f(t-T)=e^{-sT}\int_0^{\infty} f(\tau)\,e^{-sT}\,d\tau$$

† $$=e^{-sT}F(s) \quad \text{where} \quad F(s)=\mathscr{L}f(t)$$

This enables the response of linear circuits to a variety of stimuli to be evaluated; for example a pulse of width T can be treated as a positive step at $t=0$ on which is superposed a negative step of equal height applied at $t=T$ as shown in figure 5.2.

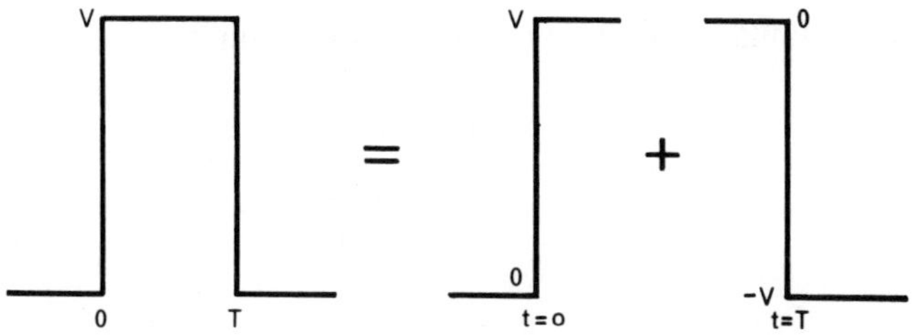

Fig. 5.2

Thus

† $$F(s)=\frac{V}{s}+\frac{-V}{s}\,e^{-sT}=\frac{V}{s}(1-e^{-sT})$$

(v) Consider now a very narrow pulse. If the height tends to infinity and the duration tends to zero the pulse is known as an *impulse.* Let the function, shown in figure 5.3, be defined by

$$\begin{aligned} f(t) &= 0; \quad t<0 \\ &= 1/k;\ 0<t<k \quad \text{where} \quad k\to 0 \\ &= 0; \quad t\geqslant k \end{aligned}$$

If

$$\int_0^\infty f(t)\,dt=1$$

the function is known as a *unit impulse*, designated $\delta(t)$.

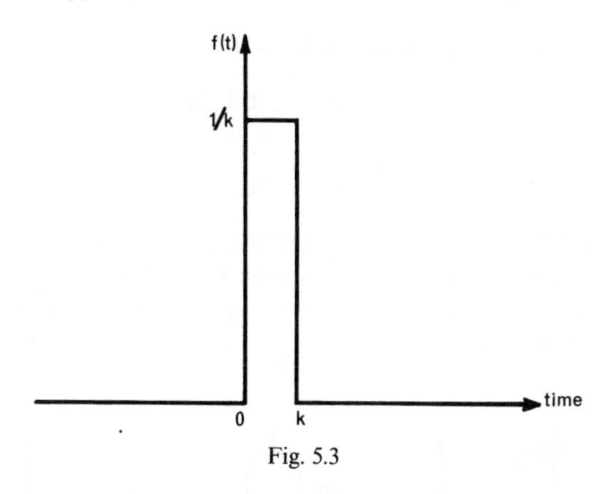

Fig. 5.3

The Laplace Transform of the unit impulse is

$$F(s)=\int_0^\infty \delta(t)\,e^{-st}\,dt$$

Since the value of the integral is zero except at $t=0$, e^{-st} can be replaced by 1, but by definition

$$\int_0^\infty \delta(t)\,dt=1$$

Therefore

† $$F(s)=1$$

5.2 SOME PROPERTIES OF THE LAPLACE TRANSFORM

The Laplace transform has important properties, the application of which can be used to facilitate the solution of linear differential equations. Some of these properties are stated below in the form of theorems.

(i) **Linearity Theorem**

If $F_1(s)$ and $F_2(s)$ are the Laplace transforms of $f_1(t)$ and $f_2(t)$ then

$$\mathscr{L}[a_1f_1(t)+a_2f_2(t)]=a_1F_1(s)+a_2F_2(s)$$

But it must be noted that the transform of the product of two functions is not the product of the Laplace transforms, that is

$$\mathscr{L}[f_1(t)\,.\,f_2(t)]\neq F_1(s)F_2(s)$$

The multiplicative operation will not be dealt with here.

(ii) **Initial Value Theorem**

As t tends to zero, the initial value $f(0+)$ of the function $f(t)$ is given by

$$f(0+)=\lim_{t\to 0} f(t)=\lim_{s\to\infty} sF(s)$$

(iii) **Final Value Theorem**

As t tends to infinity, the final value $f(\infty)$ of the function $f(t)$ is given by

$$f(\infty)=\lim_{t\to\infty} f(t)=\lim_{s\to 0} sF(s)$$

5.3 THE TRANSFER FUNCTION OF A LINEAR NETWORK

If, in the linear network of figure 5.4, a stimulus θ_i produces a response θ_0 when the initial conditions are zero, *the Laplace transform of the response divided by the Laplace transform of the stimulus is known as the Transfer Function of the network.*

We can write

$$\frac{\theta_0(s)}{\theta_i(s)}=F(s)=\text{Transfer Function}$$

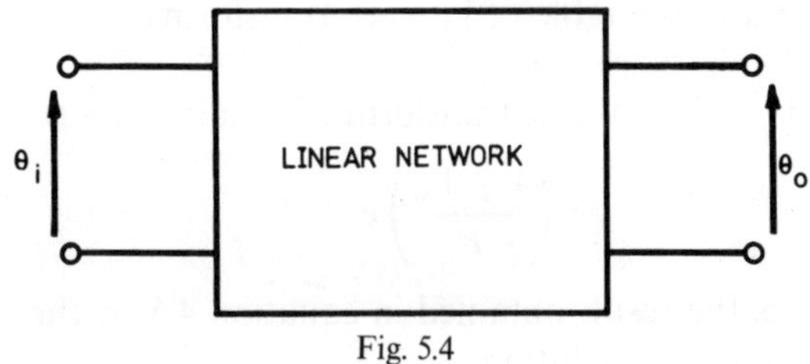

Fig. 5.4

If the stimulus is a unit impulse $\delta(t)$, then $\theta_i(s)=1$ and the Transfer Function of a linear network can therefore be defined as *the Laplace Transform of the unit impulse response.*

5.4 THE APPLICATION OF THE LAPLACE TRANSFORM TO THE SOLUTION OF ELECTRIC CIRCUIT PROBLEMS

The Laplace transform will now be applied to the solution of the *CR* circuit problem which has already been dealt with by classical methods on pages 25–27.

For convenience the circuit is redrawn in figure 5.5.

Step 1 Write down the differential equation of the circuit for $t>0$.

$$V=iR+\frac{1}{C}\int_{-\infty}^{t} i\mathrm{d}t$$

$$=iR+V_0+\frac{1}{C}\int_{0}^{t} i\mathrm{d}t \qquad (5.6)$$

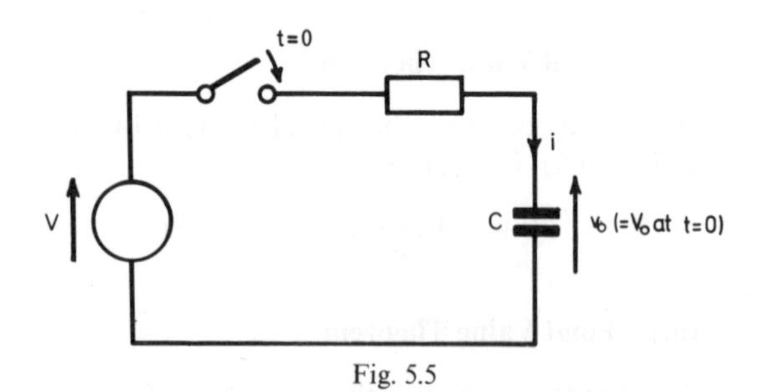

Fig. 5.5

Step 2 Refer to the table of Laplace transforms (Table 5.2 page 41) and transform each term of the equation

$$\frac{V}{s}=\bar{i}R+\frac{V_0}{s}+\frac{\bar{i}}{Cs} \qquad (5.7)$$

Step 3 Re-arrange equation 5.7 so that the *s* term appears in one or more of the forms shown in the right hand column of Table 5.2. Thus

$$\frac{(V-V_0)}{s}=\bar{i}\frac{R}{s}(s+1/CR)$$

and

$$\bar{i}=\left(\frac{V-V_0}{R}\right)\frac{1}{(s+1/CR)} \qquad (5.8)$$

The term $1/(s+1/CR)$ is of the form $1/(s+\alpha)$ which may be found in the table of Laplace transforms.

Step 4 The inverse transform of equation 5.8 is

$$i=\left(\frac{V-V_0}{R}\right)\mathrm{e}^{-t/CR} \qquad (5.9)$$

which is the result obtained in equation 4.5 by the classical method of solution.

A similar procedure is adopted to obtain v_0

$$v_0=\frac{1}{C}\int_{-\infty}^{t} i\mathrm{d}t$$

$$=V_0+\frac{1}{C}\int_{0}^{t} i\mathrm{d}t$$

Transform and substitute for $\bar{i}$

$$\bar{v}_0=\frac{V_0}{s}+\frac{\bar{i}}{Cs}$$

$$=\frac{V_0}{s}+(V-V_0)\frac{1/CR}{s(s+1/CR)}$$

from equation 5.8.

Detransform

$$v_0=V_0+(V-V_0)[1-\mathrm{e}^{-t/CR}] \qquad (5.10)$$

which is the result obtained in equation 4.9.

5.4.1 The Transformation of Circuits and Sources

In the same way that voltage sources and current sources were represented by circuit models, the transformed voltage/current relationships for circuit elements can be represented by transformed circuit models. The Thevenin and Norton Theorems can be applied to the transformed circuits, $1/Cs$ and Ls being treated in the same way as resistance.

(i) Capacitor with initial voltage V_0.

the transformed voltage/current relationship is

$$\bar{v}=\frac{V_0}{s}+\frac{\bar{i}}{Cs}$$

This expression can be represented by the transformed circuit model shown in figure 5.6a. Application of Norton's Theorem gives the transformed circuit of figure 5.6b.

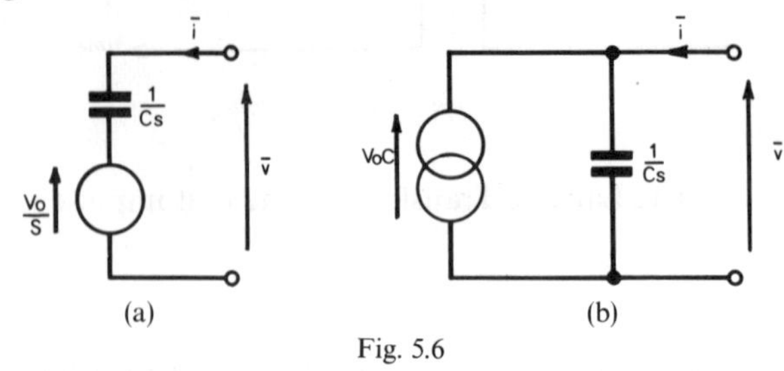

Fig. 5.6

(ii) Inductor with initial current I_0

The transformed voltage/current relationship is

$$\bar{v}=sL\bar{i}-LI_0$$

which is represented by the Thevenin and Norton transformed circuits of figure 5.7.

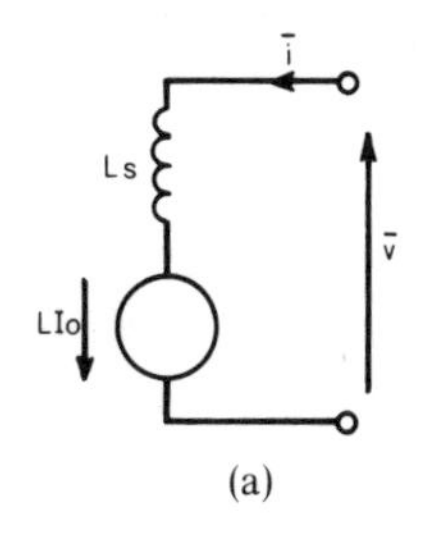

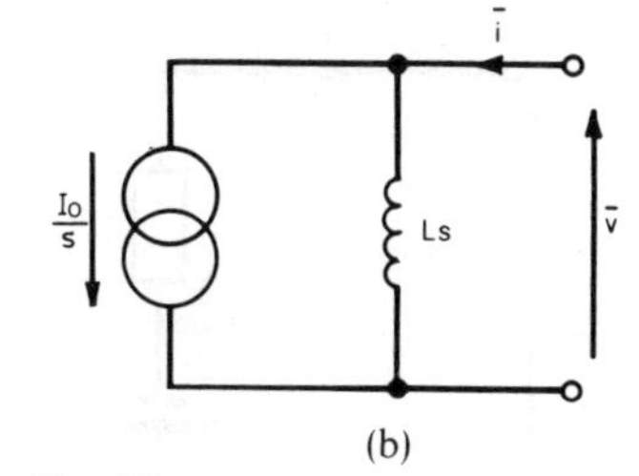

Fig. 5.7

(iii) Resistor

The transformed voltage/current relationship is $\bar{v}=\bar{i}R$ and the transformed circuit is as shown in figure 5.8.

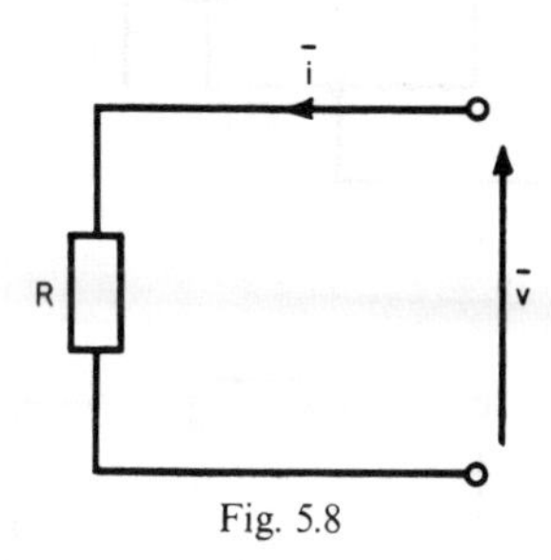

Fig. 5.8

If we now transform the circuit shown in figure 5.5, for $t>0$, the circuit of figure 5.9 is obtained.

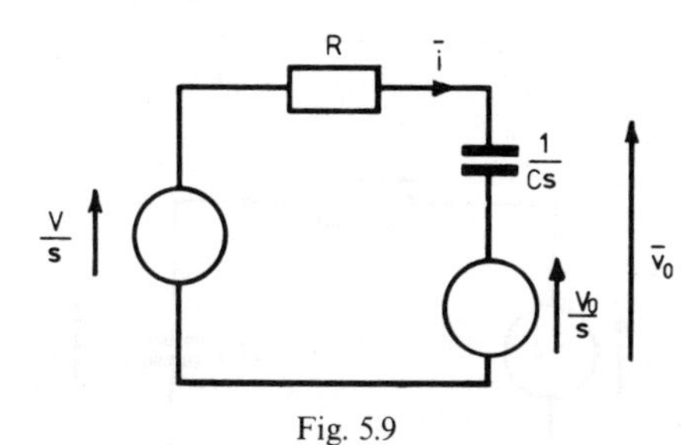

Fig. 5.9

The Kirchhoff voltage equation for this circuit is

$$\frac{V}{s}-\bar{i}R-\frac{\bar{i}}{Cs}-\frac{V_0}{s}=0$$

Re-arranging the terms gives

$$\frac{V}{s}=\bar{i}R+\frac{V_0}{s}+\frac{\bar{i}}{Cs}$$

which is identical with equation 5.7.

We can therefore *either* (i) write down the differential equation for the circuit and transform each term *or* (ii) draw the transformed circuit and write down the Kirchhoff equation for it. Both methods lead to the equation required to proceed to Step 3 of the procedure given on page 36.

A study of the transformed circuits of figures 5.6, 5.7 and 5.8 shows that the transformed voltage across the transformed circuit element divided by the transformed current through it is $1/Cs$, Ls or R respectively. The three quantities have the same dimensions and are known as *transformed impedances*, defined by $\bar{Z}=\bar{v}/\bar{i}$.

In figure 5.10a

$$\bar{v}=\bar{i}R+\bar{i}/Cs$$

Therefore

$$\frac{\bar{v}}{\bar{i}}=\bar{Z}_1=(R+1/Cs)$$

which has the same form as equation 2.3.

Similarly for figure 5.10b

$$\bar{i}=\bar{i}_1+\bar{i}_2=\frac{\bar{v}}{1/Cs}+\frac{\bar{v}}{R}$$

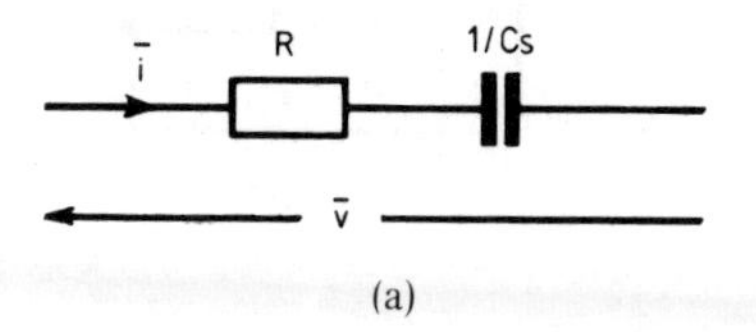

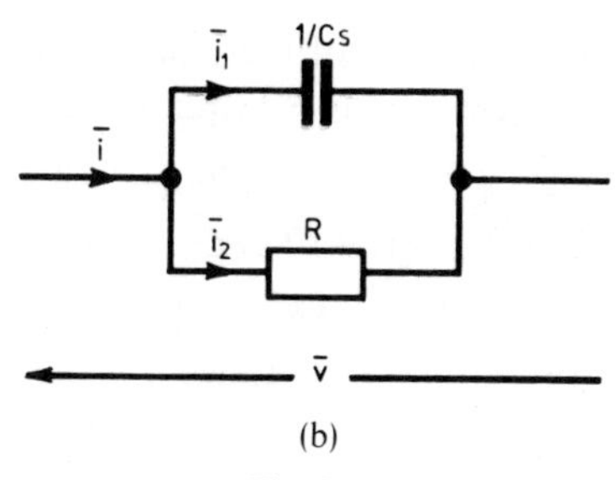

Fig. 5.10

Therefore

$$\frac{\bar{i}}{\bar{v}}=\frac{1}{\bar{Z}_2}=\left(\frac{1}{R}+\frac{1}{1/Cs}\right)$$

which has the same form as equation 2.6.

Hence

$$\bar{Z}_2=\frac{R.1/Cs}{R+1/Cs}\left(=\frac{\text{Product}}{\text{Sum}}\text{ as in equation 2.14}\right).$$

It is apparent that we are able to apply the methods of circuit analysis to $1/Cs$ and L s in the same way as they have been applied to R. This can be shown by considering the circuit of figure 5.11a, for which it is required to determine v_0.

The transformed circuit is shown in figure 5.11b.

Let the series combination R_1, $1/C_1s$ be denoted by

$$\bar{Z}_1=\left(R_1+\frac{1}{C_1s}\right)=\frac{1+sT_1}{C_1s}$$

where $T_1=C_1R_1$, and let the parallel combination R_2, $1/C_2s$ be

$$\bar{Z}_2=\frac{R_2.1/C_2s}{R_2+1/C_2s}=\frac{R_2}{1+C_2R_2s}=\frac{R_2}{1+sT_2}$$

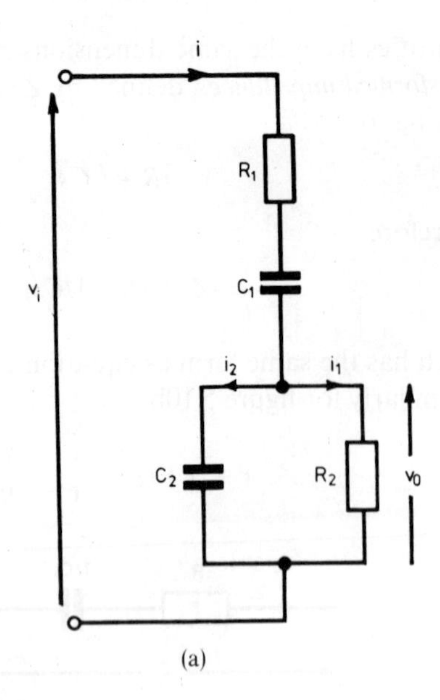

(a)

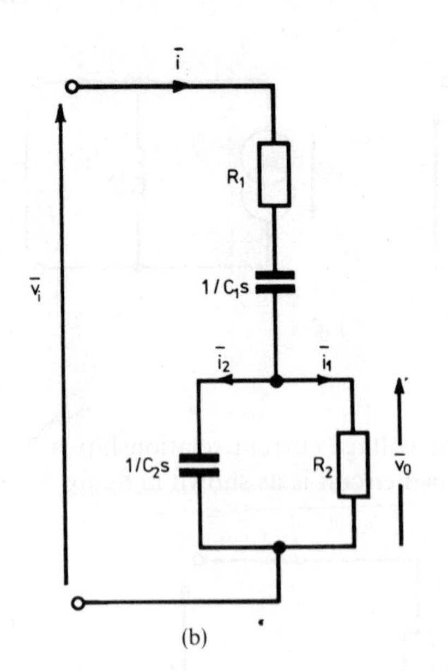

(b)

Fig. 5.11

where $T_2 = C_2R_2$.

Then by an extension of the rule for the division of voltage across series resistors [equation 2.10 page 10]

$$\bar{v}_0 = \bar{v}_i \frac{\bar{Z}_2}{\bar{Z}_1 + \bar{Z}_2} = \frac{\bar{v}_i \,.\, R_2/(1+sT_2)}{[(1+sT_1)/C_1s] + R_2/(1+sT_2)}$$

This technique may be used as an alternative to the direct application of Kirchhoff's Laws to the transformed circuit.

5.5 FURTHER EXAMPLES OF THE APPLICATION OF THE LAPLACE TRANSFORM TO THE SOLUTION OF ELECTRIC CIRCUIT PROBLEMS

Example

To determine the Impulse Response of the circuit of figure 5.12a.

Solution

The transformed circuit (for $t > 0$), assuming the capacitor to be initially uncharged, is shown in figure 5.12b and the transformed circuit equation is

$$1 = \bar{i}(R + 1/Cs)$$

But

$$\bar{v}_0 = \frac{\bar{i}}{Cs} = \frac{1}{Cs(R+1/Cs)} = \frac{1}{CR(s+1/CR)}$$

From the table of Laplace transforms

$$v_0 = \frac{1}{CR}\,e^{-t/CR}$$

The voltage v_R across R may also be determined since

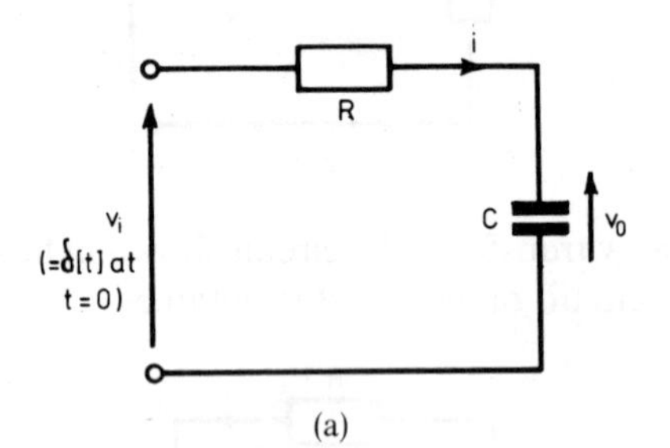

(a)

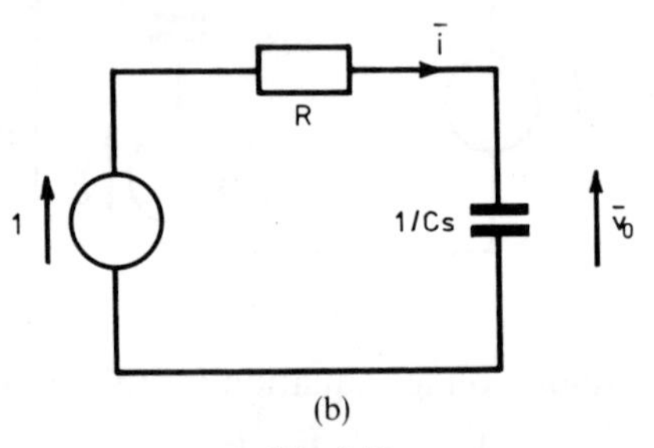

(b)

Fig. 5.12

$$\bar{v}_R = \bar{i}R$$

$$= \frac{R}{R+1/Cs} = \frac{s}{(s+1/CR)}$$

$$= 1 - \frac{1/CR}{(s+1/CR)}$$

Hence

$$v_R = \delta(t) - \frac{1}{CR}\,e^{-t/CR}$$

Alternatively v_R could have been determined from the relationship $v_R = v_i - v_C$.

The voltage waveforms across the capacitor and resistor are shown in figures 5.13a and b respectively, and the student should satisfy himself that these are what would be expected from physical considerations.

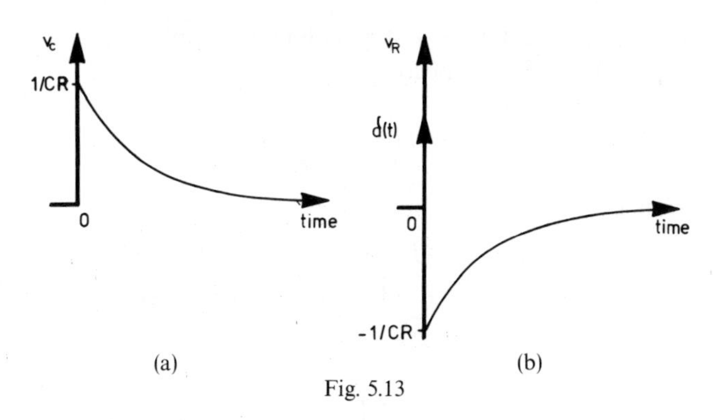

Fig. 5.13

Example

To determine the voltage across the capacitor of the circuit of figure 5.14a when a voltage $v_i = V \sin \omega t$ is applied at $t=0$.

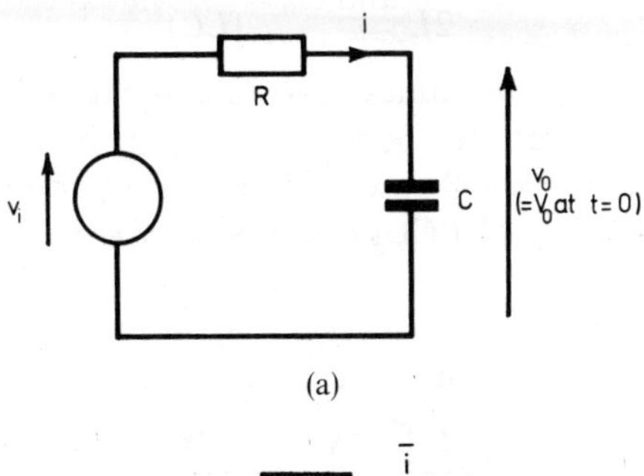

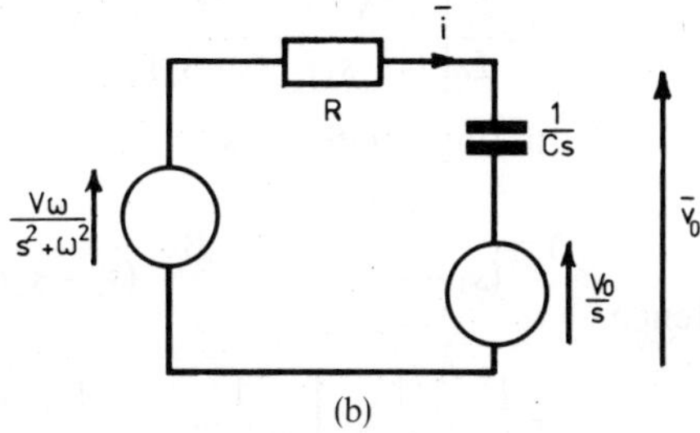

Fig. 5.14

Solution

From the table of Laplace transforms, it is seen that the Laplace transform of sin ωt is $\omega/(s^2+\omega^2)$; this is shown on the transformed circuit figure 5.14b.

The Kirchhoff equations for 5.14b are

$$\frac{V\omega}{(s^2+\omega^2)} - \frac{V_0}{s} = \bar{i}\left(R + \frac{1}{Cs}\right)$$

and

$$\bar{v}_0 = \frac{\bar{i}}{Cs} + \frac{V_0}{s}$$

hence

$$\bar{v}_0 = \frac{V_0}{s} - \frac{V_0}{s(R+1/Cs)Cs} + \frac{V\omega}{(s^2+\omega^2)} \cdot \frac{1}{(R+1/Cs)Cs}$$

$$= \frac{V_0}{s} - \frac{V_0}{s(1+CRs)} + \frac{V\omega}{(s^2+\omega^2)}\frac{1}{(1+CRs)}$$

$$= \frac{V_0}{s} - \frac{V_0}{sT(s+1/T)} + \frac{V\omega}{(s^2+\omega^2)}\frac{1}{T(s+1/T)}$$

where $T = CR$

$$\bar{v}_0 = V_0\left[\frac{1}{s} - \frac{1/T}{s(s+1/T)}\right] + \frac{V\omega}{(s^2+\omega^2)}\frac{1/T}{(s+1/T)}$$

By the method of Partial Fractions

$$\bar{v}_0 = \frac{V_0}{(s+1/T)} + \frac{V\omega}{T}\left[\frac{\mathrm{A}s+\mathrm{B}}{(s^2+\omega^2)} + \frac{\mathrm{D}}{(s+1/T)}\right]$$

Equating coefficients

$$\mathrm{A} = \frac{-T^2}{1+(\omega T)^2}; \quad \mathrm{B} = \frac{T}{1+(\omega T)^2}$$

$$\mathrm{D} = \frac{T^2}{1+(\omega T)^2}$$

Hence

$$\bar{v}_0 = \frac{V_0}{(s+1/T)} + \frac{V\omega}{T}\left[\frac{1}{1+(\omega T)^2}\left\{\frac{-sT^2}{(s^2+\omega^2)} + \frac{T}{(s^2+\omega^2)} + \frac{T^2}{(s+1/T)}\right\}\right]$$

Therefore

$$v_0 = \frac{V\omega}{T} \cdot \frac{1}{1+(\omega T)^2}\left\{-T^2 \cos \omega t + \frac{T}{\omega} \sin \omega t\right\} + \left\{\frac{V\omega T}{1+(\omega T)^2} + V_0\right\} \mathrm{e}^{-t/T}$$

$$= \frac{V}{[1+(\omega T)^2]^{1/2}}\left\{\frac{\sin \omega t}{[1+(\omega T)^2]^{1/2}} - \frac{\omega T \cos \omega t}{[1+(\omega T)^2]^{1/2}}\right\} + \left\{\frac{V\omega T}{1+(\omega T)^2} + V_0\right\} \mathrm{e}^{-t/T}$$

$$= \frac{V}{[1+(\omega T)^2]^{1/2}}\{\sin \omega t \cos \phi - \cos \omega t \sin \phi\} + \left\{\frac{V \sin \phi}{[1+(\omega T)^2]^{1/2}} + V_0\right\} \mathrm{e}^{-t/T}$$

where $\phi = \tan^{-1}(\omega CR)$

That is

$$v_0 = \underbrace{\frac{V}{[1+(\omega T)^2]^{1/2}} \sin(\omega t - \phi)}_{\text{Steady state component}} + \underbrace{\left\{V_0 + \frac{V \sin \phi}{[1+(\omega T)^2]^{1/2}}\right\} \mathrm{e}^{-t/T}}_{\text{Transient component}} \qquad (5.11)$$

This has the general form shown in figure 5.15.

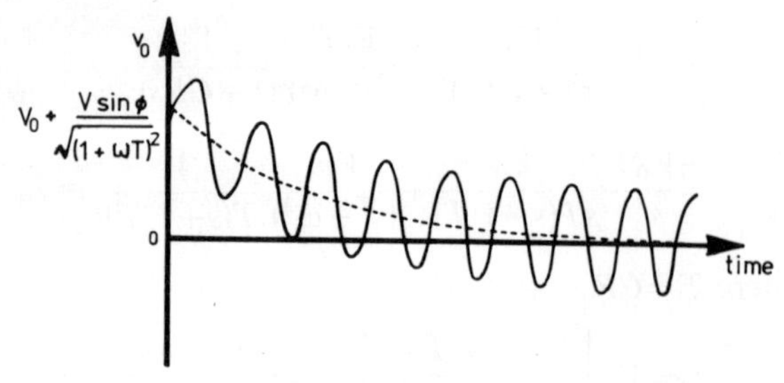

Fig. 5.15

Example

To determine the response of a series LCR circuit to a step voltage applied at $t=0$.
(NOTE This section should not be dealt with until the student is familiar with complex numbers.)

Solution

The circuit is shown in figure 5.16a and the transformed circuit (for $t>0$) in figure 5.16b.

The sources LI_0 and V_0/s in the transformed circuit result from the initial conditions (that is $i=I_0$, $v_c=V_0$ at $t=0$).

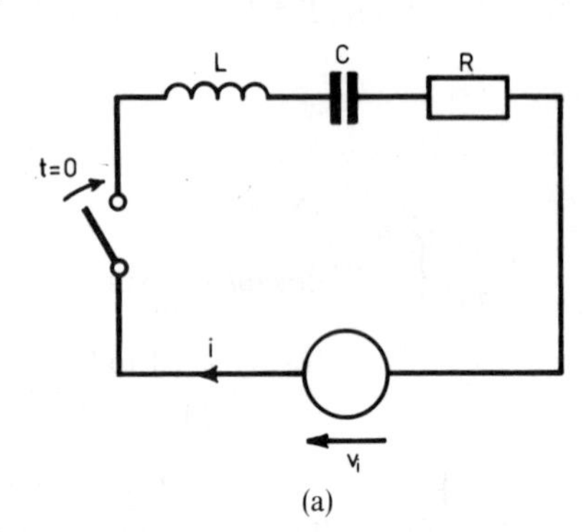

(a)

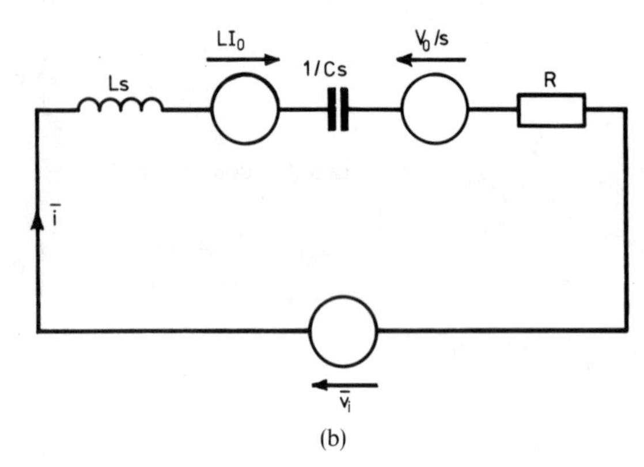

(b)

Fig. 5.16

The equation for the transformed circuit is

$$\bar{v}_i=\bar{i}\left(Ls+\frac{1}{Cs}+R\right)-LI_0+\frac{V_0}{s} \tag{5.12}$$

In order to simplify the algebra, it is assumed that $I_0=0$, $V_0=0$ and that v_i is a step voltage V applied at $t=0$. Equation 5.12 then becomes

$$\frac{V}{s}=\bar{i}\left(Ls+\frac{1}{Cs}+R\right)$$

Hence

$$\bar{i}=\frac{V/L}{(s^2+Rs/L+1/LC)}=\frac{V/L}{(s-s_1)(s-s_2)} \tag{5.13}$$

where

$$s_1, s_2=-\frac{R}{2L}\pm\left[\left(\frac{R}{2L}\right)^2-\frac{1}{LC}\right]^{1/2} \tag{5.14}$$

$$=-\alpha\pm(\alpha^2-\omega_0{}^2)^{1/2}=-\alpha\pm(\beta^2)^{1/2}$$

where

$$\alpha=\frac{R}{2L} \text{ and } \omega_0=\frac{1}{(LC)^{1/2}}$$

Depending on the values of R, L, C the term within the square root sign can be positive, negative or zero. The three conditions will now be examined separately.

(i) $(R/2L)^2>(1/LC)$, known as the *overdamped* condition.

In this case $s_1=(-\alpha+\beta)$ and $s_2=(-\alpha-\beta)$ are real; equation 5.13 can be written

$$\bar{i}=\frac{V}{L}\left[\frac{A}{(s-s_1)}+\frac{B}{(s-s_2)}\right]$$

and by equating coefficients

$$A=\frac{1}{(s_1-s_2)} \quad \text{and} \quad B=\frac{1}{(s_2-s_1)}.$$

Hence

$$\bar{i}=\frac{V}{L}\frac{1}{(s_1-s_2)}\left[\frac{1}{(s-s_1)}-\frac{1}{(s-s_2)}\right] \tag{5.15}$$

From the table of Laplace transforms

$$i=\frac{V}{L}\cdot\frac{1}{(s_1-s_2)}[e^{s_1t}-e^{s_2t}]$$

$$=\frac{V}{L}\cdot\frac{1}{2\beta}[e^{(-\alpha+\beta)t}-e^{(-\alpha-\beta)t}] \tag{5.16}$$

$$=\frac{V}{\beta L}e^{-\alpha t}\left[\frac{e^{\beta t}-e^{-\beta t}}{2}\right]$$

that is

† $$i=\frac{V}{\beta L}e^{-\alpha t}\sinh\beta t \tag{5.17}$$

Since α and β are real and $|\alpha|>|\beta|$, s_1 and s_2 are negative, so that both exponentials in equation 5.16 decay with time and the current has the form shown in figure 5.17a. The voltage across the capacitor is

$$v_c = \frac{1}{C}\int i\mathrm{d}t$$

and has the waveform shown in figure 5.17b

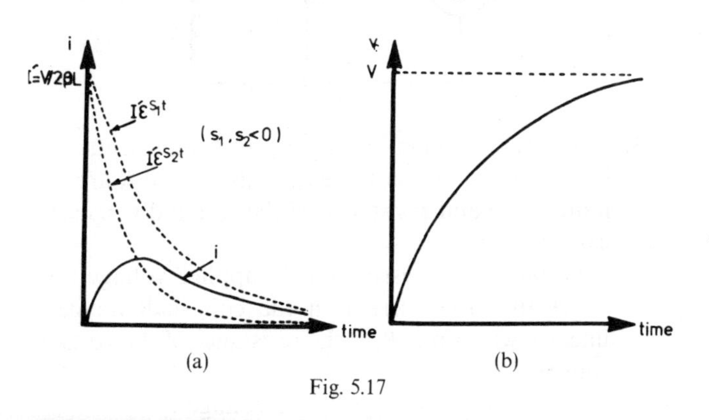

Fig. 5.17

(ii) $(R/2L)^2 < (1/LC)$, known as the *underdamped condition.*

In this case $\alpha < \omega_0$ and β^2 is negative; if we put $\beta^2 = -\omega_n{}^2$ then $s_1 = (-\alpha + j\omega_n)$, $s_2 = (-\alpha - j\omega_n)$, and the roots are complex, giving, from equation 5.13

$$\bar{i} = \frac{V/L}{[s-(-\alpha+j\omega_n)][s-(-\alpha-j\omega_n)]}$$

$$= \frac{V/L}{(s+\alpha)^2+\omega_n{}^2}$$

$$= \frac{V}{\omega_n L}\cdot\frac{\omega_n}{(s+\alpha)^2+\omega_n{}^2} \qquad (5.18)$$

From the table of Laplace transforms

† $$i = \frac{V}{\omega_n L}\,e^{-\alpha t}\sin\omega_n t \qquad (5.19)$$

The current waveform is shown in figure 5.18a and the corresponding capacitor voltage waveform in figure 5.18b.

It should be noted here that $\omega_n{}^2 = (\omega_0{}^2 - \alpha^2)$, $f_n = \omega_n/2\pi$ is known as the natural frequency of the circuit and its value varies as R is varied; $f_0 = \omega_0/2\pi$ is the undamped natural frequency ($=\omega_n$ when $R=0$).

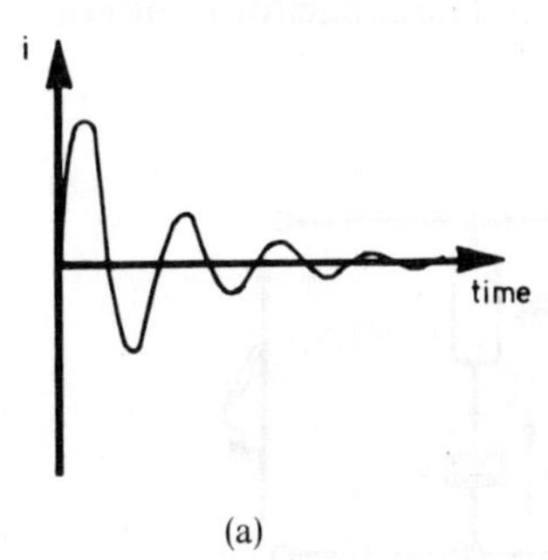

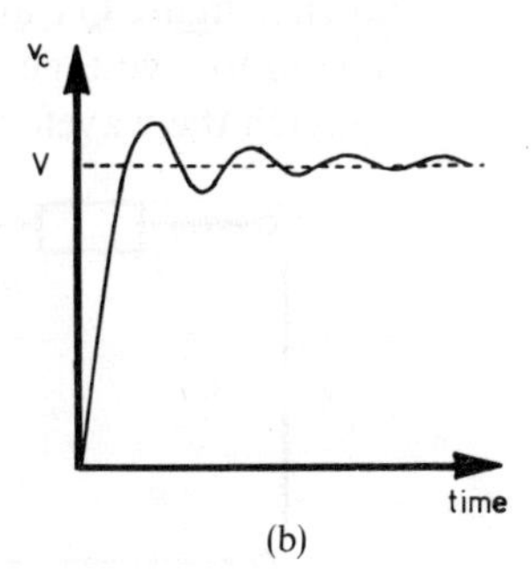

Fig. 5.18

(iii) $(R/2L)^2 = (1/LC)$, known as the *critically damped* condition.

In this case $\beta = 0$ and the roots s_1 and s_2 are equal; $s_1 = s_2 = -\alpha$.

From equation 5.13

$$\bar{i} = \frac{V/L}{(s+\alpha)^2} \qquad (5.20)$$

From the table of Laplace transforms

† $$i = \frac{V}{L}\,t\,e^{-\alpha t} \qquad (5.21)$$

which is shown in figure 5.19a, with the corresponding capacitor voltage in figure 5.19b.

TABLE 5.2
Table of Laplace Transforms

$\mathscr{L}$ f(t) is defined by $\int_0^\infty f(t)\,e^{-st}\,.\,dt$ and is written as F(s)

$\mathscr{L}$ f(t)	F(s)
$\frac{d}{dt}f(t)$	$sF(s) - f(0)$
$\frac{d^n}{dt^n}f(t)$	$s^nF(s) - s^{n-1}f(0) - s^{n-2}f'(0)\ldots$
$\int_0^t f(t)dt$	$\frac{1}{s}F(s)$
$e^{-\alpha t}f(t)$	$F(s+\alpha)$
Unit Impulse δ	1
Unit step H(t)	$\frac{1}{s}$
Delayed function	$e^{-sT}F(s)$
Pulse of width T	$\frac{1-e^{-sT}}{s}$
Ramp t	$\frac{1}{s^2}$
$e^{-\alpha t}$	$\frac{1}{(s+\alpha)}$
$1-e^{-\alpha t}$	$\frac{\alpha}{s(s+\alpha)}$
$t\,e^{-\alpha t}$	$\frac{1}{(s+\alpha)^2}$
$\sin\omega t$	$\frac{\omega}{s^2+\omega^2}$
$\cos\omega t$	$\frac{s}{s^2+\omega^2}$
$\sinh\beta t$	$\frac{\beta}{s^2-\beta^2}$
$\cosh\beta t$	$\frac{s}{s^2-\beta^2}$

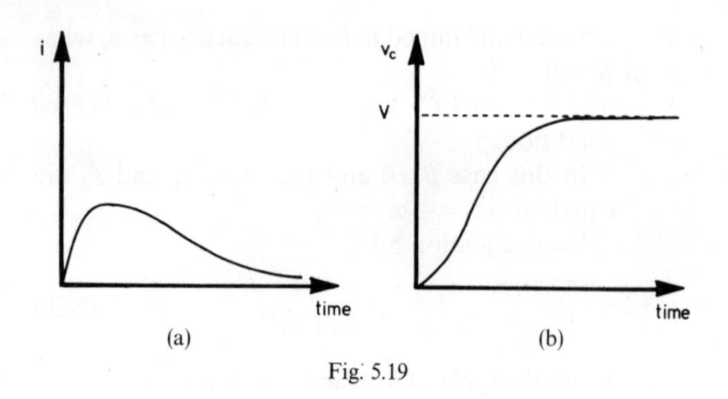

Fig. 5.19

The critically damped condition is the transitional stage between the oscillatory response obtained in the underdamped condition and the non-oscillatory response that results when the circuit is overdamped.

PROBLEMS

5.1. The network of figure Q.1 is frequently used as a compensated attenuator in a cathode ray oscilloscope.

(i) Show that the output and input voltages are of the same form if $C_1R_1=C_2R_2$

(ii) If $R_1=R_2$, $C_1=5C_2$ and the input is a step voltage of amplitude V, show that the output is

$$v_0=\frac{V}{2}+\frac{V}{3}e^{-(t/3C_2R_2)}$$

Sketch the waveform

(iii) Sketch the output waveform for the condition

$$R_1=R_2,\ C_1=C_2/5$$

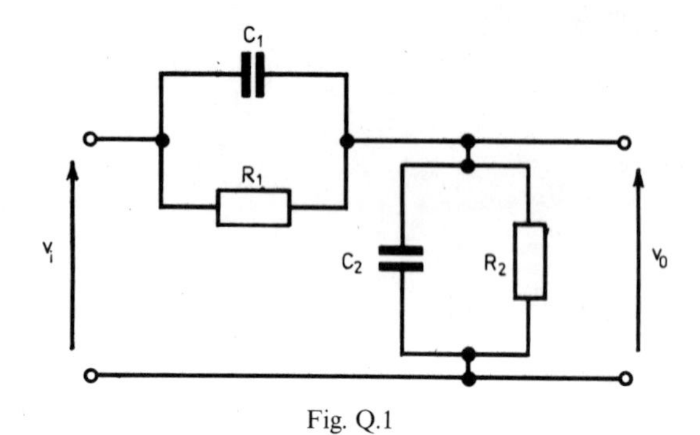

Fig. Q.1

5.2. A step voltage V is applied, at $t=0$, to a circuit consisting of a resistor R connected in series with a leaky capacitor C which has an effective parallel resistance R_p. Derive an expression for the voltage across the capacitor as a function of time.

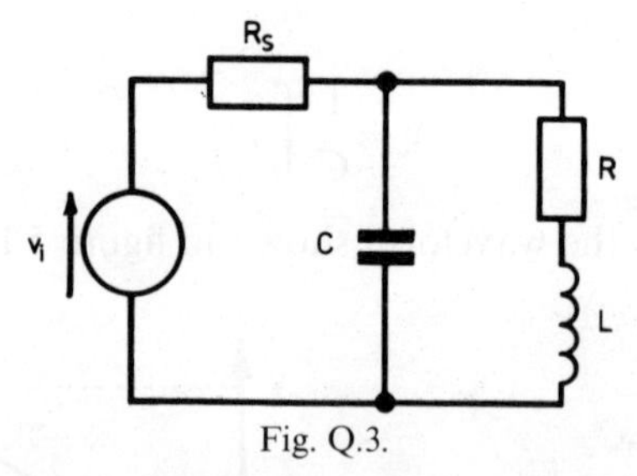

Fig. Q.3.

5.3. The circuit shown in figure Q.3 represents the scanning coil of a cathode ray tube. L and R are the inductance and resistance of the coil and C its self-capacitance.

Obtain an expression for the applied voltage v_i in order that the current in the coil shall increase linearly with time. R_s is the resistance of the voltage source.

Sketch the waveform of the voltage v_i.

5.4. In the circuit of figure Q.4 derive an expression for v_0 when v_i is a step of amplitude V applied at $t=0$. Assume that the capacitors are initially uncharged.

Sketch the output waveform.

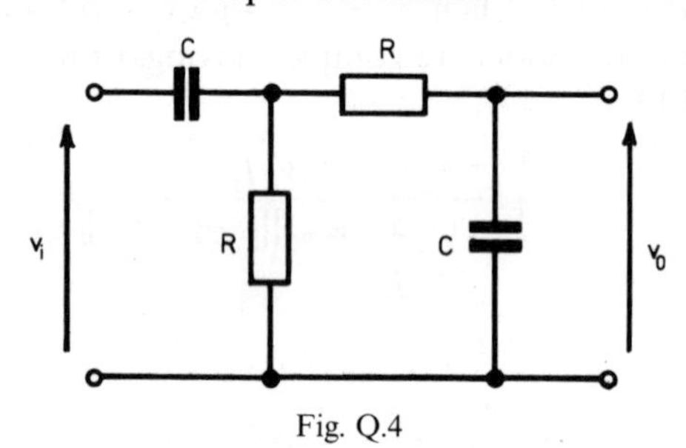

Fig. Q.4

5 5 A voltage defined by $v_i=0;\ t<0$

$$v_i=V\,e^{-\alpha t}\ t>0$$

is applied to a circuit consisting of a resistor R in series with a capacitor C which is initially charged to a voltage $V/2$.

Derive an expression for the capacitor voltage as a function of time.

5.6. Obtain, using the Laplace Transform or otherwise, an expression for the voltage v_0 as a function of time, when a step voltage V is applied to the network shown in figure Q.6 at $t=0$. The capacitor is initially charged to a voltage V_0.

Sketch the waveform of v_0.

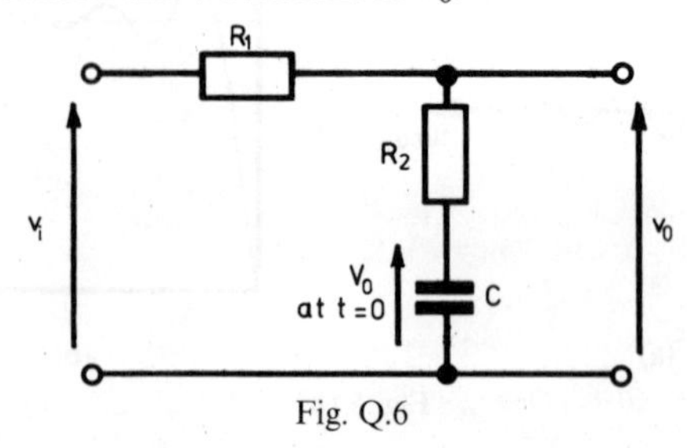

Fig. Q.6

CHAPTER SIX

Circuits With Sinusoidal Excitation

6.1 INTRODUCTION

In the previous two chapters it has been shown that the response of a network to a stimulus consists of two parts, the transient component and the steady state component. While the transient component is very important, many electrical systems operate for most of the time in the steady state, after the transient has decayed to a negligible value; the steady state behaviour of electric circuits will now be considered.

The study of the steady state performance of electric circuits conveniently deals with sinusoidal excitation. There are several reasons for the choice:

(i) Many practical systems, including the National Grid and radio-communications systems, have substantially sinusoidal waveforms associated with them when operating in the steady state.

(ii) The natural response of an underdamped linear *RLC* circuit, and of the equivalent non-electrical systems, is sinusoidal.

(iii) The differentiation and integration with respect to time of a time-varying sinusoidal function results in a function of the same form; thus when a sinusoidal input is applied to a linear circuit element the associated steady state output is also sinusoidal.

(iv) Sinusoids are readily handled mathematically and the application of Fourier techniques enables one to extend the analysis to any periodic waveform.

6.2 PERIODIC WAVEFORMS

A periodic wave is one that repeats at regular intervals of time and the sinusoidal wave is an example of a periodic wave.

If the value of a periodic sinusoidal function representing a waveform is $f(t_1)$ at time t_1 and is similar at times (t_1+nT) where n is an integer, then T is known as the *period* or *periodic time* of the function. During the time interval T the function describes one complete cycle, and the number of cycles per second or *the frequency* is $f=1/T$ Hertz (Hz).

The average or mean value of the function is

$$\text{Mean}=\left[\frac{1}{T}\int_{t_1}^{t_1+T} f(t)\,dt\right]=\left[\frac{1}{T}\int_0^T f(t)\,dt\right]$$

since the function is periodic.

The *mean square value* of the function is

$$\text{Mean Square}=\left[\frac{1}{T}\int_{t_1}^{t_1+T} f^2(t)\,dt\right]=\left[\frac{1}{T}\int_0^T f^2(t)\,dt\right]$$

The root mean square or *r.m.s.* value of the function is Root Mean Square (r.m.s.)

$$=\left[\frac{1}{T}\int_{t_1}^{t_1+T} f^2(t)\,dt\right]^{1/2}=\left[\frac{1}{T}\int_0^T f^2(t)\,dt\right]^{1/2}$$

The r.m.s. value is of great importance in electrical engineering as the following example shows.

When a periodic current $i(t)$ flows through a resistor R the instantaneous voltage across the resistor is, by Ohm's Law, $v(t)=i(t)R$ and the power dissipated at any instant is $p(t)=v(t)\times i(t)=i^2(t)R$.

In general, the average power dissipation is measured and because of the periodic nature of the voltage and current, the power dissipation will be similar in magnitude in every cycle.

The average power is

$$P=\frac{1}{T}\int_0^T p(t)\,dt$$

$$=\frac{1}{T}\int_0^T i^2(t)R\,dt$$

$$=R\left[\frac{1}{T}\int_0^T i^2(t)\,dt\right]$$

† that is $P=Ri^2$

But at all instants of time $v(t)=i(t)R$, hence

† $$P=\frac{v_{\text{r.m.s.}}^2}{R}$$

It has already been shown that for d.c. $P=I^2R$, hence the *r.m.s. value of a periodic current can be defined as the value of direct current which causes an equal average power to be dissipated in a given resistor.*

6.3 PROPERTIES OF SINUSOIDAL WAVEFORMS

The term sinusoidal waveform is used for waveforms defined by

$$f(t) = A \sin(\omega t + \phi)$$

that is, it also includes cosinusoidal waveforms since $\sin(\omega t+\phi)=[\sin \omega t \cos \phi + \cos \omega t \sin \phi]$. Hence $\omega = 2\pi f$ is the *angular frequency* and is expressed in radians per second; A is the *peak value* or *amplitude* of the waveform and ϕ, defined later, is known as the *phase angle*. The parameters are shown in figures 6.1a and b, where $f(t)=A \sin \omega t$ is plotted. In figure 6.1a t is the abscissa, whereas in figure 6.1b ωt, termed the *electrical angle*, is the abscissa; the latter is often a more convenient parameter as can be seen when calculating average and r.m.s. values.

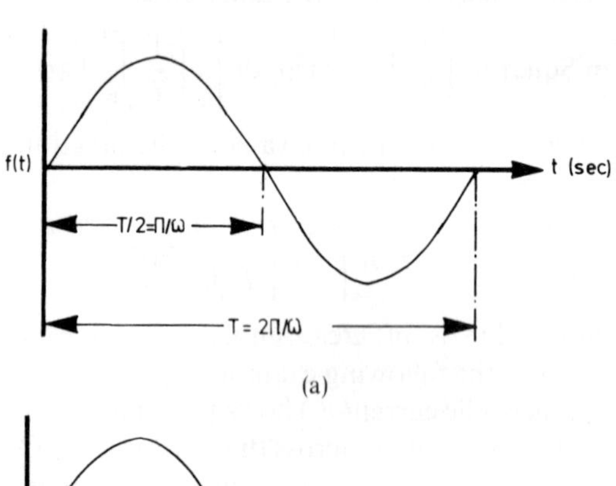

(a)

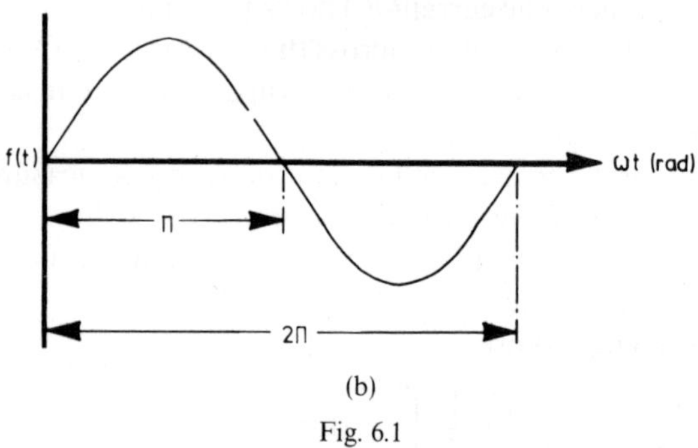

(b)

Fig. 6.1

It is apparent from figure 6.1 that the mean or average value of a sinusoidal waveform over a complete cycle is zero, since the positive and negative half cycles enclose equal areas. By convention the mean value of a sinusoidal waveform is defined as the mean over half a cycle, from one zero crossing to the next.

$$V_{mean} = \frac{A}{\pi/\omega}\int_0^{\pi/\omega} \sin \omega t \, dt$$

$$= \frac{\omega A}{\pi}\left[-\frac{1}{\omega}\cos \omega t\right]_{t=0}^{t=\pi/\omega}$$

$$= \frac{2A}{\pi}$$

In practice it is usually more convenient to integrate with respect to ωt

$$V_{mean} = \frac{A}{\pi}\int_0^{\pi} \sin \omega t \, d(\omega t)$$

$$= \frac{A}{\pi}\left[-\cos \omega t\right]_0^{\pi}$$

$$V_{mean} = \frac{2A}{\pi}$$

The root mean square value of the sinusoidal waveform is

$$V_{r.m.s.} = \left[\frac{A^2}{2\pi}\int_0^{2\pi} \sin^2 \omega t \, d(\omega t)\right]^{1/2}$$

$$= \left[\frac{A^2}{2\pi}\int_0^{2\pi} \frac{(1-\cos 2\omega t)}{2} d(\omega t)\right]^{1/2}$$

$$= \left[\frac{A^2}{4\pi}\left[\omega t - \frac{\sin 2\omega t}{2}\right]_0^{2\pi}\right]^{1/2}$$

$$V_{r.m.s.} = \frac{A}{\sqrt{2}}$$

The ratio $(V_{r.m.s.}/V_{mean})$ is known as the *form factor* and is an indication of the 'peakiness' of the waveform: the larger the form factor, the more 'peaky' is the waveform. The significance of the form factor will be understood better when Non-sinusoidal Periodic Waveforms have been studied (Chapter 12).

In figure 6.2 the periodic functions $f_1(t)=A \sin \omega t$ and $f_2(t)=A \sin(\omega t+\phi)$ are plotted; ϕ is the phase difference in radians, between the functions. It is seen that $f_2(t)$ crosses the zero *before* the corresponding crossing of $f_1(t)$; we say that $f_2(t)$ *leads* $f_1(t)$ by an angle ϕ, or that $f_1(t)$ *lags* $f_2(t)$ by an angle ϕ.

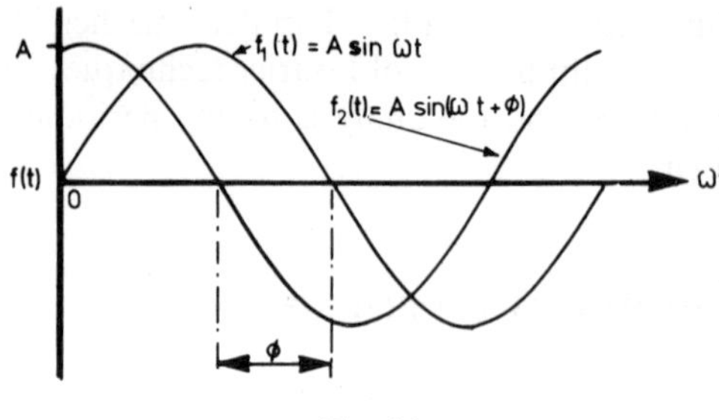

Fig. 6.2

6.4 WAVEFORM RELATIONSHIPS FOR LINEAR CIRCUIT ELEMENTS

The current/voltage relationships for circuits containing resistance, capacitance and inductance are now considered

(i) **Resistance**

If

$$i = I_m \sin \omega t$$

then

$$v_R = iR$$

$$= I_m R \sin \omega t \quad (6.1)$$

$$= V_m \sin \omega t \quad (6.2)$$

The voltage across the resistor is therefore in phase with the current through the resistor.

(ii) **Capacitance**

If

$$i = I_m \sin \omega t$$

since

$$v_c = \frac{1}{C} \int i dt$$

then

$$v_c = -\frac{I_m}{\omega C} \cos \omega t$$

$$= \frac{I_m}{\omega C} \sin (\omega t - \pi/2) \quad (6.3)$$

$$= V_m \sin (\omega t - \pi/2) \quad (6.4)$$

The voltage across the capacitor therefore lags the current by $\pi/2$, or the current leads the voltage by $\pi/2$.

(iii) **Inductance**

If

$$i = I_m \sin \omega t$$

since

$$v_L = L \frac{di}{dt}$$

then

$$v_L = \omega L I_m \cos \omega t$$

$$= \omega L I_m \sin (\omega t + \pi/2) \quad (6.5)$$

$$= V_m \sin (\omega t + \pi/2) \quad (6.6)$$

The voltage across the inductor therefore leads the current by $\pi/2$, or the current lags the voltage by $\pi/2$.

The current and voltage waveforms are shown in figure 6.3 and the results are summarized in Table 6.1.

An inspection of equations 6.1 to 6.6 shows that the maximum, or peak, voltages across the resistor, capacitor

TABLE 6.1

Resistor	Current and voltage are in phase
Capacitor	Current leads voltage by $\pi/2$
Inductor	Current lags voltage by $\pi/2$

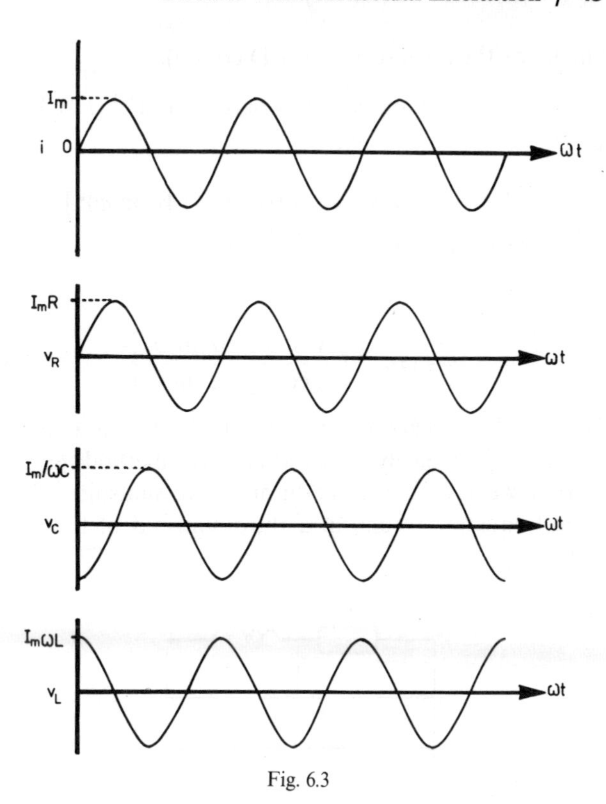

Fig. 6.3

and inductor are respectively $I_m R$, $I_m/\omega C$ and $I_m \omega L$. It is apparent that the quantities $1/\omega C$ and ωL have the dimensions of resistance. *$1/\omega C$ is the reactance of the capacitor and ωL is the reactance of the inductor.* The reciprocal of reactance is analogous to conductance $G(=1/R)$; *ωC is the susceptance of the capacitor and $1/\omega L$ is the susceptance of the inductor.* The symbol for reactance is X and that for susceptance is B.

6.5 THE PHASOR REPRESENTATION OF SINUSOIDAL QUANTITIES

When a current $i = I_m \sin \omega t$ is passed through a circuit consisting of resistance R in series with inductance L, as shown in figure 6.4a, the voltage across the circuit is $v = v_R + v_L$ where $v_R = I_m R \sin \omega t$ and $v_L = I_m \omega L \sin (\omega t + \pi/2)$. The voltages v_R and v_L are shown in figure 6.4b and v, obtained by adding their instantaneous values, is shown in figure 6.4c.

The process of adding graphically the instantaneous values of two sinusoids of the same frequency but differing in amplitude and phase is tedious and a shorter method of obtaining the resultant is required.

In the general case

$$v = A \sin (\omega t + \theta) + B \sin (\omega t + \phi)$$

$$= A(\sin \omega t \cos \theta + \cos \omega t \sin \theta)$$

$$+ B(\sin \omega t \cos \phi + \cos \omega t \sin \phi)$$

$$= (A \cos \theta + B \cos \phi) \sin \omega t + (A \sin \theta + B \sin \phi) \cos \omega t$$

which has the form (C sin ωt + D cos ωt)

$$=(C^2+D^2)^{1/2}\sin(\omega t+\alpha) \text{ where } \alpha=\tan^{-1}(D/C)$$

or

$$v=[(A\cos\theta+B\cos\phi)^2+(A\sin\theta+B\sin\phi)^2]^{1/2}\times\sin(\omega t+\alpha) \quad (6.7)$$

where

$$\alpha=\tan^{-1}\left[\frac{A\sin\theta+B\sin\phi}{A\cos\theta+B\cos\phi}\right] \quad (6.8)$$

This result appears rather formidable, but it may be obtained quite easily by an alternative method, particularly if we note that the addition of two sinusoids of the same frequency results in a third sinusoid of that frequency.

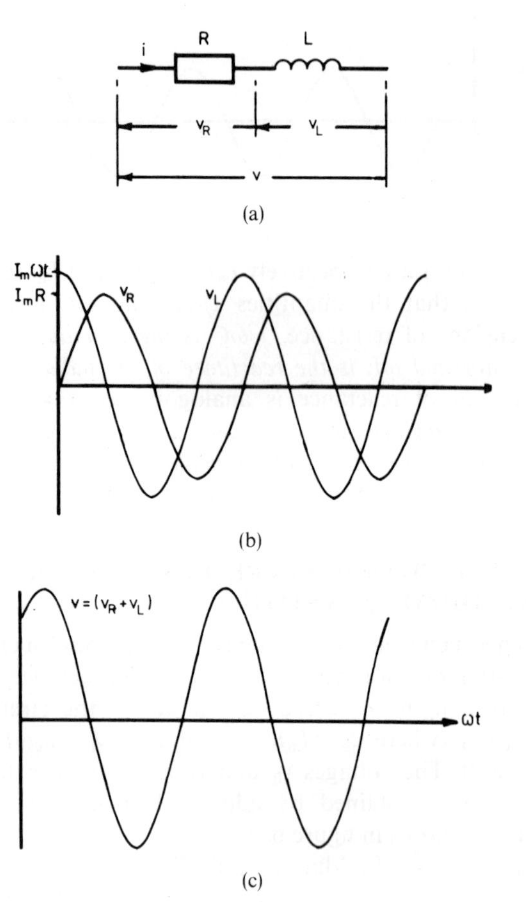

Fig. 6.4

The instantaneous value v of a voltage $v=V_m \sin \omega t$ may be obtained by representing the sinusoid as a line of length V_m rotating at a constant angular velocity ω radian/sec in an anticlockwise direction as shown in figure 6.5. *The instantaneous value of v at time t is the perpendicular projection of the line on to the vertical axis.* The rotating line is known as a *phasor*.

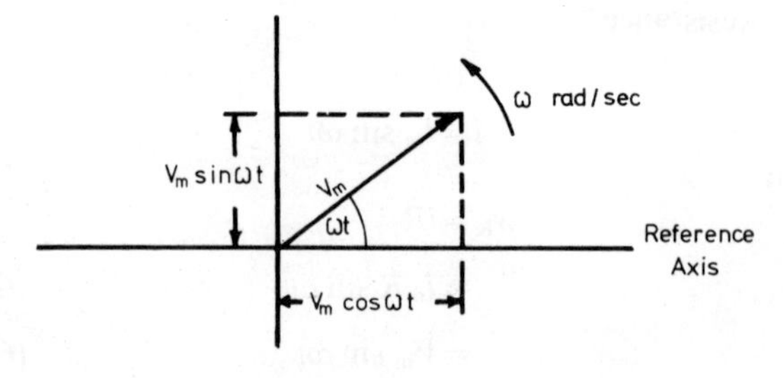

Fig. 6.5

Because the sinusoidal voltages and associated currents in a linear circuit are of the same frequency, all the phasors are rotating with the same angular velocity. We need therefore consider only their *relative* positions and can take one phasor as a reference when performing arithmetic operations. If we wish to add A sin ωt and B sin $(\omega t+\phi)$ it is convenient to set $t=0$ and the resulting phasor diagram is as shown in figure 6.6.

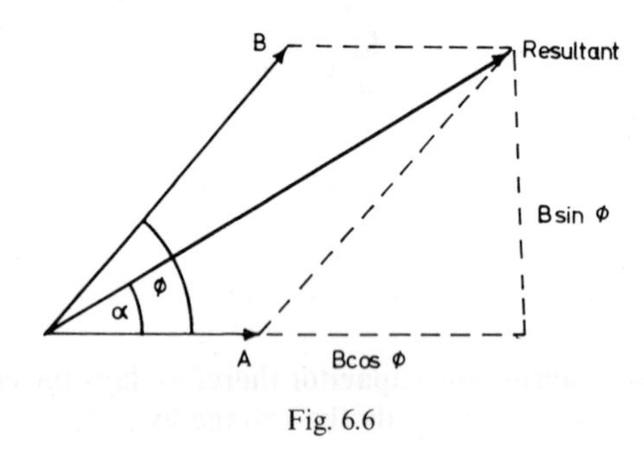

Fig. 6.6

It may be seen by inspection of figure 6.6 that the expressions for the magnitude and phase angle of the resultant are the same as those obtained from equations 6.7 and 6.8 by setting $\theta=0$. The phasor diagram forms the basis of a reasonably quick method of adding (or subtracting) sinusoidal voltages and currents. *The magnitudes and the relative phase angles* of sinusoids of the same frequency provide sufficient information to enable these arithmetic operations to be performed.

The phasor diagram for the series *RL* circuit considered at the beginning of this section can be drawn in either of the forms shown in figure 6.7.

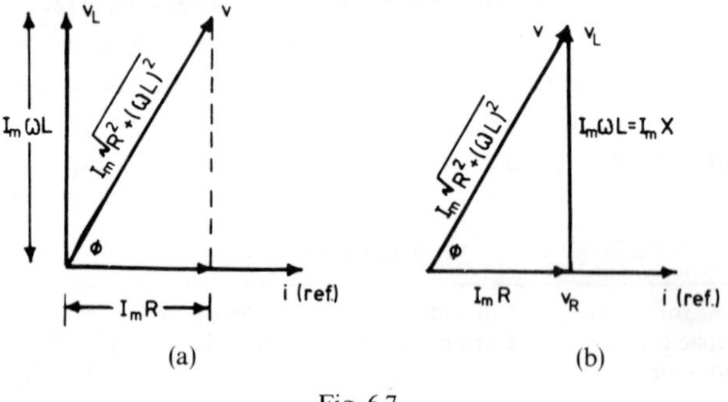

Fig. 6.7

The diagrams show that

$$\phi=\tan^{-1}\left(\frac{I_m\omega L}{I_m R}\right)=\tan^{-1}\left(\frac{\omega L}{R}\right) \quad (6.9)$$

and

$$|v|=[(I_m R)^2+(I_m\omega L)^2]^{1/2} \quad (6.10)$$

Hence

$$v=I_m[R^2+(\omega L)^2]^{1/2}\sin(\omega t+\phi) \quad (6.11)$$

The reference phasor in figure 6.7 is the current, since it is common to both circuit elements. In general, current is the reference phasor in series circuits and voltage is the reference phasor in parallel circuits.

The voltage v_L which is at right angles to the reference current on the phasor diagram is known as the *quadrature component* of v.

From figure 6.7 it is seen that the resultant voltage v *leads* the current i by an angle $\phi=\tan^{-1}(X/R)$ where $X=\omega L$. For the circuit consisting of a capacitor in series with a resistor in figure 6.8a, the phasor diagram is shown in figure 6.8b. It is seen that the resultant voltage v *lags* the current i by an angle $\phi=\tan^{-1}(X/R)$ where $X=1/\omega C$.

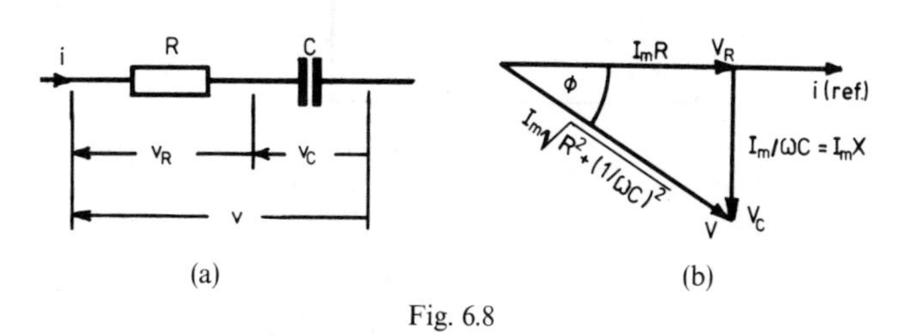

Fig. 6.8

It is usual to measure r.m.s. values instead of peak values of currents and voltages. The length of a phasor is therefore generally made equal to the r.m.s. value of the sinusoid it represents. This is equivalent to the application of a scale factor $1/\sqrt{2}$ but, if r.m.s. values are used throughout, the result is unaffected.

The following notation is used in the text for representing instantaneous, peak and r.m.s. values, and phasors

v, i = instantaneous values
V_m, I_m = peak values
V, I = r.m.s. values
$\boldsymbol{V}, \boldsymbol{I}$ = phasors

It will be seen that the quantities in bold capital letters are complex, whereas the peak and r.m.s. values are real numbers.

The ratio of r.m.s. voltage to r.m.s. current (or peak voltage to peak current) in the circuits of figures 6.4 and 6.8 is respectively

$$\frac{I_m[R^2+(\omega L)^2]^{1/2}}{\sqrt{2}}\bigg/\frac{I_m}{\sqrt{2}}=[R^2+(\omega L)^2]^{1/2} \quad (6.12)$$

and

$$I_m\frac{[R^2+(1/\omega C)^2]^{1/2}}{\sqrt{2}}\bigg/\frac{I_m}{\sqrt{2}}=[R^2+(1/\omega C)^2]^{1/2} \quad (6.13)$$

This ratio has the dimensions of resistance and is known as the *impedance* of the circuit. The symbol for impedance is $\boldsymbol{Z}$ and we have the general relationship

$$Z=(R^2+X^2)^{1/2}$$

If a scale factor $1/I_m$ is applied to eliminate current from the phasor diagrams in figures 6.7b and 6.8b, the corresponding impedance diagrams shown in figure 6.9 are obtained.

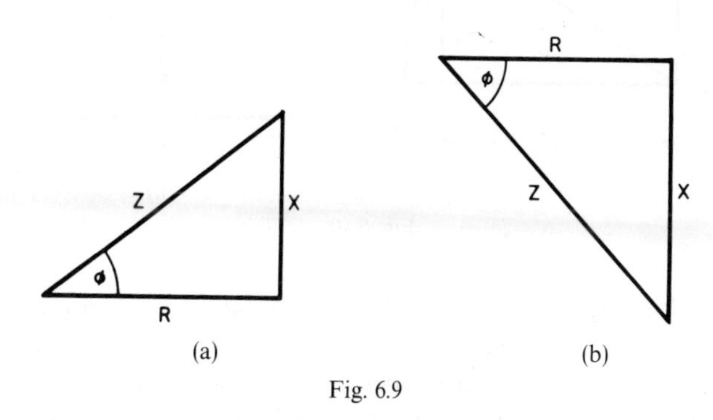

Fig. 6.9

It is apparent from figure 6.9 that to specify an impedance completely, both the magnitude Z and the phase angle ϕ must be stated, that is

† $$\boldsymbol{Z}=Z\underline{/\phi}=|\boldsymbol{Z}|\underline{/\phi}$$

where

† $$Z=(R^2+X^2)^{1/2}$$

and

† $$\phi=\tan^{-1}(X/R)$$

Note that *in an inductive circuit* $\boldsymbol{Z}$ *has a positive (or leading) phase angle and in a capacitive circuit* $\boldsymbol{Z}$ *has a negative (or lagging) phase angle.*

6.6 COMPLEX NUMBER REPRESENTATION OF SINUSOIDAL QUANTITIES

The trigonometric expressions, such as those in equations 6.9 and 6.10 may become cumbersome when adding or subtracting phasors and it is more convenient to use complex numbers.

A complex number in a plane has two components which may be represented by lengths along two perpendicular axes. By convention the horizontal axis is known as the *Real* axis and the vertical axis is known as the *Imaginary* axis or, for a closer relationship to real systems, the two components are referred to as the *In-phase* and *Quadrature* components respectively.

The phasor shown in figure 6.10a has horizontal and vertical components $a = V\cos\phi$ and $b = V\sin\phi$ respectively and the phasor is specified completely by these components. It is possible however to express this information in a 'shorthand notation' as $\boldsymbol{V} = a + jb$ *where j is an operator denoting an anticlockwise rotation through an angle* $\pi/2$, a *is the magnitude of the real part of* $\boldsymbol{V}$ *and* b *is the magnitude of the imaginary part.*

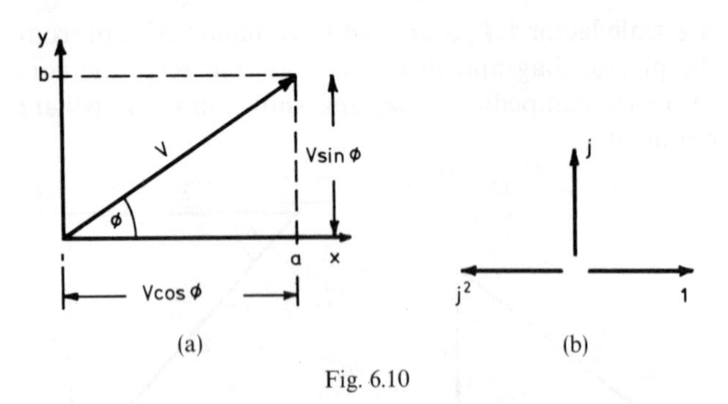

Fig. 6.10

The reason for the use of the term *imaginary part* may be seen by referring to figure 6.10b in which a reference phasor of unit length is operated on twice by j; the first operation results in a phasor $j \times 1 = j$ and the second operation gives $j \times j = j^2$, but the latter is a phasor equal in magnitude but opposite in direction to the original unit phasor as there are two successive 90° rotations. Therefore $j^2 = -1$ or $j = \sqrt{-1}$ which is not a real number and is known as an imaginary number.

The algebraic rules relating to alternating quantities represented by complex numbers will now be dealt with briefly.

In the above figures $\boldsymbol{w}_1$ and $\boldsymbol{w}_2$ are two complex numbers represented by $\boldsymbol{w}_1 = p_1 + jq_1$ and $\boldsymbol{w}_2 = p_2 + jq_2$. In polar co-ordinates $\boldsymbol{w}_1 = |\boldsymbol{w}_1|\underline{/\phi_1}$ and $\boldsymbol{w}_2 = |\boldsymbol{w}_2|\underline{/\phi_2}$.

(i) **Addition**

† $$\boldsymbol{w} = \boldsymbol{w}_1 + \boldsymbol{w}_2 = (p_1 + p_2) + j(q_1 + q_2) \qquad (6.14)$$

as shown in figure 6.11a.

(ii) **Subtraction**

† $$\boldsymbol{w} = (\boldsymbol{w}_1 - \boldsymbol{w}_2) = (p_1 - p_2) + j(q_1 - q_2) \qquad (6.15)$$

as shown in figure 6.11b.

(iii) **Multiplication**

$$\boldsymbol{w} = \boldsymbol{w}_1 \times \boldsymbol{w}_2 = (p_1 + jq_1)(p_2 + jq_2)$$
$$= (p_1p_2 - q_1q_2) + j(p_1q_2 + p_2q_1)$$

as shown in figure 6.11c.

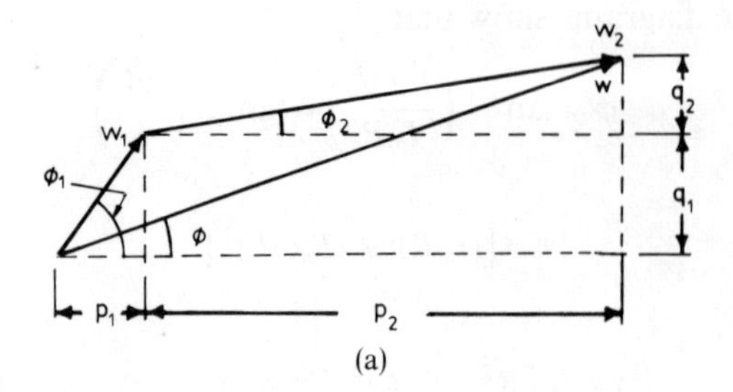

(a)

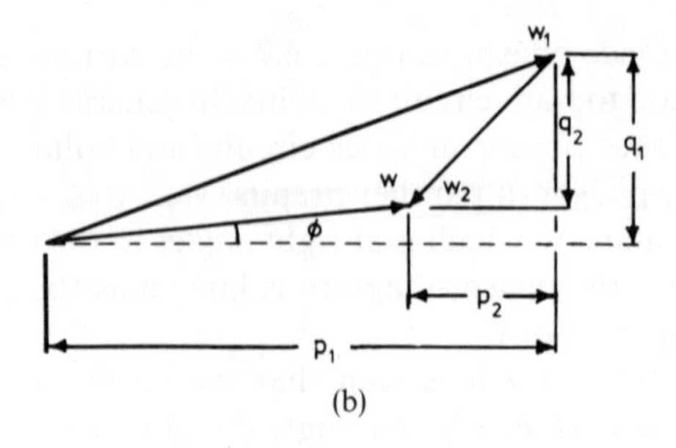

(b)

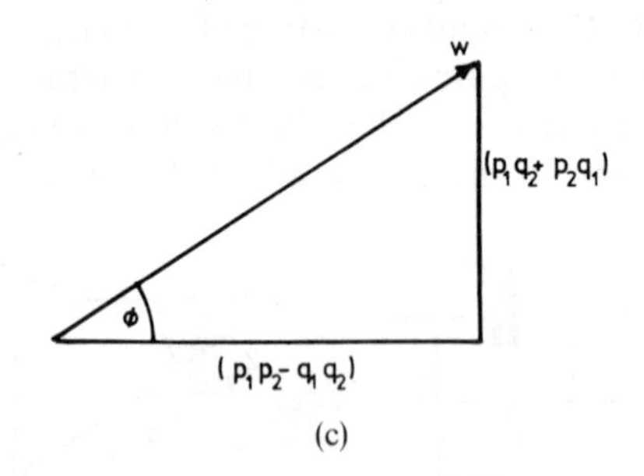

(c)

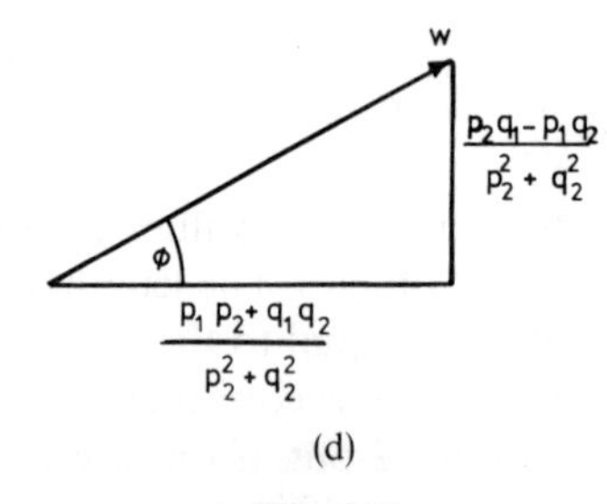

(d)

Fig. 6.11

This result is more conveniently expressed in polar form:

$$|\boldsymbol{w}| = [(p_1p_2 - q_1q_2)^2 + (p_1q_2 + p_2q_1)^2]^{1/2}$$
$$= [p_1{}^2 + q_1{}^2)(p_2{}^2 + q_2{}^2)]^{1/2}$$
$$= |\boldsymbol{w}_1| \times |\boldsymbol{w}_2|$$

Also

$$\tan\phi = \frac{p_1q_2 + p_2q_1}{p_1p_2 - q_1q_2} = \frac{q_2/p_2 + q_1/p_1}{1 - q_1/p_1 \cdot q_2/p_2}$$
$$= \frac{\tan\phi_2 + \tan\phi_1}{1 - \tan\phi_1\tan\phi_2}$$

which leads to $\phi = (\phi_1 + \phi_2)$ from the expansion of $\tan(\phi_1 + \phi_2)$.

If w_1 and w_2 are in polar form

† $$w = |w| \angle\phi = w_1 \times w_2 = |w_1||w_2| \angle(\phi_1 + \phi_2) \quad (6.16)$$

(iv) **Division**

$$w = \frac{w_1}{w_2} = \frac{(p_1 + jq_1)}{(p_2 + jq_2)} = \frac{(p_1 + jq_1)(p_2 - jq_2)}{(p_2 + jq_2)(p_2 - jq_2)}$$

$$= \frac{(p_1p_2 + q_1q_2) + j(p_2q_1 - p_1q_2)}{p_2^2 + q_2^2}$$

$$= \frac{(p_1p_2 + q_1q_2)}{p_2^2 + q_2^2} + j\frac{(p_2q_1 - p_1q_2)}{p_2^2 + q_2^2}$$

as shown in figure 6.11d.

By a similar method to that used for the multiplication of complex numbers it may be shown that

† $$w = |w| \angle\phi = \frac{w_1}{w_2} = \frac{|w_1|}{|w_2|} \angle(\phi_1 - \phi_2) \quad (6.17)$$

(v) **Rationalization**

When a complex number appears in the denominator of a fraction, as in (iv) above, the process of rationalization is applied in order to ensure that only real terms are present in the denominator. *Rationalization consists of multiplying the numerator and the denominator of the fraction by the complex conjugate of the denominator*, (p − jq) *being the complex conjugate of* (p + jq). *If* (p + jq) = Z *then* (p − jq) = $\overset{*}{Z}$. represents the conjugate

Thus $m = \dfrac{p + jq}{x + jy} = \dfrac{(p + jq)(x - jy)}{(x + jy)(x - jy)}$

or

† $$\frac{p + jq}{x + jy} = \frac{(px + qy) + j(qx - py)}{x^2 + y^2} \quad (6.18)$$

(vi) **Powers**

As an extension of multiplication it may be shown that

† $$m^n = |m|^n \angle n\phi$$

also (6.19)

† $$m^{1/n} = |m|^{1/n} \angle\phi/n$$

From the above examples it follows that, as a general rule, it is preferable to use Cartesian co-ordinates for addition and subtraction of complex numbers and Polar co-ordinates for multiplication and division.

† It should be noted that *if* $a + jb = c + jd$, *then* $a = c$ *and* $b = d$; that is the real term on the left-hand side of the equation is equal to the real term on the right-hand side and the imaginary term on the left-hand side is equal to the imaginary term on the right-hand side.

6.7 THE EXPONENTIAL REPRESENTATION OF SINUSOIDAL QUANTITIES

As an alternative to the complex number representation of sinusoids it is useful to employ the exponential form which embraces both the sine and cosine waves.

The series for e^{ϕ} is

$$e^{\phi} = 1 + \phi + \frac{\phi^2}{2!} + \frac{\phi^3}{3!} + \frac{\phi^4}{4!} + \frac{\phi^5}{5!} + \frac{\phi^6}{6!} \cdots$$

Replacing ϕ by $j\phi$ gives

$$e^{j\phi} = 1 + j\phi - \frac{\phi^2}{2!} - \frac{j\phi^3}{3!} + \frac{\phi^4}{4!} + \frac{j\phi^5}{5!} - \frac{\phi^6}{6!} \cdots$$

$$= \left[1 - \frac{\phi^2}{2!} + \frac{\phi^4}{4!} - \frac{\phi^6}{6!} \cdots\right] + j\left[\phi - \frac{\phi^3}{3!} + \frac{\phi^5}{5!} \cdots\right]$$

$$= \cos\phi + j\sin\phi \text{ by definition of these series}$$

The complex number $V\angle\phi = V(\cos\phi + j\sin\phi)$ shown graphically in figure 6.10a may also be represented by $Ve^{j\phi}$.

It follows that

† $$\begin{aligned} V\cos\phi &= \text{Real part of } Ve^{j\phi} = \text{Re } Ve^{j\phi} \\ V\sin\phi &= \text{Imaginary part of } Ve^{j\phi} = \text{Im } Ve^{j\phi} \end{aligned} \quad (6.20)$$

It has been shown in section 6.5 that a sinusoid $v = V_m \sin\omega t$ can be represented by a line of length V_m rotating at a constant angular velocity ω radians/second; because this phasor has real and imaginary parts $V_m \cos\omega t$ and $V_m \sin\omega t$ respectively, it follows that it can also be expressed as $V_m e^{j\omega t}$.

6.8 INTRODUCTION TO COMPLEX FREQUENCY

We will now take a significant step forward, without giving too detailed an explanation. Let us replace the frequency variable $j\omega$ by a complex variable $s = (\alpha + j\omega)$ then

$$\begin{aligned} v &= V_m e^{st} \\ &= V_m e^{(\alpha + j\omega)t} \\ &= V_m e^{\alpha t} e^{j\omega t} \end{aligned} \quad (6.21)$$

The real part of the complex variable represents a damping term and the imaginary part represents the angular frequency; in particular if α is negative the amplitude of the function $|v| = V_m e^{\alpha t}$ will decrease exponentially with time.

The quantity s is referred to as a *complex frequency* and we will now see that it is a unifying concept of which the d.c. and sinusoidal techniques of analysis developed in the previous sections are special cases. The following conditions will be considered, with reference to equation 6.21:

(i) $\alpha = 0, \omega = 0$, then $v = V_m$ which is a constant or d.c. voltage.

(ii) $\omega = 0$, then $v = V_m e^{\alpha t}$ which is an exponential waveform.

(iii) $\alpha = 0$, then $v = V_m e^{j\omega t} = V_m(\cos \omega t + j \sin \omega t)$ which represents undamped cosine and sine waves.

(iv) $v = V_m e^{\alpha t} \cos \omega t$, which if α is negative is an exponentially damped cosine wave and may be written in exponential form as follows

$$= \frac{V_m e^{\alpha t}}{2} [e^{j\omega t} + e^{-j\omega t}]$$

$$= \frac{V_m}{2} e^{(\alpha + j\omega)t} + \frac{V_m}{2} e^{(\alpha - j\omega)t}$$

$$= \frac{V_m}{2} e^{s_1 t} + \frac{V_m}{2} e^{s_2 t} \quad (6.22)$$

where

$$s_1 = (\alpha + j\omega) \text{ and } s_2 = \overset{*}{s}_1 = (\alpha - j\omega)$$

We see therefore that to define the damped cosine wave a conjugate complex pair of frequencies is required.

(v) It follows from (iv) that if $\alpha = 0$,

$$v = V_m \cos \omega t$$

$$= \frac{V_m}{2} e^{j\omega t} + \frac{V_m}{2} e^{-j\omega t} \quad (6.23)$$

which may be represented by two phasors of amplitude $V_m/2$ rotating in opposite directions as shown in figure 6.12.

It is apparent from the above examples that the concept of *complex frequency* can form the basis of a powerful technique for the analysis of electric circuits. It is convenient to represent the real and imaginary parts of the complex frequency on a plane, known as the s-plane or complex frequency plane, in which the horizontal axis represents the real component of s and the vertical axis represents the imaginary component. Typical waveforms (in the time domain) associated with the complex frequency plane are shown in figure 6.13, although only positive values of ω are shown, as the concept of 'negative frequency', corresponding to the second term on the right hand side of equations 6.22 and 6.23 is not dealt with at this stage.

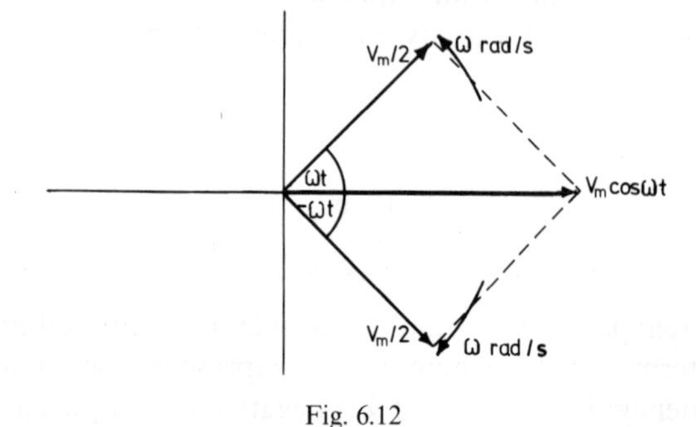

Fig. 6.12

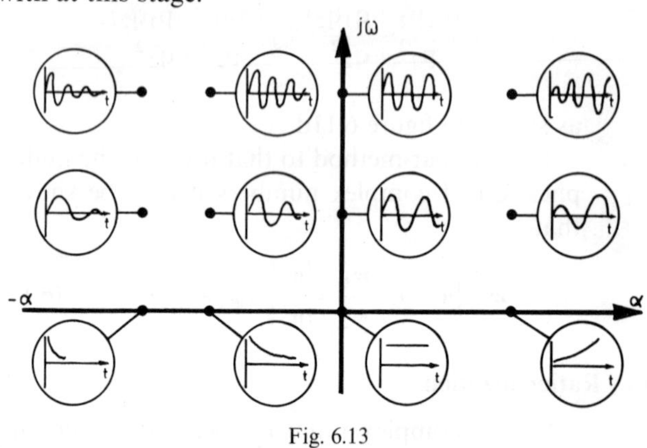

Fig. 6.13

From figure 6.13 it may be seen that waves having amplitudes that decay with time, fall in the left hand half of the complex frequency plane (corresponding in practice to stable systems) and that sine waves of constant amplitude occur along the vertical axis which corresponds to $\alpha = 0$ or zero damping. It is seen therefore that the steady state sinusoidal condition is obtained by setting $s = j\omega$ and going from the complex frequency (s) domain to the real frequency (ω) domain. When the Laplace transform method of solving differential equations was introduced it was stated, on page 33, that at that stage s had no significance other than that it was an auxiliary variable of such a value so that the associated integral was convergent. Complex numbers had not then been introduced, but it can now be noted that in the Laplace transform method s is in fact a complex variable of the form $s = (\alpha + j\omega)$.

A study of the results of the worked examples in Section 5.5 shows that *the rate of decay of the transient term depends only on the circuit constants and is independent of the initial conditions and excitation, although the two latter factors do affect the initial amplitude of the transient term. The steady state term depends on the periodic excitation and is independent of the initial conditions.* In Section 5.1 the transformed voltage/current relationships for capacitance and inductance were given as

$$\bar{v} = \frac{V_0}{s} + \frac{\bar{i}}{Cs} \text{ and } \bar{v} = sL\bar{i} - LI_0$$

If the initial conditions are ignored these become

$$\bar{v}=\frac{\bar{i}}{Cs} \quad \text{or} \quad \frac{\bar{v}}{\bar{i}}=\frac{1}{Cs}$$

and

$$\bar{v}=Ls\bar{i} \quad \text{or} \quad \frac{\bar{v}}{\bar{i}}=Ls$$

By setting $s=\mathrm{j}\omega$ we obtain the steady state equivalents, namely the reactances, $1/\mathrm{j}\omega C$ and $\mathrm{j}\omega L$.

Referring to the impedance diagrams of figure 6.9 we can write

† $$\boldsymbol{Z}=R+\mathrm{j}X$$

so that for an inductive circuit consisting of R and L in series

† $$\boldsymbol{Z}=R+\mathrm{j}\omega L$$

and for a capacitive circuit consisting of R and C in series

† $$\boldsymbol{Z}=R-\mathrm{j}/\omega C$$

or

† $$\boldsymbol{Z}=R+1/\mathrm{j}\omega C$$

Let us now consider a current $i=I_{\mathrm{m}}\,\mathrm{e}^{\mathrm{j}\omega t}$ flowing in a circuit consisting of R, L and C in series, as shown in figure 6.14.

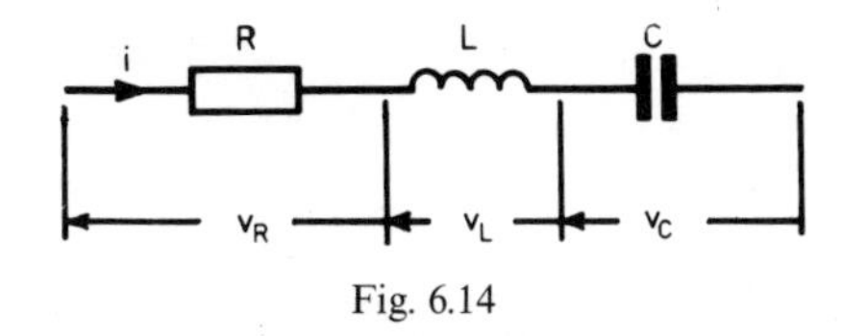

Fig. 6.14

Then

$$v_{\mathrm{R}}=iR=RI_{\mathrm{m}}\,\mathrm{e}^{\mathrm{j}\omega t}$$

$$v_{\mathrm{L}}=\frac{L\mathrm{d}i}{\mathrm{d}t}=\mathrm{j}\omega LI_{\mathrm{m}}\,\mathrm{e}^{\mathrm{j}\omega t}=\mathrm{j}\omega L\,i$$

$$v_{\mathrm{C}}=\frac{1}{C}\int i\mathrm{d}t=\frac{1}{\mathrm{j}\omega C}I_{\mathrm{m}}\,\mathrm{e}^{\mathrm{j}\omega t}=\frac{i}{\mathrm{j}\omega C}$$

from which it is seen that, in the steady state, the operations of differentiation and integration are, in effect, replaced by $\mathrm{j}\omega$ and $1/\mathrm{j}\omega$ multipliers respectively. One should note the similarity of the Laplace transform in which *if initial conditions are ignored* the operations of differentiation and integration involve s and $1/s$ respectively.

PROBLEMS

6.1. Determine the mean and r.m.s. values of the periodic waveforms shown in figure Q.1.

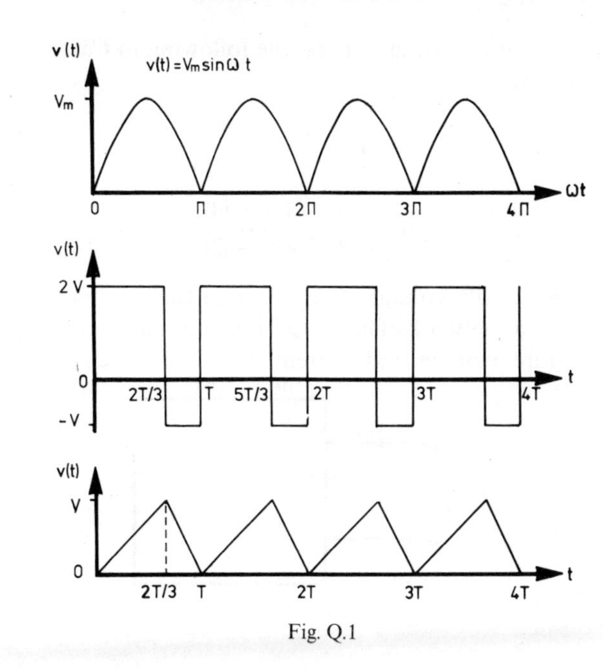

Fig. Q.1

6.2. A voltage $v=20\sin 10^6t$ V is applied to a two-terminal network consisting of a loss-free capacitor in series with a resistor. The steady-state current in the circuit is $i=9\sin(10^6t+26.5°)$ mA. Determine the values of the capacitor and resistor and draw a phasor diagram for the circuit showing all voltages and the current.

6.3. A coil of inductance 100 mH and effective resistance 100 Ω is connected in series with a 0.5 μF capacitor. If the steady-state current flowing in the circuit is $i=50\sin(2000\,\pi t+30°)$ mA, derive expressions for the voltages across the capacitor, the coil and the whole circuit. Sketch the waveforms.

Show the three voltages and the current on a phasor diagram drawn to scale.

6.4. Simplify the following expressions and give the results in polar form

(i) $(4+\mathrm{j}3)+(5+\mathrm{j}6)$

(ii) $\dfrac{(5+\mathrm{j}6)(3-\mathrm{j}2)}{(3-\mathrm{j}4)(4+\mathrm{j}4)}$

(iii) $\dfrac{(4+\mathrm{j}3)-(2+\mathrm{j}1)}{(3+\mathrm{j}2)}$

6.5. Express the following in Cartesian form and Exponential form

(i) $5\angle 30°$

(ii) $(10\angle 60° - 4\angle 45°)$

(iii) $\dfrac{5\angle 30°}{(2+\mathrm{j}2)}$

6.6. By rationalizing, express the following in Cartesian form

(i) $\dfrac{(3+j4)}{(2-j3)}$

(ii) $\dfrac{(4+j6)+(4+j4)}{(2+j3)+(1-j2)}$

6.7. When the voltage $v(t)$ applied to the two-terminal linear network of figure Q.7 is sinusoidal, the steady-state voltage and current can be represented by

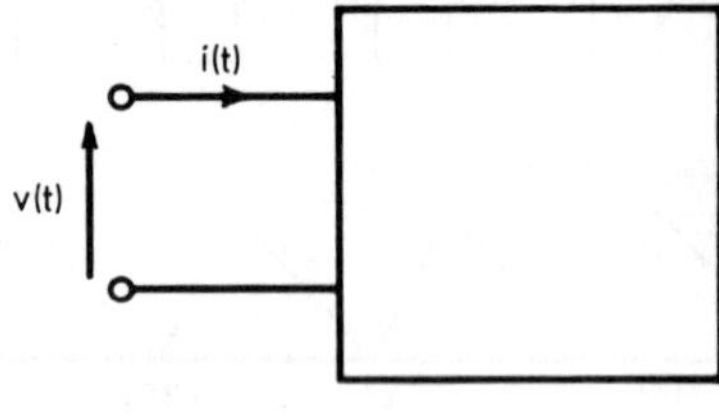

Fig. Q.7

phasors $\boldsymbol{V}$ and $\boldsymbol{I}$ respectively. For this network

$$\frac{\boldsymbol{V}}{\boldsymbol{I}}=\frac{1}{1+j\omega}$$

Derive an expression for $i(t)$ if $v(t)$ is not sinusoidal but is defined by

$$v(t)=0,\ t\leqslant 0$$
$$=Ae^{-\alpha t},\ t>0$$

6.8. A thyristor, or solid-state switch, is connected in series with an 800 Ω resistor across an a.c. supply voltage $v=400\sin\omega t$ V.

The thyristor is switched 'on' when the voltage across it reaches 200 V and is turned 'off' when the voltage across it falls to zero.

Calculate, from first principles, the power dissipated in the resistor, assuming zero voltage drop across the thyristor when it is conducting.

CHAPTER SEVEN

Voltage and Current Relationships in A.C. Circuits

7.1 INTRODUCTION

Several methods of representing alternating quantities have been discussed in the previous chapter and the application of phasors and complex quantities to electric circuits has been introduced. These concepts will now be applied directly to the analysis of electric circuits which, when excited by sinusoids, are known as *a.c. circuits.*

In general, the j notation will be used, but *it is recommended that, whenever applicable, a phasor diagram should be constructed step by step, as the calculation proceeds; it will be found that this usually leads to a better understanding of the problem.*

7.2 THE APPLICATION OF COMPLEX NOTATION TECHNIQUES TO THE ANALYSIS OF LINEAR CIRCUITS

To illustrate the use of the complex notation techniques described in Section 6.6, some worked examples are now presented.

Example In the circuit of figure 7.1a, determine the voltage v_{ab} in terms of the applied voltage v

Solution

The angular velocity of the applied voltage is $\omega = 5000$ rad/s

$$\therefore X_c = \frac{1}{\omega C} = \frac{1}{5\times10^3\times0.1\times10^{-6}} = 2\ \text{k}\Omega$$

$$X_L = \omega L = 5\times10^3\times800\times10^{-3} = 4\ \text{k}\Omega$$

Let $\boldsymbol{Z}_1$ represent R_1 in series with C and let $\boldsymbol{Z}_2$ represent R_2 in series with L as shown in figure 7.1b.

Then

$$\boldsymbol{Z}_1 = (4 - \text{j}2)\ \text{k}\Omega$$

$$\boldsymbol{Z}_2 = (3 + \text{j}4)\ \text{k}\Omega$$

From figure 7.1b

$$\boldsymbol{V} = \boldsymbol{I}(\boldsymbol{Z}_1 + \boldsymbol{Z}_2)$$

$$\boldsymbol{V}_{ab} = \boldsymbol{I}\boldsymbol{Z}_2$$

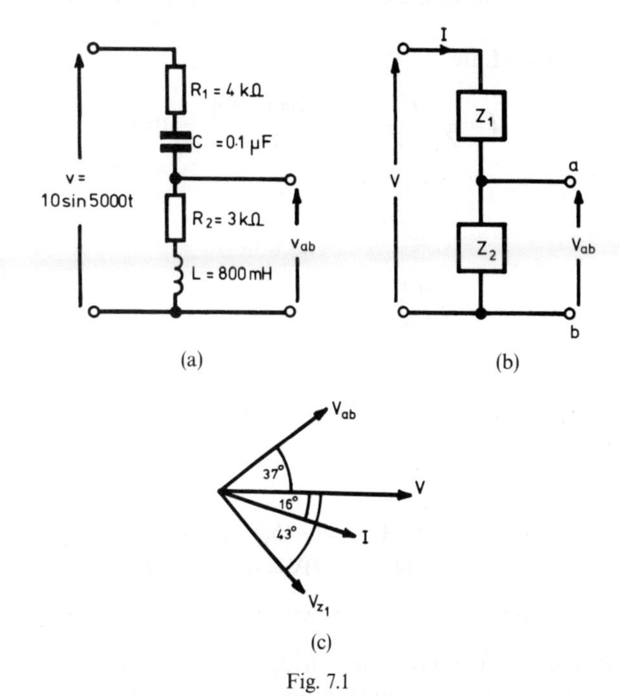

(a) (b) (c)

Fig. 7.1

Therefore

$$\boldsymbol{V}_{ab} = \boldsymbol{V}\cdot\frac{\boldsymbol{Z}_2}{\boldsymbol{Z}_1 + \boldsymbol{Z}_2}$$

(cf. equation 2.10, page 10).

and taking $\boldsymbol{V}$ as the reference voltage, $\boldsymbol{V} = 10\underline{/0^\circ} = 10(1 + \text{j}0)$

$$\boldsymbol{V}_{ab} = \frac{10(1+\text{j}0)(3+\text{j}4)}{(4-\text{j}2)+(3+\text{j}4)} = \frac{10(3+\text{j}4)}{(7+\text{j}2)}$$

If the answer is required in polar form it is preferable at this stage to convert the numerator and denominator to polar co-ordinates

$$\boldsymbol{V}_{ab} = \frac{10(3^2+4^2)^{1/2}\underline{/\tan^{-1} 4/3}}{(7^2+2^2)^{1/2}\underline{/\tan^{-1} 2/7}}$$

$$= \frac{50\underline{/53^\circ}}{7.3\underline{/16^\circ}} = 6.9\underline{/37^\circ}\ V$$

and

$$v_{ab} = 6.9 \sin(5000t + 37^\circ)\ V$$

If the answer is required in cartesian form it may be preferable to rationalize

$$V_{ab}=\frac{10(3+j4)(7-j2)}{(7+j2)(7-j2)}$$

$$=\frac{10(29+j22)}{7^2+2^2}$$

$$=(5.5+j4.2)\ V$$

It is also possible to calculate the magnitude and phase of the current in the circuit, with respect to the reference V

By Ohm's Law

$$I=\frac{V}{Z_1+Z_2}=\frac{10(1+j0)}{(4-j2)+(3+j4)}\text{mA}$$

$$=\frac{10\angle 0^\circ}{(7+j2)}$$

$$=\frac{10\angle 0^\circ}{7.3\angle 16^\circ}$$

$$=1.4\angle -16^\circ\ \text{mA}$$

Clearly the voltage across Z_1 is the difference of V and V_{ab}.

Hence

$$V_{Z_1}=10(1+j0)-(5.5+j4.2)$$
$$=(4.5-j4.2)\text{V}=6.2\angle -43^\circ\ V$$

The phasor diagram is shown in figure7.1c.

Example The Owen a.c. bridge shown in figure 7.2a is used to measure the inductance L and effective resistance r of a coil. Derive the balance equations for the bridge.

Solution

When the bridge is balanced, no current flows in the detector.

Therefore

$$I_2=I_3 \text{ and } I_1=I_4,$$

also, A and B are at the same potential.

That is

$$I_3(r+j\omega L)=I_4R_4$$

and

$$I_3(R_2-j/\omega C_2)=-I_4\,.\,j/\omega C_1$$

therefore

$$r+j\omega L=\frac{R_4(R_2-j/\omega C_2)}{-j/\omega C_1}$$

$$=j\omega C_1R_2R_4+\frac{\omega C_1R_4}{\omega C_2}$$

$$=\frac{R_4C_1}{C_2}+j\omega C_1R_2R_4$$

Equating the real parts and the imaginary parts gives

$$r=R_4C_1/C_2$$

$$L=C_1R_2R_4$$

It should be noted that, in this case, the balance conditions are independent of the frequency of the source.

The phasor diagram for the balanced bridge is shown in figure 7.2b.

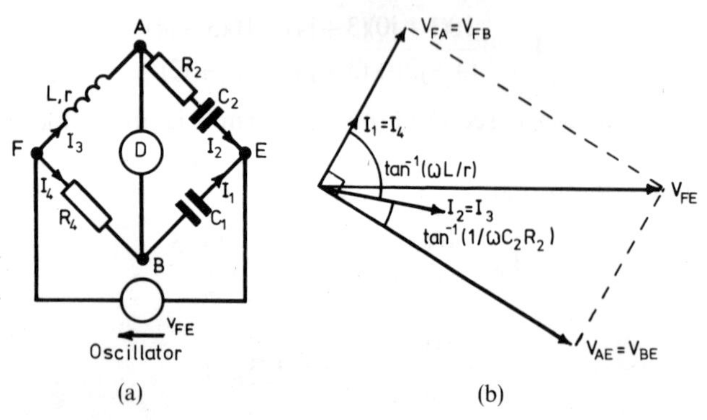

(a) (b)

Fig. 7.2

Example Calculate the current in each impedance in the circuit shown in figure 7.3.

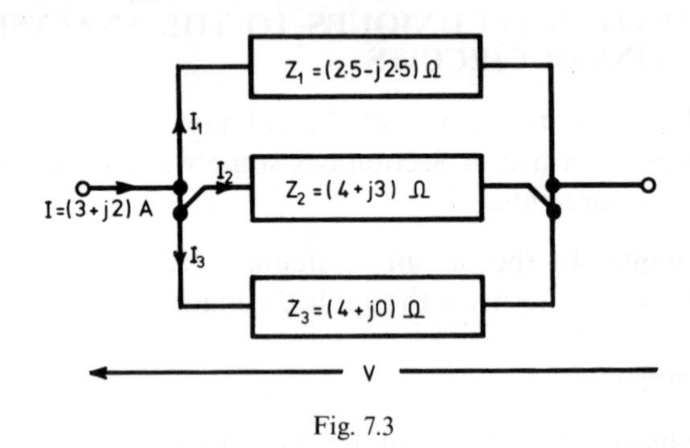

Fig. 7.3

Solution

By Ohms Law $I_1=V/Z_1=VY_1$ where $Y_1=1/Z_1$ is the *admittance* of the upper branch

$$I_2=V/Z_2=VY_2$$

$$I_3=V/Z_3=VY_3$$

$$I=(I_1+I_2+I_3)=V(Y_1+Y_2+Y_3)$$

Now

$$I_1=VY_1=\frac{IY_1}{Y_1+Y_2+Y_3}$$

(cf. equation 2.11, page 11).

We will evaluate $\boldsymbol{Y}_1$, $\boldsymbol{Y}_2$ and $\boldsymbol{Y}_3$

$$\boldsymbol{Y}_1=\frac{1}{2.5-\mathrm{j}2.5}=\frac{1+\mathrm{j}1}{5}=(0.2+\mathrm{j}0.2)S$$

$$\boldsymbol{Y}_2=\frac{1}{4+\mathrm{j}3}=\frac{4-\mathrm{j}3}{25}=(0.16-\mathrm{j}0.12)S$$

$$\boldsymbol{Y}_3=\tfrac{1}{4}=(0.25+\mathrm{j}0)S$$

Therefore

$$\boldsymbol{I}_1=\frac{(3+\mathrm{j}2)(0.2+\mathrm{j}0.2)}{(0.61+\mathrm{j}0.08)}=\frac{3.61\angle 34^\circ\ 0.28\angle 45^\circ}{0.62\angle 7^\circ}=1.63\angle 72^\circ\ \mathrm{A}$$

$$\boldsymbol{I}_2=\frac{(3+\mathrm{j}2)(0.16-\mathrm{j}0.09)}{(0.61+\mathrm{j}0.08)}=\frac{3.61\angle 34^\circ\ .\ 0.18\angle -29^\circ}{0.62\angle 7^\circ}$$

$$=1.05\angle -2^\circ\ \mathrm{A}$$

$$\boldsymbol{I}_3=\frac{(3+\mathrm{j}2)0.25}{(0.61+\mathrm{j}0.08)}=\frac{3.61\angle 34^\circ\ .\ 0.25\angle 0^\circ}{0.62\angle 7^\circ}=1.45\angle 27^\circ\ \mathrm{A}$$

The currents, together with the reference voltage, are shown on the phasor diagram, figure 7.4.

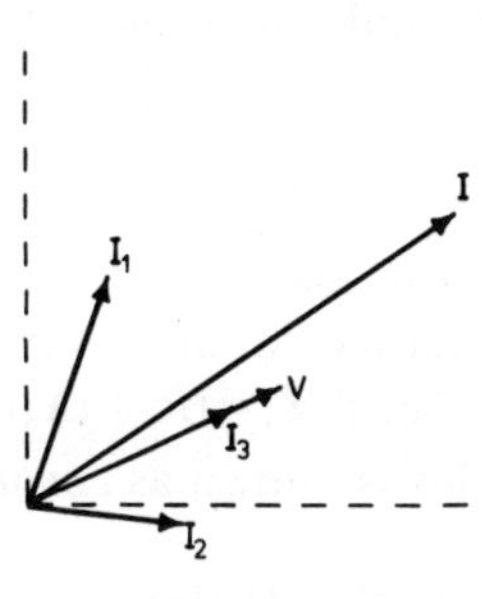

Fig. 7.4

7.3 ADMITTANCE, CONDUCTANCE AND SUCEPTANCE RELATIONSHIPS

Conductance, susceptance and admittance have already been mentioned (pages 2, 45 and 54) and expressions will now be derived relating these quantities to resistance, reactance and impedance.

For a circuit consisting of a resistor and an inductor in series

$$\boldsymbol{Z}=R+\mathrm{j}X$$

The admittance of this circuit is

$$\boldsymbol{Y}=(G+\mathrm{j}B)=\frac{1}{\boldsymbol{Z}}=\frac{1}{(R+\mathrm{j}X)}=\frac{R-\mathrm{j}X}{R^2+X^2}=\frac{R}{|\boldsymbol{Z}|^2}-\mathrm{j}\frac{X}{|\boldsymbol{Z}|^2}$$

Thus

† $$G=\frac{R}{|\boldsymbol{Z}|^2}\ \text{and}\ B=-\frac{X}{|\boldsymbol{Z}|^2} \qquad (7.1)$$

*It should be noted that when **Z** has a positive phase angle **Y** has a negative phase angle and vice versa.*

Example

The impedance of a circuit, measured at a frequency of 1 MHz, is (400 − j300) Ω. Express this in the form of resistance in parallel with capacitance.

Solution

The admittance of the circuit is

$$\boldsymbol{Y}=\frac{1}{\boldsymbol{Z}}=\frac{1}{400-\mathrm{j}300}=\frac{(4+\mathrm{j}3)}{100\times 25}$$

$$=\frac{4}{2500}+\mathrm{j}\frac{3}{2500}=(G+\mathrm{j}B)=\left(\frac{1}{R}+\mathrm{j}\omega C\right)$$

Hence

$$R=\frac{2500}{4}=625\ \Omega\ \text{and}\ \omega C=\frac{3}{2500}\ \mathrm{S}$$

giving

$$C=\frac{3\times 10^{12}}{2500\times 2\pi\times 10^6}\ \mathrm{pF}=191\ \mathrm{pF}$$

Conversely if the admittance of the circuit is given, and the equivalent series elements are required, one writes down an expression for the impedance of the circuit.

Example

Measurements on a two-terminal network, carried out on a radio-frequency admittance bridge at a frequency of 30 MHz, gave the following results: Conductance scale reading = 1.32 mS; Susceptance scale reading = −4.97 mS. Determine the equivalent series elements of the network.

Solution

$$\boldsymbol{Y}=(1.32-\mathrm{j}4.97)\ \mathrm{mS}$$
$$=(1.32-\mathrm{j}4.97)\times 10^{-3}\ \mathrm{S}$$

To determine the equivalent series elements it is necessary to obtain an expression for the impedance of the network

$$\boldsymbol{Z}=\frac{1}{\boldsymbol{Y}}=\frac{10^3}{1.32-\mathrm{j}4.97}\ \Omega$$

$$=\frac{10^3(1.32+\mathrm{j}4.97)}{1.32^2+4.97^2}\ \Omega$$

$$=(50+\mathrm{j}188)\ \Omega=(r+\mathrm{j}\omega L)$$

Hence

$$r=50\ \Omega$$

$$L=\frac{188}{\omega}\ \mathrm{H}=\frac{188}{2\pi\times 30\times 10^6}\ \mathrm{H}=1\ \mu\mathrm{H}$$

and the equivalent circuit is a resistance of 50 Ω in series with an inductance of 1 μH.

7.4 NETWORK THEOREMS APPLIED TO A.C. CIRCUITS

Kirchhoff's Laws apply to a.c. circuits and need not be restated. Thevenin's Theorem and Norton's Theorem and the Superposition Theorem also apply but with *resistance* replaced by *impedance*; they are stated below, together with the Maximum Power Theorem and some additional theorems.

7.4.1 Thevenin's Theorem

A two-terminal linear network of generators and impedances can be replaced by **a single voltage source in series with an impedance.** *The e.m.f. of the source is equal to the open-circuit voltage at the terminals of the network; the value of the impedance is equal to the impedance measured between the terminals of the network when all generators are replaced by their internal impedances.*

7.4.2 Norton's Theorem

A two-terminal linear network of generators and impedances can be replaced by **a single current source in parallel with an impedance.** *The source current is equal to the current that flows between the terminals when they are short-circuited; the value of the impedance is equal to the impedance measured between the terminals when all generators are replaced by their internal impedances.*

7.4.3 The Superposition Theorem

In any linear network containing more than one source, the current flowing in any branch of the network is the algebraic sum of the currents that would flow in that branch if each source were considered separately, with all other sources replaced at the time by impedances equal in value to their internal impedances.

7.4.4 The Maximum Power Transfer Theorem

A source of internal impedance $\boldsymbol{Z}_s$ *supplies maximum power to a load impedance* $\boldsymbol{Z}_L$ *when the load impedance is the complex conjugate of the source impedance; that is when*

$$\boldsymbol{Z}_L = \overset{*}{\boldsymbol{Z}}_s \qquad (7.2)$$

In figure 7.5 a generator of internal impedance $\boldsymbol{Z}_s = (R_s + jX_s)$ supplies power to a load $\boldsymbol{Z}_L = (R_L + jX_L)$; the conditions for maximum power transfer will now be examined.

The current load is

$$\boldsymbol{I} = \frac{\boldsymbol{E}}{\boldsymbol{Z}_s + \boldsymbol{Z}_L} = \frac{\boldsymbol{E}}{(R_s + R_L) + j(X_s + X_L)}$$

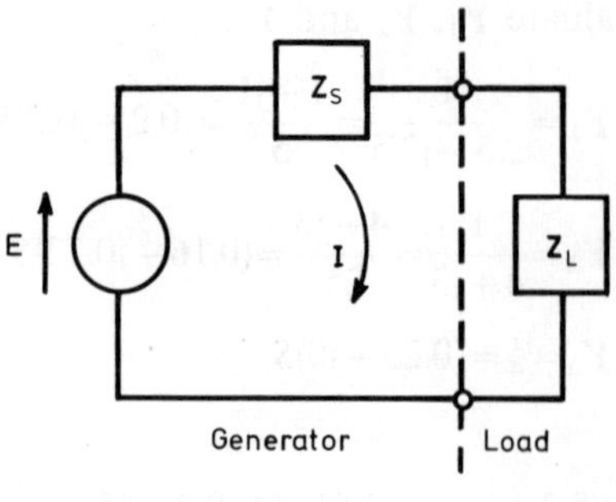

Fig. 7.5

The power dissipated in the load is $|\boldsymbol{I}|^2 R_L$ (since no power is dissipated in the reactive component).

Therefore

$$P = \frac{|\boldsymbol{E}|^2 R_L}{(R_s + R_L)^2 + (X_s + X_L)^2}$$

X_s and X_L may be positive (inductive) or negative (capacative); hence if X_L is varied to maximize P, the maximum value of P occurs when $(X_s + X_L) = 0$; that is, when $X_L = -X_s$ and the power in the load becomes

$$P_1 = \frac{|\boldsymbol{E}|^2 R_L}{(R_s + R_L)^2}$$

If R_L is now varied to maximize P_1, then $(dP_1/dR_L) = 0$ giving $R_s = R_L$. It follows that the condition for maximum power transfer is that if $\boldsymbol{Z}_s = (R_s + jX_s)$, then $\boldsymbol{Z}_L = (R_s - jX_s)$ or $\boldsymbol{Z}_L = \overset{*}{\boldsymbol{Z}}_s$. This is known as *conjugate matching*.

7.4.5 The Compensation Theorem

In a linear network of generators and impedances, if an impedance $\boldsymbol{Z}$*, carrying a current* $\boldsymbol{I}$*, is changed by an amount* $\delta\boldsymbol{Z}$*, the change in current at that point in the circuit is the same as that produced by an ideal voltage source of e.m.f.* $(\boldsymbol{I}\delta\boldsymbol{Z})$*, connected in series with* $(\boldsymbol{Z} + \delta\boldsymbol{Z})$ *when all other generators in the network are replaced by their internal impedances.*

The theorem is useful in calculating the effect of component tolerances on the performance of the network.

Example

Calculate the change in the current supplied by the voltage source in figure 7.6a when the value of the 2 kΩ resistor is increased by 10%.

Solution

In figure 7.6a

$$\boldsymbol{I}_2 = \left(\frac{8}{1 + \frac{6}{5}} \cdot \frac{3}{5}\right) \text{mA} = \frac{24}{11} \text{mA}$$

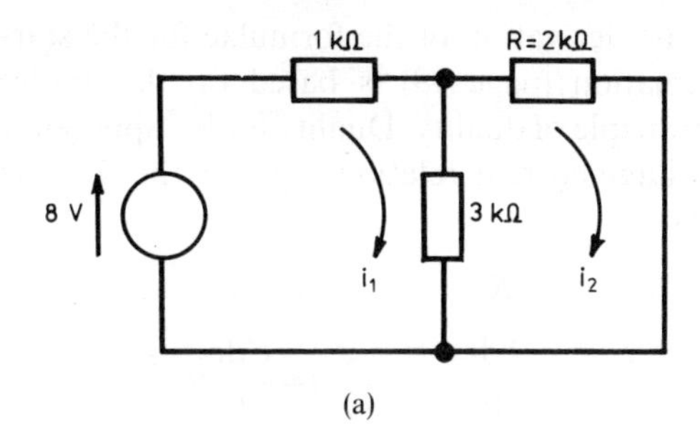

(a)

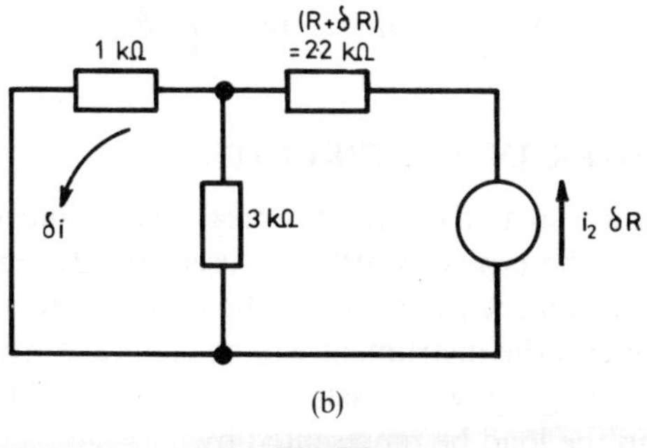

(b)

Fig. 7.6

Applying the Compensation Theorem; the e.m.f. of the added voltage source is $I_2 \delta R = (\frac{24}{11} \times 0.2)\ V$ as shown in figure 7.6b. The added source produces a *reduction* in I_1 given by

$$\delta I = \left[\left(\frac{24}{11} \times 0.2\right) \cdot \frac{1}{2.2 + \frac{3}{4}} \cdot \frac{3}{4}\right] \text{mA} = 0.11 \text{ mA}$$

which is equal to the reduction in I_1 when R is increased by 10%.

7.4.6 The Reciprocity Theorem

In any passive network of linear, bilateral impedances, if a voltage V *applied in one branch of the network produces a current* I *in another branch, the ratio* V/I *(known as the transfer impedance) will be the same as that obtained if* V *and* I *are interchanged.*

Example

If, in the network of figure 7.7, a 1 volt source applied between A and B causes a short-circuit current of $0.03\underline{/-116^\circ}$ A to flow between X and Y, calculate the current in the 4 Ω resistor when a 5 volt source is connected between X and Y, with AB short-circuited.

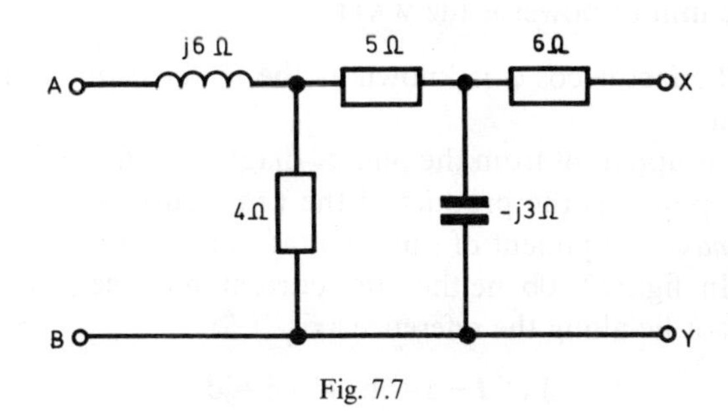

Fig. 7.7

Solution

Application of the Reciprocity Theorem gives the current in the inductor as

$$I = 5 \times 0.03\underline{/-116^\circ}\ \text{A}$$

hence the current in the 4 Ω resistor is

$$(5 \times 0.03\underline{/-116^\circ}) \cdot \frac{\text{j}6}{4}\ \text{A} = 0.22\underline{/-26^\circ}\ \text{A}$$

The phase of this current is relative to the voltage applied between X and Y.

7.4.7 The Star-Delta (T-Π) Transformation

The formulae are of the same form as for d.c. circuits, the resistances being replaced by complex impedances as stated below.

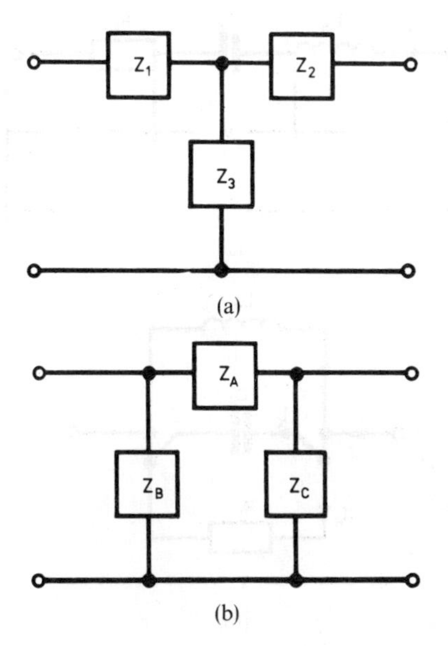

Fig. 7.8

$$Z_1 = \frac{Z_A Z_B}{Z_A + Z_B + Z_C};\quad Z_2 = \frac{Z_C Z_A}{Z_A + Z_B + Z_C};\quad Z_3 = \frac{Z_B Z_C}{Z_A + Z_B + Z_C} \tag{7.3}$$

†

$$Z_A = \frac{\Sigma Z_1 Z_2}{Z_3};\quad Z_B = \frac{\Sigma Z_1 Z_2}{Z_2};\quad Z_C = \frac{\Sigma Z_1 Z_2}{Z_1}$$

7.5 DUAL RELATIONSHIPS

Some voltage/current relationships for the series and parallel circuits of figure 7.9 are set out below.

$V = V_L + V_C + V_R \qquad I = I_L + I_C + I_R$

$$V = I\left[R_s + j\left(\omega L_s - \frac{1}{\omega C_s}\right)\right]$$

$$I = V\left[\frac{1}{R_p} + j\left(\omega C_p - \frac{1}{\omega L_p}\right)\right]$$

$$Z = \frac{V}{I} = \left[R_s + j\left(\omega L_s - \frac{1}{\omega C_s}\right)\right]$$

$$= R_s + j(X_L - X_C)$$

$$Y = \frac{I}{V} = \left[\frac{1}{R_p} + j\left(\omega C_p - \frac{1}{\omega L_p}\right)\right]$$

$$= G_p + j(B_C - B_L)$$

$$= G_p - j(B_L - B_C)$$

There is a similarity in the forms of the relationships for the series and parallel circuits and the pattern may be seen from Table 7.1. The pairs of quantities are said to be *duals* of each other.

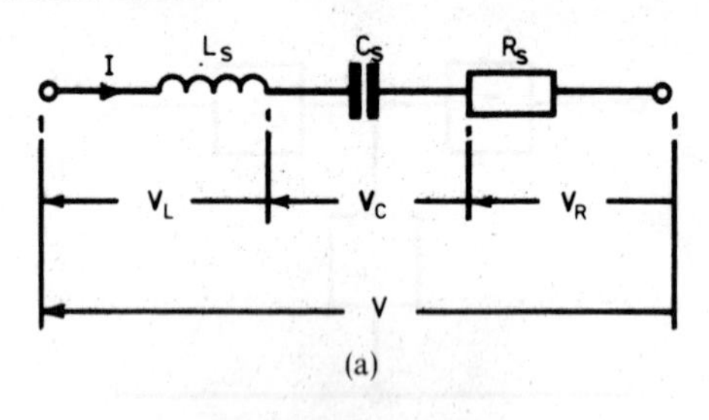

(a)

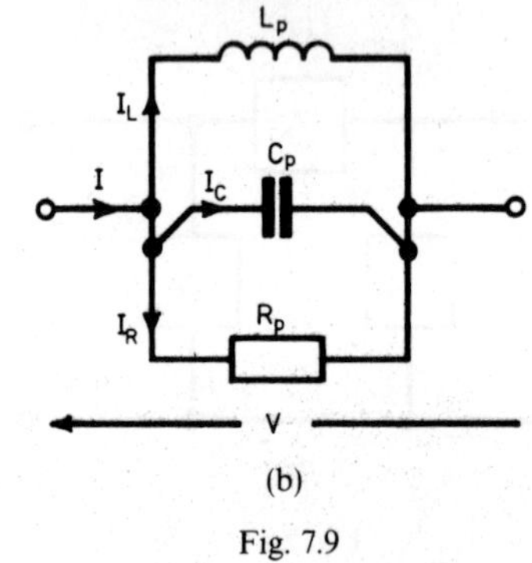

(b)

Fig. 7.9

TABLE 7.1

Quantity	Dual
Series	Parallel
Voltage	Current
Resistance	Conductance
Reactance	Susceptance
Impedance	Admittance
Inductance	Capacitance
Open-Circuit	Short-Circuit

The principle of duality is useful because it enables one to write down circuit equations, with a considerable saving in labour, from a knowledge of the dual circuit. Indeed the derivation of the formulae for the star-delta transformation (page 19) is based on the application of the principle of duality. Duality is also apparent in the basic voltage/current relationships for the three circuit elements:

$$v = iR \qquad i = vG$$

$$v = \frac{L\,di}{dt} \qquad i = \frac{C\,dv}{dt}$$

$$v = \frac{1}{C}\int i\,dt \qquad i = \frac{1}{L}\int v\,dt$$

7.6 POWER IN A.C. CIRCUITS

The power in an a.c. circuit is measured by means of a wattmeter; the type of wattmeter used will depend to a large extent on the frequency of the current and voltage but in general the instrument will be calibrated to indicate the average power dissipated in the load. Let the current in the load be represented by

$$i = I_m \sin \omega t$$

and the voltage across the load by

$$v = V_m \sin(\omega t + \phi)$$

The instantaneous power dissipated is

$$p = vi = V_m I_m \sin(\omega t + \phi) \sin \omega t$$

$$= \frac{V_m I_m}{2}[\cos\phi - \cos(2\omega t + \phi)] \tag{7.4}$$

If p is plotted against ωt it is seen that the instantaneous power characteristic has a frequency which is twice the supply frequency.

The average value of the second term in equation 7.4 over a complete cycle is zero, hence the average power dissipated in the load is

$$P = \frac{V_m I_m}{2}\cos\phi = \frac{V_m}{\sqrt{2}} \cdot \frac{I_m}{\sqrt{2}}\cos\phi$$

or

† $$P = VI\cos\phi \tag{7.5}$$

where V and I are the r.m.s. values of voltage and current. The unit of power is the WATT.

The factor $\cos\phi$ is known as the *power factor* of the circuit.

It is apparent from the phasor diagram of figure 7.10a that power is the product of the r.m.s. current and the *in phase* component of r.m.s. voltage or vice-versa.

In figure7.10b neither the current nor the voltage phasor lie along the reference axis.

Let $I = a + jb$, $V = c + jd$

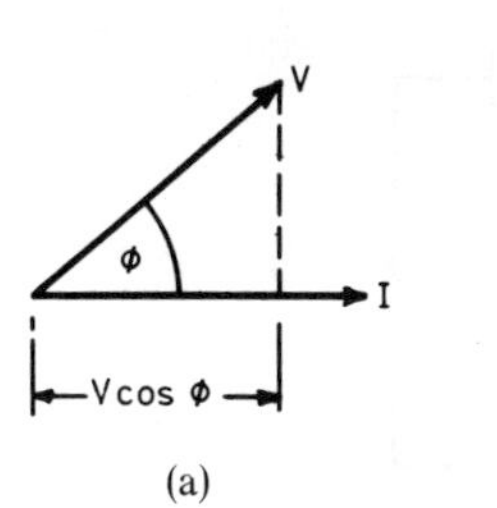

(a)

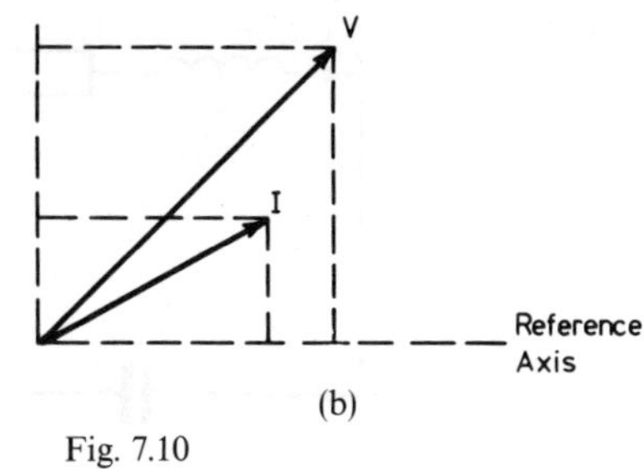

(b)

Fig. 7.10

The in-phase components of $\boldsymbol{I}$ and $\boldsymbol{V}$ are a and c along the reference axis and b and d at right angles to the reference axis; the total power being (ac + bd).

It is important to note that this is not the same as Re($\boldsymbol{VI}$) since

$$\boldsymbol{IV} = (a + jb)(c + jd) = \underbrace{(ac - bd)}_{\text{NOT POWER}} + j(bc + ad)$$

$$\left.\begin{array}{l}\text{But } \mathrm{Re}(\boldsymbol{I}\overset{*}{\boldsymbol{V}}) = \mathrm{Re}(a + jb)(c - jd) = (ac + bd) \\ \text{and } \mathrm{Re}(\overset{*}{\boldsymbol{I}}\boldsymbol{V}) = \mathrm{Re}(a - jb)(c + jd) = (ac + bd)\end{array}\right\}\text{POWER}$$

The expression for power $P = VI \cos\phi$ will now be examined in more detail.

For a resistor the current and voltage are in phase, so that $\phi = 0$, $\cos\phi = 1$ and the circuit is said to have unity power factor. For a *capacitive circuit*, in which the current leads the voltage by an angle ϕ the power factor is said to be *leading* and for an *inductive circuit* the power factor is *lagging*.

In general terms

$$\dagger \qquad Power\ Factor = \frac{P}{VI} = \frac{Watts}{Voltamperes}$$

and this relationship holds for non-sinusoidal waveforms, but it must be noted that in such cases the Power Factor is not $\cos\phi$, since the term phase angle has no significance for non-sinusoidal waveforms.

For a given amount of power P, transmitted at a supply voltage V, the current is given by $I = P/(V \cos\phi)$ from which it can be seen that the current decreases as the power factor is increased from a low value towards unity. The tariff imposed by the Electricity Supply Authority encourages consumption of electricity at a high power factor, consumers being charged on a kilovoltampere (kVA) basis rather than on the kilowatts (kW) of power used.

In practice low power factor loads are usually inductive, for example induction motors, and *power factor improvement* is achieved by connecting either capacitors, or a synchronous motor operating at a leading power factor, in parallel with the inductive load.

Figure 7.11b is the phasor diagram for the circuit of figure 7.11a. If the scale is changed by a factor I, the power triangle of figures 7.11c and 7.11d results. The

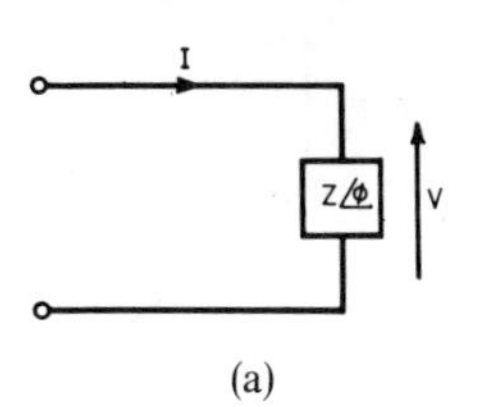

(a)

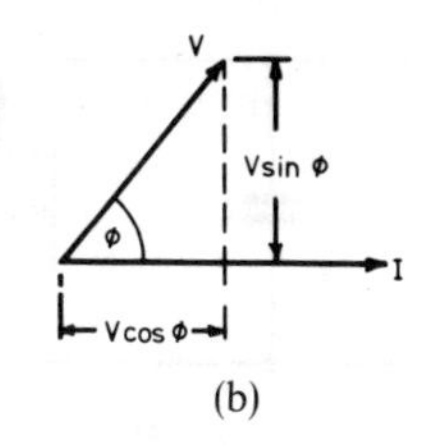

(b)

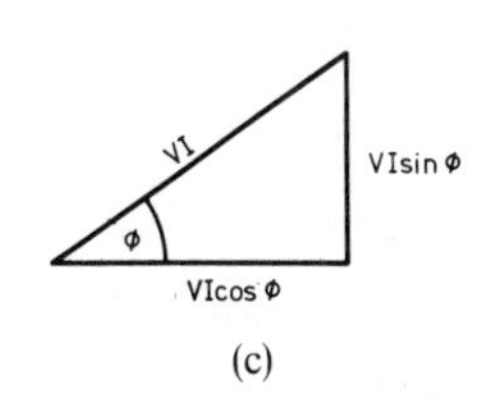

(c)

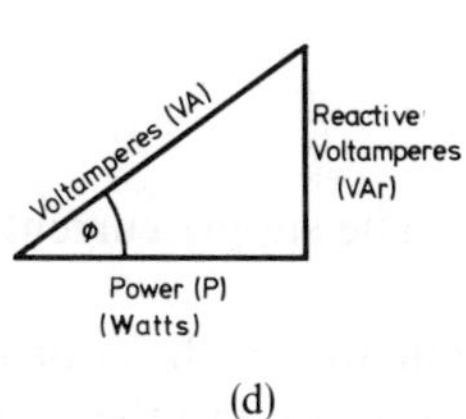

(d)

Fig. 7.11

voltamperes are sometimes referred to as the *apparent power* and the reactive component $VI \sin\phi$ as the *reactive power*. Figure 7.11 applies to an inductive load; for a capacitive load the triangle is inverted.

Example

An electric motor takes a current of 25 A, at a lagging power factor of 0.6, from a 440 V, 50 Hz, supply. What value of capacitor must be connected in parallel with the motor to raise the overall power factor to 0.95 lagging?

Solution

The circuit diagram and phasor diagram are shown in figures 7.12a and b.

In figure 7.12b

$$I_L = 25 \text{ A}$$
$$\phi_1 = \cos^{-1} 0.6 = 53^\circ$$
$$\phi_2 = \cos^{-1} 0.95 = 18^\circ$$

and it is required to determine I_C and hence C.

From the diagram

$$OA = I_L \cos\phi_1 = 15 \text{ A}$$
$$AI_L = I_L \sin\phi_1 = 20 \text{ A}$$
$$AI = OA \tan\phi_2$$
$$= 15 \times 0.325 = 4.9 \text{ A}$$

Therefore

$$I_C = AI_L - AI = (20 - 4.9)$$
$$= 15.1 \text{ A}$$

But $I_C = V\omega C$

hence $$C = \frac{I_C}{V\omega} = \frac{15.1 \times 10^6}{440 \times 2\pi \times 50}\ \mu F$$
$$= 109\ \mu F$$

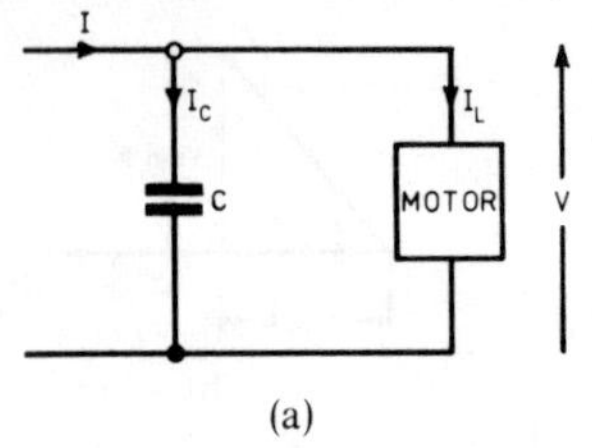

(a) (b)

Fig. 7.12

$$\text{The supply current OI} = \frac{\text{OA}}{\cos \phi_2} = \frac{15}{0.95} = 15.8 \text{ A}$$

compared with its original value of 25 A, although the power input to the motor is unchanged.

It should be noted that if the scale of the phasor diagram is changed by a factor V, it becomes a 'power' diagram and the problem can be solved in terms of kVA, kW and kVAr instead of the currents used in the solution above.

7.7 RESONANCE IN A.C. CIRCUITS

It can be seen from the phasor diagram of figure 7.12b that if the value of the capacitor is increased, thereby increasing I_C, a point is reached where $I_C = I_L \sin \phi_1$ and the supply current I is in phase with the supply voltage C. Under these conditions the circuit is said to *resonate*.

Resonance is defined as the condition in a circuit containing reactances, and possibly resistance, when the supply current is in phase with the supply voltage; that is, the circuit behaves as if it is resistive.

From this definition it follows that if

TABLE 7.2

$$\left.\begin{aligned} Z &= R + jX \\ &= Z\underline{/\phi} \\ &= \frac{a+jb}{c+jd} \\ Y &= G + jB \\ &= Y\underline{/\theta} \\ &= \frac{l+jm}{p+jq} \end{aligned}\right\} \text{then at resonance} \left\{\begin{aligned} X &= 0 \\ \phi &= 0 \\ \frac{b}{a} &= \frac{d}{c} \\ B &= 0 \\ \theta &= 0 \\ \frac{m}{l} &= \frac{q}{p} \end{aligned}\right.$$

7.7.1 Resonance in Parallel Circuits

The condition for resonance in the circuit of figure 7.13a will now be established. A coil of inductance L and effective series resistance r is connected in parallel with a capacitor C. In practice the loss in a capacitor is often sufficiently small to be neglected in comparison with the loss in a coil.

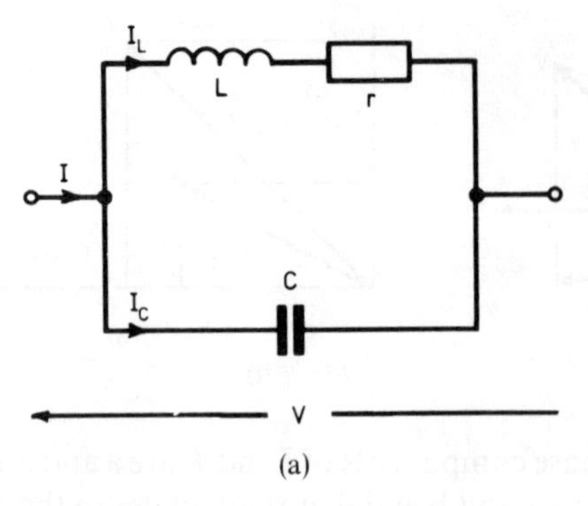

(a)

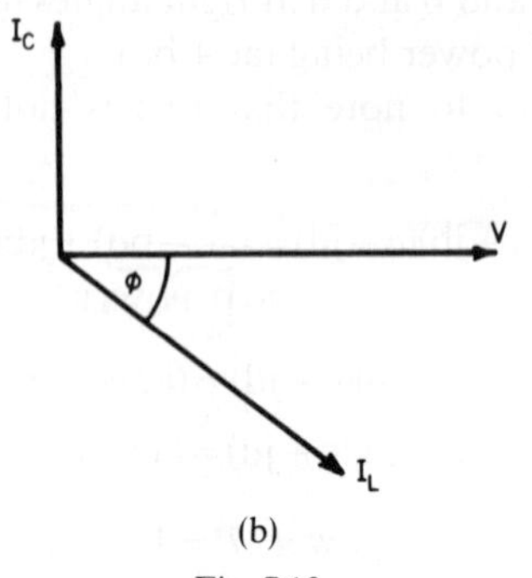

(b)

Fig. 7.13

The admittance of the circuit is

$$\begin{aligned} Y &= j\omega C + \frac{1}{r + j\omega L} \\ &= j\omega C + \frac{r}{r^2 + (\omega L)^2} - \frac{j\omega L}{r^2 + (\omega L)^2} \\ &= \frac{r}{r^2 + (\omega L)^2} + j\omega \left[C - \frac{L}{r^2 + (\omega L)^2} \right] \end{aligned}$$

At resonance the j term is zero, so that

$$\left[C - \frac{L}{r^2 + (\omega L)^2} \right] = 0$$

or

$$(\omega L)^2 = \frac{L}{C} - r^2$$

and the resonant frequency is

$$f_r = \frac{\omega_r}{2\pi} = \frac{1}{2\pi} \left[\frac{1}{LC} - \left(\frac{r}{L} \right)^2 \right]^{1/2} \tag{7.6}$$

The admittance at resonance is

$$Y_{res} = \frac{r}{r^2 + (\omega_r L)^2}$$

and the impedance at resonance is

$$\begin{aligned} Z_D &= r + \frac{(\omega_r L)^2}{r} \\ &= \left[r + \frac{(L/C) - r^2}{r} \right] \end{aligned}$$

or

$$Z_D = \frac{L}{Cr} \tag{7.7}$$

where Z_D is known as the *Dynamic Impedance* of the circuit.

It should be noted that if the circuit is considered to be loss-free,

$$Z_D = \infty \text{ and } f_r = f_0 = \frac{1}{2\pi(LC)^{1/2}}$$

The phasor diagram for the circuit is shown in figure 7.13b and it is possible to derive the conditions for resonance directly from this diagram:

At resonance $I_c = I_L \sin \phi$

But

$$\tan \phi = \frac{\omega L}{r}$$

hence

$$\sin \phi = \frac{\omega L}{[r^2 + (\omega L)^2]^{1/2}}$$

$$I_L = \frac{V}{[r^2 + (\omega L)^2]^{1/2}}$$

Therefore

$$I_L \sin \phi = \frac{V\omega L}{r^2 + (\omega L)^2}$$

But

$$I_c = V\omega C$$

Therefore

$$\text{At resonance } V\omega_r C = \frac{V\omega_r L}{r^2 + (\omega_r L)^2}$$

$$\text{giving } \omega_r = \left[\frac{1}{LC} - \left(\frac{r}{L}\right)^2\right]^{1/2} \text{ as before}$$

It is possible to represent the losses in a coil by a parallel resistor R, *which is not equal to r*, as shown in figure 7.14a.

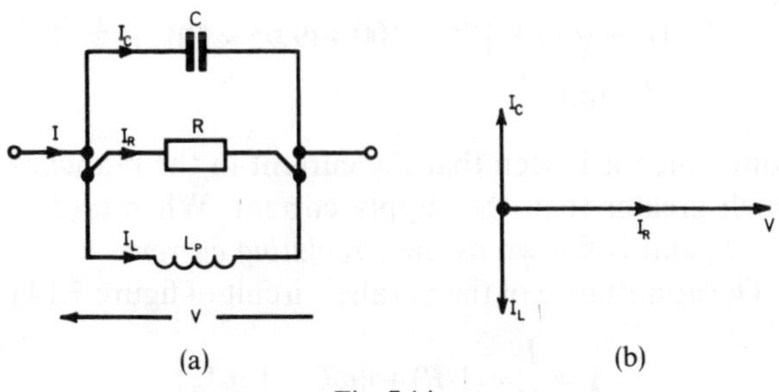

(a) (b)

Fig. 7.14

The admittance of the circuit is

$$\boldsymbol{Y} = \frac{1}{j\omega L_p} + \frac{1}{R} + j\omega C$$

$$= \frac{1}{R} + j\left(\omega C - \frac{1}{\omega L_p}\right)$$

At resonance the 'j' term is zero so that

$$Y_{res} = \frac{1}{R} \quad \text{or} \quad Z_D = R \tag{7.8}$$

and

$$\left(\omega_r C - \frac{1}{\omega_r L_p}\right) = 0 \quad \text{giving} \quad \omega_r = \left(\frac{1}{L_p C}\right)^{1/2}$$

or

† $$f_r = \frac{1}{2\pi}\left(\frac{1}{L_p C}\right)^{1/2} \tag{7.9}$$

From the phasor diagram in figure 7.14b it is apparent that, at resonance, $I_c = I_L$ hence $V\omega_r C = (V/\omega_r L_p)$ giving $\omega_r = (1/L_p C)^{1/2}$.

It is useful to study the relationships that exist between the values of the circuit elements in the series and parallel representations of the resistance of a coil.

If the two circuits in figure 7.15 are equivalent their impedances can be equated

$$\boldsymbol{Z} = r + j\omega L_s = \frac{j\omega L_p R}{R + j\omega L_p} = \frac{(\omega L_p)^2 R + j\omega L_p R^2}{R^2 + (\omega L_p)^2}$$

Hence

† $$r = \frac{(\omega L_p)^2 R}{R^2 + (\omega L_p)^2}$$

† $$L_s = \frac{L_p R^2}{R^2 + (\omega L_p)^2} \tag{7.10}$$

In practice approximations can often be made; for example, if $R \gg (\omega L_p)$ (and the validity of this should be checked numerically in each case) the expressions for r and L_s reduce to

$$\left.\begin{aligned} r &= \frac{R}{(R/\omega L_p)^2 + 1} \doteqdot \frac{(\omega L_p)^2}{R} \\ L_s &= \frac{L_p}{1 + (\omega L_p/R)^2} \doteqdot L_p \end{aligned}\right\} \tag{7.11}$$

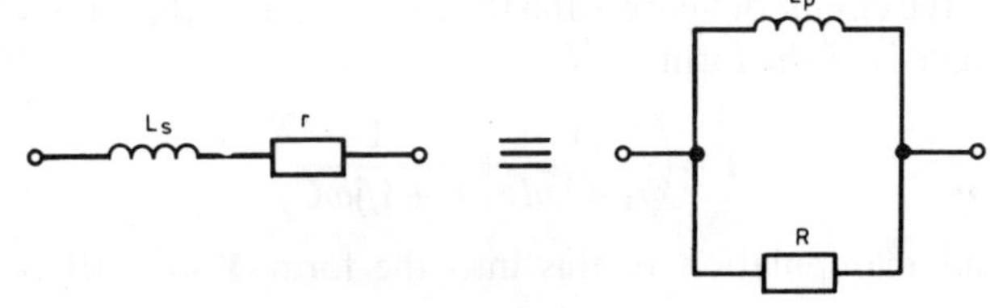

Fig. 7.15

Similarly if admittances are equated

$$\boldsymbol{Y}=\frac{1}{R}+\frac{1}{\mathrm{j}\omega L_{\mathrm{p}}}=\frac{1}{r+\mathrm{j}\omega L_{\mathrm{s}}}=\frac{r}{r^2+(\omega L_{\mathrm{s}})^2}-\frac{\mathrm{j}\omega L_{\mathrm{s}}}{r^2+(\omega L_{\mathrm{s}})^2}$$

Hence

$$R=\frac{r^2+(\omega L_{\mathrm{s}})^2}{r}$$

$$L_{\mathrm{p}}=\frac{r^2+(\omega L_{\mathrm{s}})^2}{\omega^2 L_{\mathrm{s}}} \qquad (7.12)$$

If $r \ll (\omega L_{\mathrm{s}})$ the expressions for R and L_{p} are

$$\left.\begin{aligned} R &\doteqdot \frac{(\omega L_{\mathrm{s}})^2}{r} \\ L_{\mathrm{p}} &\doteqdot L_{\mathrm{s}} \end{aligned}\right\} \qquad (7.13)$$

It should be observed that as the losses are reduced $r \to 0$, $R \to \infty$, $L_{\mathrm{s}} \to L_{\mathrm{p}}$. In those infrequent cases where the losses in the capacitor cannot be neglected it is necessary to include an additional resistor as shown in figure 7.16.

Clearly the form shown in figure 7.16a is preferable, since R_{L} and R_{C} can be combined as a single resistor.

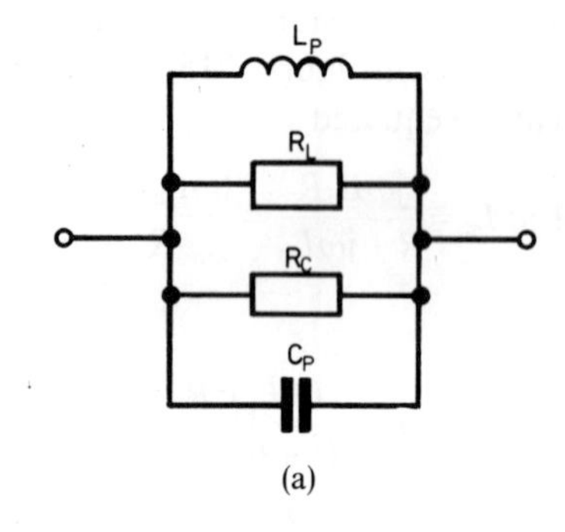

(a)

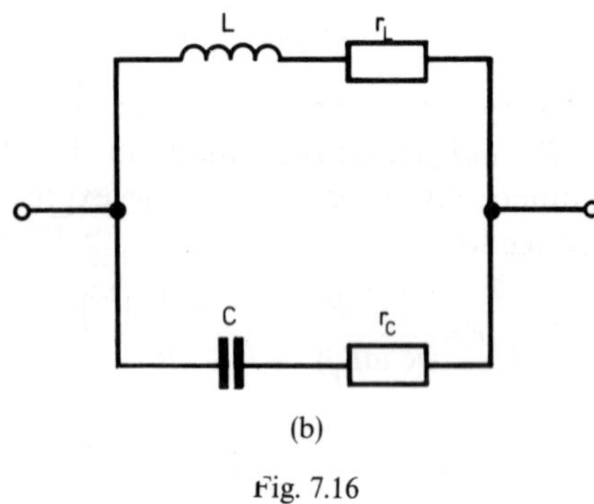

(b)

Fig. 7.16

In the circuit of figure 7.16b the expression for the admittance is of the form

$$\boldsymbol{Y}=\left(\frac{1}{r_{\mathrm{L}}+\mathrm{j}\omega L}+\frac{1}{r_{\mathrm{c}}+1/\mathrm{j}\omega C}\right)$$

and manipulation of this into the form $\boldsymbol{Y}=G+\mathrm{j}B$ is tedious.

When a parallel circuit is at resonance the currents flowing in the circuit elements are greater than the supply current. The following example shows the method of calculating the values of the currents.

Example

In the circuit of figure 7.17, if the frequency of the supply is adjusted to the resonant frequency, calculate the supply current and the current in each branch of the circuit.

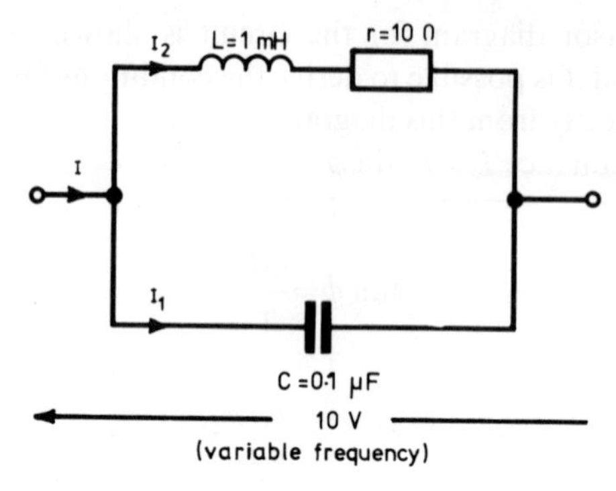

Fig. 7.17

Solution

The supply current is

$$I=\frac{V}{Z_{\mathrm{D}}}=\frac{VrC}{L}=\frac{10\times 10\times 0.1\times 10^{-6}}{10^{-3}}\ \mathrm{A}=10\ \mathrm{mA}$$

The resonant frequency of the circuit is $f_{\mathrm{r}}=\omega_{\mathrm{r}}/2\pi$ where

$$\omega_{\mathrm{r}}=\left[\frac{1}{LC}-\left(\frac{r}{L}\right)^2\right]^{1/2}$$

$$=(10^{10}-10^{8})^{1/2}$$

$$=9.95\times 10^4\ \mathrm{rad/s}$$

The capacitor current is

$$I_1=V\omega_{\mathrm{r}}C=10\times 9.95\times 10^4\times 0.1\times 10^{-6}\ \mathrm{A}$$

$$=99.5\ \mathrm{mA}$$

The current in the coil is

$$I_2=\frac{V}{[r^2+(\omega_{\mathrm{r}}L)^2]^{1/2}}=\frac{10}{[100+(9.95\times 10)^2]^{1/2}}\ \mathrm{A}$$

$$=100\ \mathrm{mA}$$

from which it is seen that the current in the branches is much greater than the supply current. When $(\omega_{\mathrm{r}}L) \gg r$, $I_1 \doteqdot I_2$ and is known as the *circulating current.*

The admittance of the parallel circuit of figure 7.14a is

$$\boldsymbol{Y}=\frac{\boldsymbol{I}}{\boldsymbol{V}}=(1/R)+\mathrm{j}(\omega C-1/\omega L_{\mathrm{p}})$$

The impedance is

$$Z=\frac{V}{I}=\frac{1}{Y}=\frac{1/R}{(1/R)^2+(\omega C-1/\omega L_p)^2}$$

$$+j\frac{(1/\omega L_p-\omega C)}{(1/R)^2+(\omega C-1/\omega L_p)^2}$$

$$=R'+jX'$$

The phase angle of the supply current with respect to the supply voltage, and the admittance and impedance characteristics of the circuit as functions of frequency, are shown in figures 7.18a, b and c.

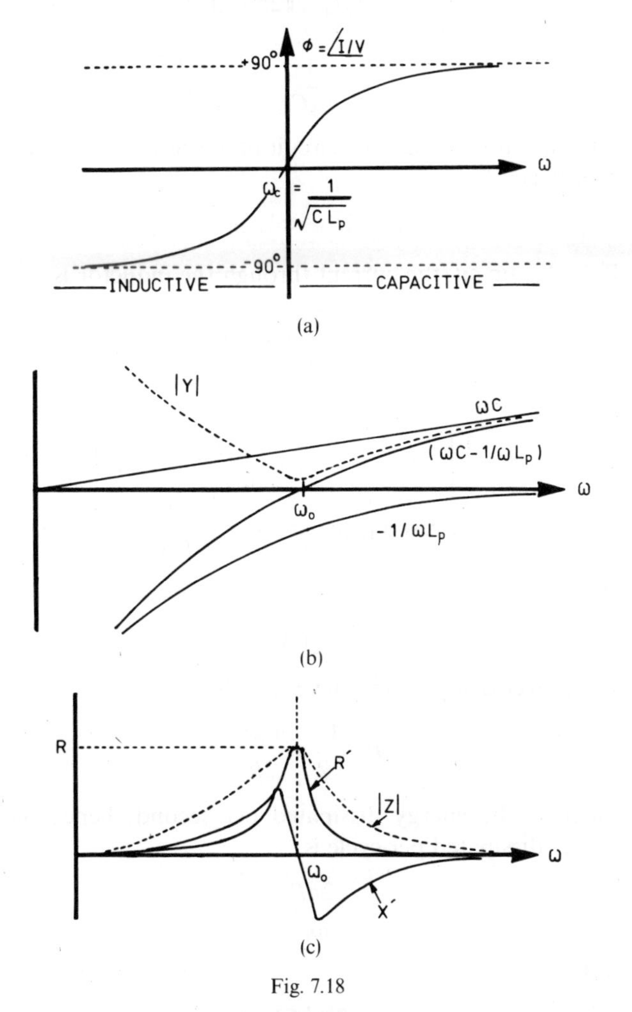

Fig. 7.18

It should be noted that the curves of figure 7.18 do not apply to the circuit of figure 7.13. In the latter case the conditions for resonance and maximum impedance do not coincide, maximum impedance occurring slightly above the resonant frequency.

7.7.2 Resonance in Series Circuits

The impedance of the series circuit shown in figure 7.19a is

$$Z=r+j\left(\omega L-\frac{1}{\omega C}\right)$$

At resonance the j term is zero, giving

† Resonant frequency $$f_r=f_0=\frac{\omega_0}{2\pi}=\frac{1}{2\pi}\left(\frac{1}{LC}\right)^{1/2} \tag{7.14}$$

† Impedance at resonance $= r$ (7.15)

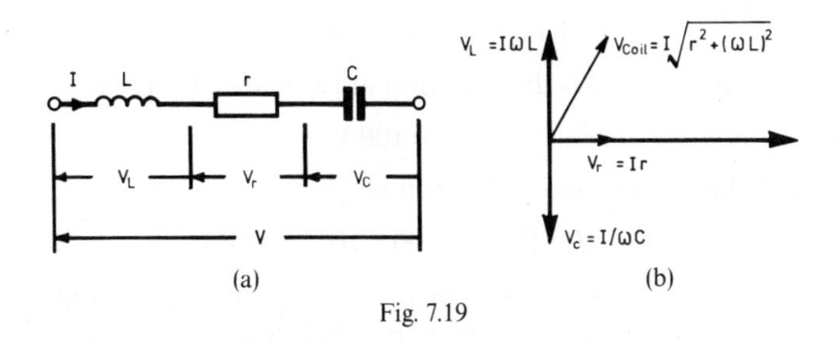

Fig. 7.19

The phase angle of the supply current with respect to the supply voltage and the impedance characteristics of the circuit, as functions of frequency, are shown in figures 7.20a and b respectively.

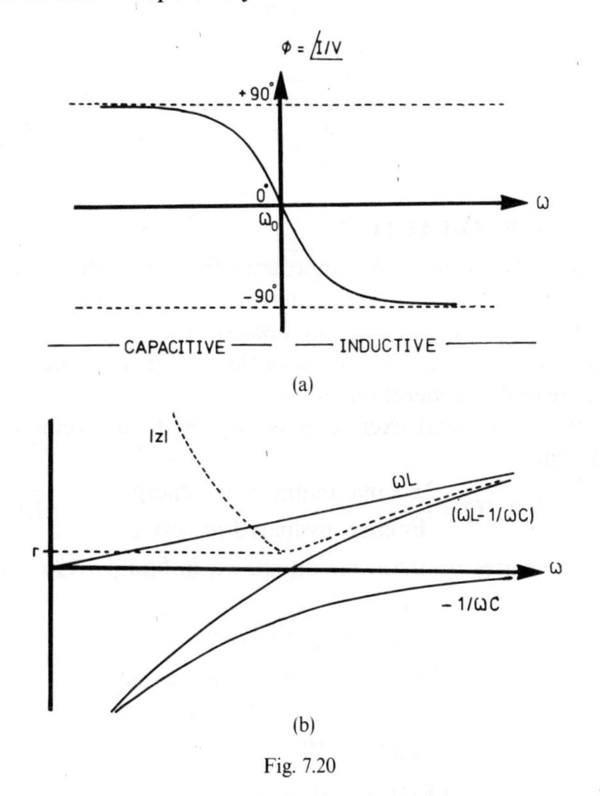

Fig. 7.20

It was shown that, in the resonant condition, the currents in the branches of the parallel circuit were much greater than the supply current. By the Principle of Duality it might be expected that in the series resonant circuit the voltages across the circuit elements are much greater than the supply voltage; this is now shown to be so.

If in the circuit of figure 7.19a $L=1$ mH, $r=10\,\Omega$, $C=0.1\ \mu$F and $V=10$ V, it is found that

$$I=\frac{V}{r}=\frac{10}{10}=1\text{ A}$$

$$\omega_r=\frac{1}{(LC)^{1/2}}=\omega_0=\frac{1}{(10^{-3}\times 0.1\times 10^{-6})^{1/2}}=10^5\text{ rad/s}$$

Therefore

$$1/\omega_0 C=\omega_0 L=100\,\Omega$$

The voltage across the capacitor at resonance is therefore

$$I/\omega_0 C=100\text{ V}$$

and the voltage across the coil is

† $$I[r^2+(\omega_0 L)^2]^{1/2}=1(100+10^4)^{1/2}=100.5\text{ V}$$

The *voltage magnification* in series resonant circuits and the *current magnification* in parallel resonant circuits must be borne in mind when selecting components for use in such circuits.

The reactance characteristics of resonant circuits are summarized in table 7.3.

TABLE 7.3

	SERIES circuit	PARALLEL circuit
BELOW the resonant frequency	CAPACITIVE	INDUCTIVE
ABOVE the resonant frequency	INDUCTIVE	CAPACITIVE

7.8 THE Q-FACTOR

The sharpness of the impedance/frequency characteristic of a resonant circuit is often measured in terms of the Q-factor of the circuit but because the Q-factor also affects the transient response of the circuit the topic will be treated in general terms.

If a sinusoidal excitation is applied to a circuit or system

† $$Q=\frac{2\pi\times\text{maximum stored energy}}{\text{Energy dissipated per cycle}}\qquad(7.16)$$

In the series resonant circuit shown in figure 7.19a the stored energy is

$$W=(\tfrac{1}{2}Cv_c^2+\tfrac{1}{2}Li^2)$$

If $i=I_m\sin\omega t$, the voltage across the capacitor is

$$v_c=-\frac{I_m}{\omega C}\cos\omega t$$

$$W=\frac{1}{2}\left[\frac{CI_m^2\cos^2\omega t}{\omega^2C^2}+LI_m^2\sin^2\omega t\right]$$

At resonance $\omega_r^2=\omega_0^2=\dfrac{1}{LC}$

Therefore

$$W=\tfrac{1}{2}(LI_m^2\cos^2\omega_0 t+LI_m^2\sin^2\omega_0 t)$$
$$=\tfrac{1}{2}LI_m^2$$

The power dissipated in the circuit is

$$P=I^2r=\frac{I_m^2 r}{2}$$

which is the energy dissipated per second, hence the energy dissipated per cycle is

$$\frac{P}{f_0}=\frac{P.2\pi}{\omega_0}$$

and

$$Q=\frac{2\pi(\frac{1}{2}LI_m^2)}{(\frac{1}{2}I_m^2 r)(2\pi/\omega_0)}$$

† $$Q=\frac{\omega_0 L}{r}=\frac{1}{\omega_0 Cr}=\frac{1}{r}\left(\frac{L}{C}\right)^{1/2}\qquad(7.17)$$

Similarly for the parallel circuit of figure 7.14 the stored energy is

$$W=(\tfrac{1}{2}Cv^2+\tfrac{1}{2}L_p i_L^2)$$

If $v=V_m\sin\omega t$, the current through the inductor is

$$i_L=-\frac{V_m}{\omega L_p}\cos\omega t$$

and

$$W=\frac{1}{2}\left[CV_m^2\sin^2\omega t+\frac{V_m^2L_p}{\omega^2L_p^2}\cos^2\omega t\right]$$

At resonance $\omega_r^2=\omega_0^2=\dfrac{1}{L_pC}$

and

$$W=\tfrac{1}{2}CV_m^2$$

The power dissipated in the circuit is

$$P=\frac{V^2}{R}=\frac{V_m^2}{2R}$$

which is the energy dissipated per second; hence the energy dissipated per cycle is

$$\frac{2\pi P}{\omega_0}$$

and

$$Q=\frac{2\pi(\frac{1}{2}CV_m^2)}{(V_m^2/2R)(2\pi/\omega_0)}$$

† $$Q=\omega_0 CR=\frac{R}{\omega_0 L_p}\qquad(7.18)$$

Putting $\omega_0=\dfrac{1}{(L_pC)^{1/2}}$ we obtain

† $$Q=R\left(\frac{C}{L_p}\right)^{1/2}\qquad(7.19)$$

In both the cases considered the stored energy W is constant. It is not a function of time but oscillates between the capacitor and the inductor.

The Q-factor of the parallel circuit of figure 7.13a in which the resistance is in series with the inductance, may be obtained by replacing the series (L, r) combination by the equivalent parallel (L_p, R) elements given by equation 7.12. For circuits having Q values greater than about 10 it may be assumed, for most practical purposes, that

$$L_p = L \quad \text{and} \quad R = \frac{(\omega L)^2}{r}$$

and the expression for the Q factor of the circuit of figure 7.13a may be obtained directly from equation 7.17 as

† $$Q = \frac{\omega_0 L}{r} = \frac{1}{r}\left(\frac{L}{C}\right)^{1/2} \tag{7.20}$$

The resonant frequency of the circuit has been shown to be

$$\omega_r = \left[\frac{1}{LC} - \left(\frac{r}{L}\right)^2\right]^{1/2}$$

which may be written

$$\omega_r = \left(\omega_0^2\left[1 - \left(\frac{r}{\omega_0 L}\right)^2\right]\right)^{1/2}$$

$$\omega_r = \omega_0[1 - (1/Q)^2]^{1/2} \tag{7.21}$$

The Q factor of an inductor or a capacitor may also be determined by applying the definition of equation 7.16. A current $i = I_m \sin \omega t$ flows in a coil of inductance L and effective resistance r. The stored energy is $W = \frac{1}{2}Li^2$ and the maximum stored energy is $W_m = \frac{1}{2}LI_m^2$.

The power dissipated in the coil is

$$P = I^2 r = \frac{I_m^2 r}{2}$$

hence the energy dissipated per cycle is

$$\frac{P}{f} = \frac{2\pi P}{\omega}$$

$$\text{and } Q = \frac{2\pi(\frac{1}{2}LI_m^2)}{(2\pi/\omega)(I_m^2 r/2)}$$

or

† $$Q = \frac{\omega L}{r} \tag{7.22}$$

For a capacitor the losses may be represented by a resistance either in series or in parallel with a loss-free capacitor.

We consider first a capacitor of capacitance C and effective series loss resistance r. If the voltage across C is $v = V_m \sin \omega t$, the maximum stored energy is $W_m = \frac{1}{2}CV_m^2$.

The current flowing in the circuit is $i = V_m \omega C \cos \omega t$, so that the power dissipated in the loss resistance is

$$P = \frac{(V_m \omega C)^2 r}{2}$$

therefore the energy dissipated per cycle is

$$\frac{P}{f} = \frac{2\pi P}{\omega}$$

and

$$Q = \frac{2\pi(\frac{1}{2}CV_m^2)}{(2\pi/\omega)(V_m \omega C)^2 r/2)}$$

or

† $$Q = \frac{1}{\omega C r} \tag{7.23}$$

If the losses in the capacitor are represented by a resistor R in parallel with C we have

The maximum stored energy is $W_{max} = \frac{1}{2}CV_m^2$.

The power dissipated is $P = V_m^2/2R$, hence the energy dissipated per cycle is

$$\frac{P}{f} = \frac{2\pi P}{\omega}$$

and

$$Q = \frac{2\pi(\frac{1}{2}CV_m^2)}{(2\pi/\omega)(V_m^2/2R)}$$

or

† $$Q = \omega C R \tag{7.24}$$

It should be noted that for the *series* L, r and C, r circuits

† $$Q = \frac{\omega L}{r} = \frac{1}{\omega C r} = \frac{X}{r} = \frac{\text{Reactance}}{\text{Resistance}}$$

and for the *parallel* circuit

† $$Q = \omega C R = \frac{B}{G} = \frac{\text{Susceptance}}{\text{Conductance}}$$

We will now relate the transient response of an LCr circuit to its Q factor.

It has been shown (pages 40–42) that when the series LCR circuit of figure 7.21a is excited by a step voltage, the nature of the current depends on the damping. In the *critically damped* condition

$$\frac{r}{2L} = \frac{1}{(LC)^{1/2}} = \omega_0 \quad \text{giving} \quad \frac{\omega_0 L}{r} = 0.5.$$

Hence

† $$Q_{crit} = 0.5 \tag{7.25}$$

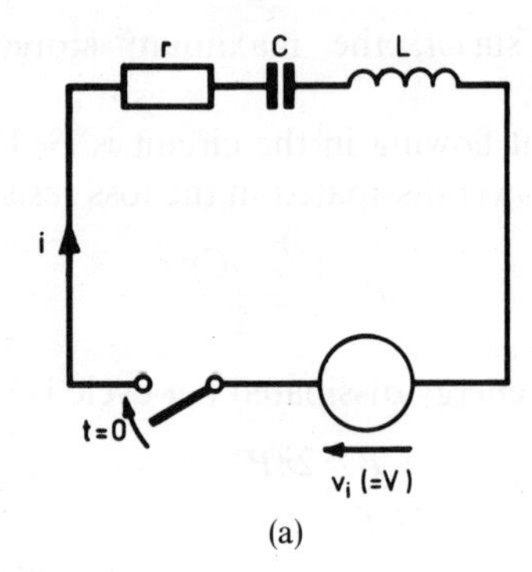

(a)

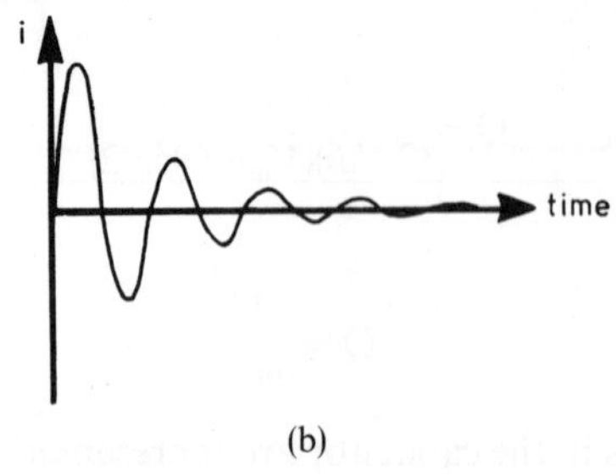

(b)

Fig. 7.21

If the damping is less than the critical value, the current has the form shown in figure 7.21b and is represented by equation 5.19

$$i = \frac{V}{\omega_n L} e^{-\alpha t} \sin \omega_n t$$

$$\text{But } \alpha = \frac{r}{2L} = \frac{\omega_0}{2Q} \quad \text{and} \quad \omega_n = (\omega_0{}^2 - \alpha^2)^{1/2}$$

giving

$$i = \frac{V}{\omega_n L} e^{-\omega_0 t/2Q} \sin \omega_n t \qquad (7.26)$$

from which it can be seen that decreasing the Q of the circuit causes the transient to decay more rapidly.

The characteristic equation

$$\left(s^2 + \frac{r}{L} s + \frac{1}{LC}\right) = 0$$

is frequently written in the form

$$s^2 + 2\xi\omega_0 s + \omega_0{}^2 = 0$$

where $\xi = 1/2Q$ is known as the *damping factor*.

7.9 CURRENT AND VOLTAGE MAGNIFICATION IN RESONANT CIRCUITS

It has been seen that, in a parallel resonant circuit, the circulating current is much greater than the supply current and that in a series resonant circuit the voltages across the circuit elements are greater than the supply voltage. Current and voltage magnification are now related to the Q-factor of the circuit.

In the parallel circuit of figure 7.22a,

$$\text{at resonance } I = \frac{V}{Z_D} = \frac{VCr}{L}$$

But

$$I_c = V\omega_r C \doteqdot V\omega_0 C \text{ if } Q \gg 1.$$

Therefore

$$\frac{I_c}{I} = \frac{V\omega_0 C}{VCr/L} = \frac{\omega_0 L}{r} = Q$$

or

$$I_c = QI$$

Now

$$I_c = \frac{V}{[r^2 + (\omega_r L)^2]^{1/2}} \doteqdot \frac{V}{\omega_0 L} \quad \text{if } Q \gg 1$$

so that at resonance in a high Q circuit

$$I_c \doteqdot I_L \doteqdot QI \qquad (7.27)$$

For the series circuit of figure 7.22b at resonance

$$V = Ir$$

$$V_L = I\omega_0 L, \; V_c = \frac{I}{\omega_0 C}$$

Therefore

$$\frac{V_L}{V} = \frac{\omega_0 L}{r} = Q \quad \text{and} \quad \frac{V_c}{V} = \frac{1}{\omega_0 Cr} = Q$$

so that, at resonance

$$V_L = V_c = QV \qquad (7.28)$$

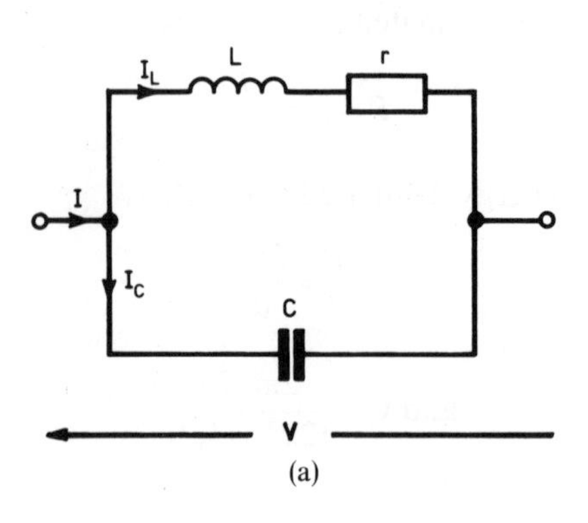

(a)

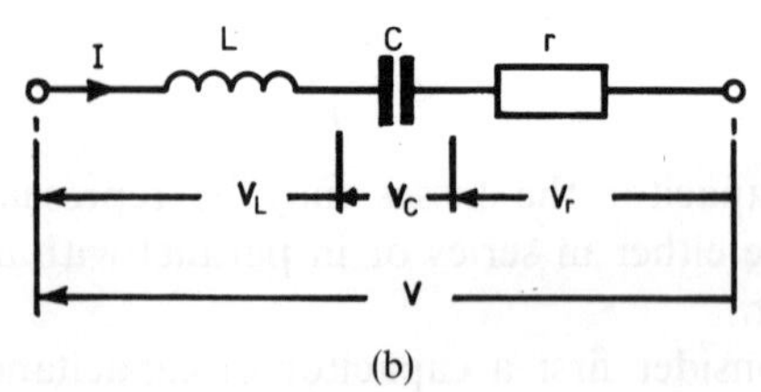

(b)

Fig. 7.22

PROBLEMS

7.1. Calculate the current in, and the voltage across, each branch of the circuit of Figure Q.1. Express the results in polar form, taking the supply voltage as the reference, and draw a phasor diagram.

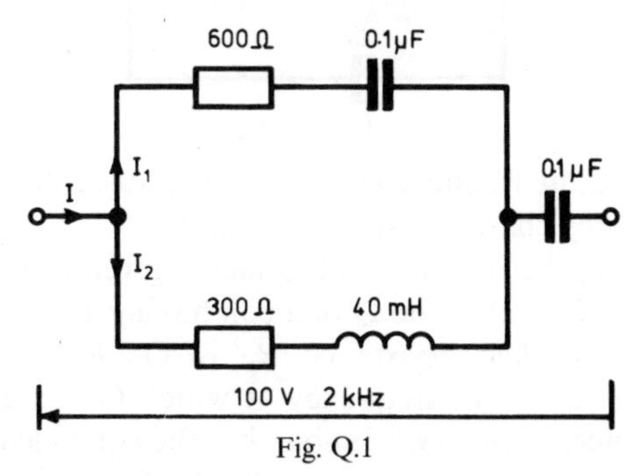

Fig. Q.1

7.2. Show that the Wien a.c. bridge circuit of Figure Q.2 balances at a frequency

$$f=\frac{1}{2\pi(C_1C_2R_1R_2)^{1/2}}$$

If $C_1=C_2$ and $R_1=R_2$ what is the relationship between R_3 and R_4 for a balance to be obtained?

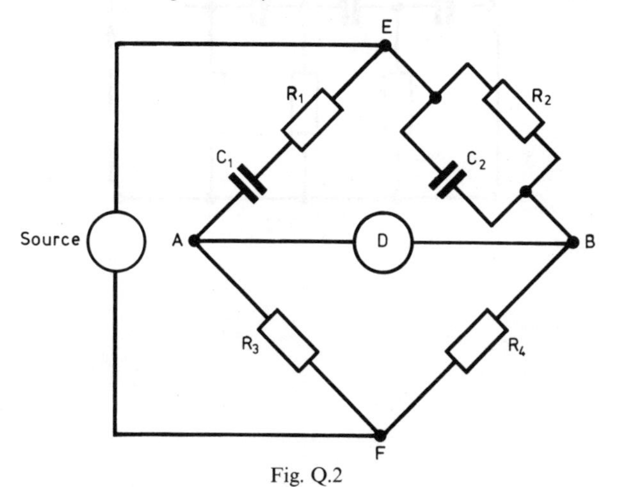

Fig. Q.2

7.3. Reduce the two-terminal linear network of figure Q.3 to

(i) a single voltage source in series with an impedance

(ii) a single current source in parallel with an admittance.

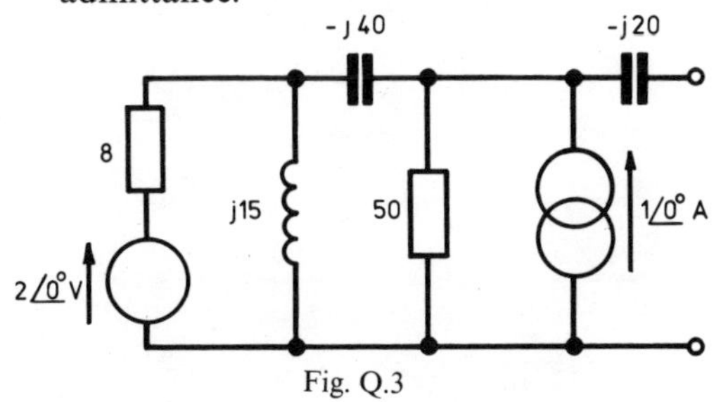

Fig. Q.3

7.4. The LC circuit shown in Figure Q.4 is used to match the output stage of a radio transmitter to an aerial. The transmitter output stage is equivalent to a voltage source E of resistance $R_1=5\,\text{k}\Omega$, and the aerial is represented by a resistance $R_2=50\,\Omega$. Calculate the values of L and C for maximum power transfer to the aerial at a frequency of 10 MHz.

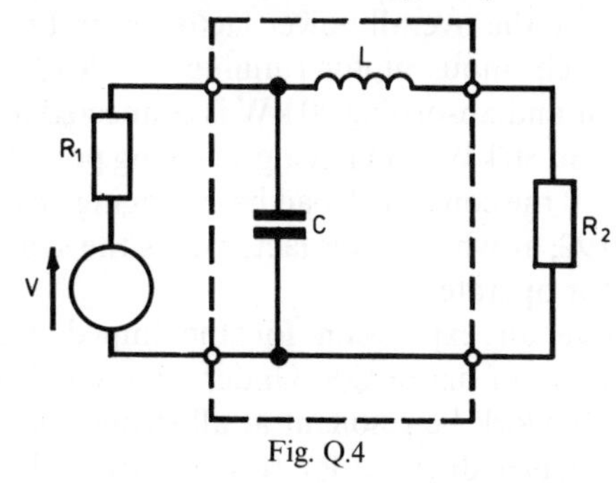

Fig. Q.4

7.5. An ammeter of resistance 0.2 Ω is connected in series with the load R_L in the circuit of figure Q.5. If the ammeter reads 4.72 A what is the true value of the current in R_L (without the ammeter in circuit)?

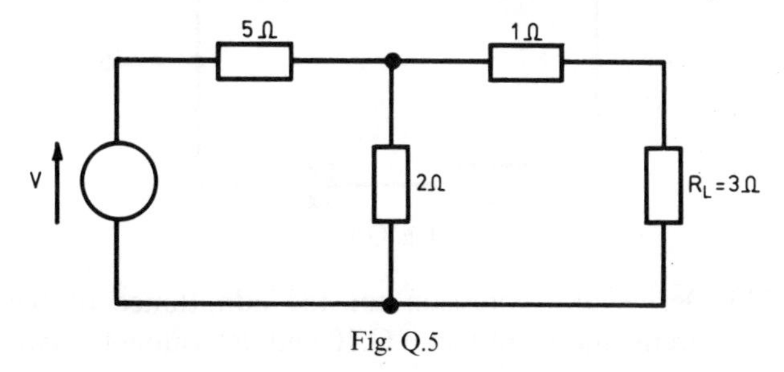

Fig. Q.5

7.6. Derive the π equivalent for the circuit of figure Q.6a; hence or otherwise, show that the ratio V_0/V_i for the circuit of figure Q.6b will be zero at one frequency if $R_2=L/2CR_1$.

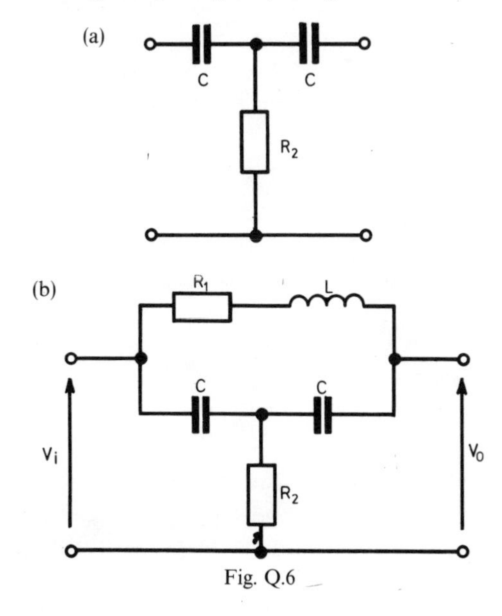

Fig. Q.6

7.7. An electric motor takes a current of 20 A at a lagging power factor of 0.7 from a 440 V, 50 Hz supply; a resistive load of 10 A is also connected to the supply. The overall power factor is to be raised by means of capacitors. Plot curves showing capacitance/overall power factor and capacitance/supply current; hence explain why it is not normal practice to raise the overall power factor to unity.

7.8. A synchronous motor running at a leading power factor and absorbing 20 kW is connected in parallel with an 80 kW load having a lagging power factor of 0.75. If the combined load has a lagging power factor of 0.92, at what power factor does the synchronous motor operate?

7.9. Derive an expression for the impedance of the network of figure Q.9. Under what conditions can the network be resonant at all frequencies? Sketch the phasor diagram for this condition showing all currents and voltages.

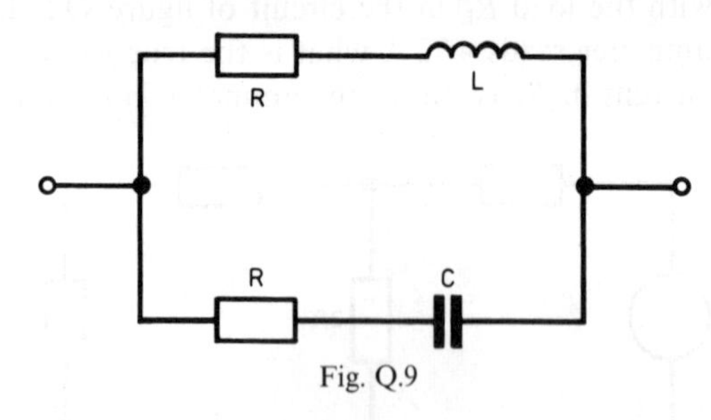

Fig. Q.9

7.10. Derive an expression for the admittance of the circuit shown in figure Q.10 and determine the two

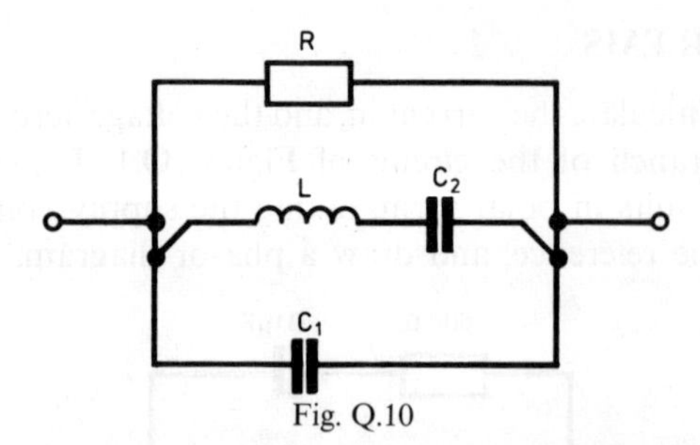

Fig. Q.10

resonant frequencies. Sketch the susceptance/ frequency characteristic of the circuit.

7.11. Using the definition of Q-factor given in equation 7.16 show that the Q of a coil having an equivalent parallel loss resistance R_p is $Q = R_p/\omega L$ where $f = \omega/2\pi$ is the frequency at which Q is measured. Hence, or otherwise show that the equivalent series resistance of the coil is $r = R_p/(1+Q^2)$.

7.12. Show that, in the circuit of figure Q.12 the output voltage V_o differs in phase by 180° from the input voltage V_i at a frequency $f = 1/(2\pi\sqrt{6.CR})$. Determine $|V_o/V_i|$ under these conditions

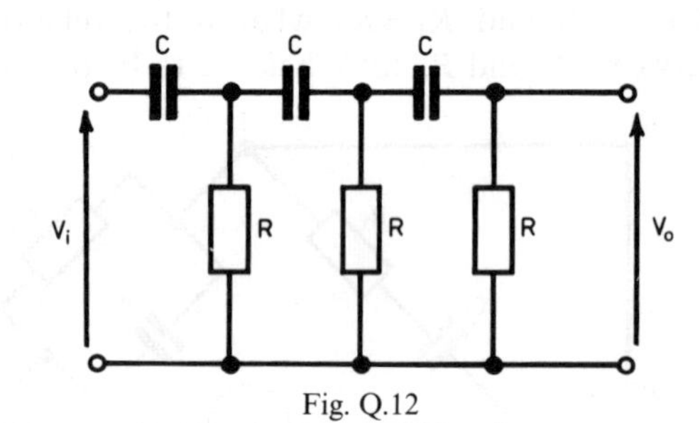

Fig. Q.12

CHAPTER EIGHT

The Steady-State Frequency Response of Circuits

8.1 INTRODUCTION

When a sinusoidal signal V_i of constant amplitude and variable frequency is applied to a linear network as shown in figure 8.1 the output V_0 is also sinusoidal, but its magnitude and phase, relative to the input, are in general, functions of the frequency of the input signal.

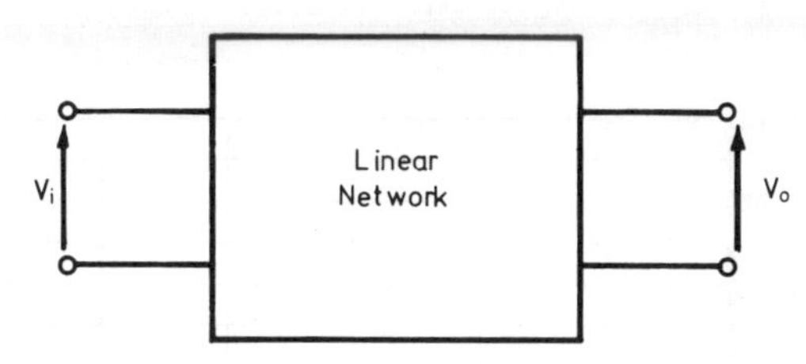

Fig. 8.1

The complex ratio $V_0/V_i = A\underline{/\phi}$ is known as the *Frequency Response Function of the network.* This representation of the steady state performance of a circuit is widely used in electronic and control system engineering. The information is usually presented graphically; the $|V_0/V_i|/\omega$ or A/ω characteristic is known as the *amplitude response* and the $\underline{/V_0/V_i}/\omega$ or ϕ/ω characteristic is the *phase response* of the circuit.

The techniques are demonstrated in the following examples.

8.2 THE LOW-PASS NETWORK

When a sinusoidal voltage V_i is applied to the circuit of figure 8.2, the steady state output voltage V_0 is given by

$$V_0 = V_i \frac{1/j\omega C}{R + 1/j\omega C}$$

$$= \frac{V_i}{1 + j\omega CR} = \frac{V_i}{1 + j\omega T} \tag{8.1}$$

where $T = CR$.

The amplitude response is

$$A = \left|\frac{V_0}{V_i}\right| = \frac{1}{[1 + (\omega T)^2]^{1/2}} \tag{8.2}$$

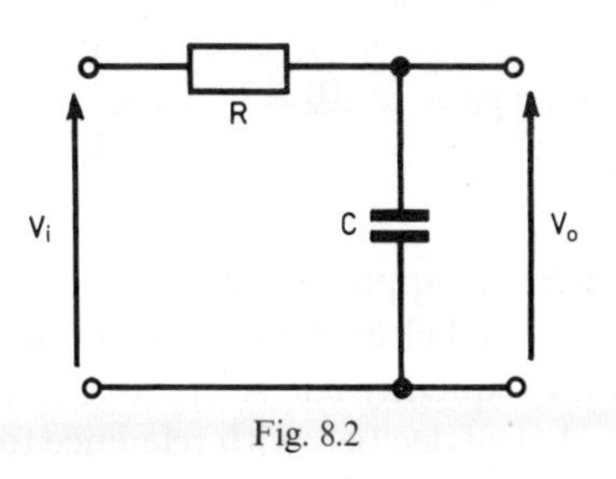

Fig. 8.2

and the phase response is

$$\phi = \underline{/V_0/V_i} = \tan^{-1}(-\omega T) \tag{8.3}$$

The amplitude and phase responses, plotted to linear scales are shown in figure 8.3 for a network in which $C = 1\mu F$, $R = 1.59\,k\Omega$ and the frequency range is 0 to 1000 Hz. The shape of the amplitude response shows why this type of network is known as a *Low Pass Network.*

In practice one is often interested in the steady-state performance of circuits over a frequency range of several decades, for example, with audio-frequency amplifiers frequencies ranging from tens of Hertz to more than 10 kHz are of interest. To cover this range and give a more uniform emphasis to all parts of the range, a logarithmic scale is used for the horizontal axis. Reference to figure 8.3a indicates that when a linear scale is employed the 10–100 Hz decade occupies a much smaller portion of the horizontal axis than the 100–1000 Hz decade.

The construction and manipulation of the amplitude response function is simplified if a logarithmic scale is also used for the ordinate. If there are two non-interacting networks in series having frequency response functions $A_1\underline{/\phi_1}$ and $A_2\underline{/\phi_2}$, the resulting frequency response function is $A\underline{/\phi} = (A_1 \times A_2)\underline{/(\phi_1 + \phi_2)}$; by using a logarithmic scale for the amplitude response the resultant magnitude is obtained as the sum of the individual terms since $\log A = \log A_1 + \log A_2$. The summation is easily performed graphically whereas multiplication does not lend itself readily to graphical procedures.

For historical reasons, the quantity plotted on the vertical axis is $20 \log_{10}|V_0/V_i|$. The fundamental logarithmic measure of *power ratio* is the *Bel*, defined by *power ratio in Bels* $=\log_{10}$[*Power out/Power in*] and since, for a given value of resistance, power is proportional to (voltage)^2 we can write:

$$\text{Voltage ratio in Bels} = \log_{10}\left[\frac{\text{voltage out}}{\text{voltage in}}\right]^2$$

$$= 2\log_{10}\left[\frac{\text{voltage out}}{\text{voltage in}}\right]$$

Since the Bel is rather a large unit, it is usually more convenient to work in terms of the *decibel (dB), which is one tenth of a Bel* so that

$$\dagger\ \text{Voltage ratio (or gain) in dB} = 20\log_{10}\left[\frac{\text{voltage out}}{\text{voltage in}}\right] \quad (8.4)$$

A similar expression applies to current ratio; it should be noted that the decibel expresses a ratio and is not an absolute unit. Frequently one refers to a voltage level as a certain number of decibels with reference to a specified voltage, for example 20 dB above 1 μV is 10 μV.

From equation 8.2 we have

$$A = \left|\frac{V_0}{V_i}\right| = \frac{1}{[1+(\omega T)^2]^{1/2}}$$

then

$$\left|\frac{V_0}{V_i}\right|_{dB} = 20\log_{10}\left[\frac{1}{[1+(\omega T)^2]^{1/2}}\right]$$

$$= -10\log_{10}[1+(\omega T)^2] \quad (8.5)$$

It is not necessary to use a logarithmic scale for the vertical axis of the phase response diagram, because when multiplying frequency response functions, the resulting phase angle is the sum of the individual phase angles.

The amplitude and phase response curves are known as *Bode Diagrams.*

Figures 8.4a and b show the amplitude and phase responses of the network of figure 8.1. Table 8.1 gives the data from which figures 8.3 and 8.4 are plotted.

$$C = 1\mu F,\ R = 1.59\ k\Omega.$$

Therefore

$$T = CR = 1\times10^{-6}\times1.59\times10^{3} = 1.59\times10^{-3}\ \text{sec}$$

Inspection of equations 8.2 and 8.3 enables Table 8.2 to be drawn up.

TABLE 8.1

f(Hz)	ω	ωT	$1+(\omega T)^2$	$\lvert V_0/V_i\rvert$	ϕ	$20\log_{10}\lvert V_0/V_i\rvert$
0	0	0	1.0	1.00	0°	0
10	62.8	0.1	1.01	0.99	−6°	−0.1
20	125.7	0.2	1.04	0.96	−11°	−0.4
40	251.3	0.4	1.16	0.91	−22°	−0.8
50	314.2	0.5	1.25	0.89	−27°	−1
70	439.8	0.7	1.49	0.82	−35°	−2
100	628.3	1.0	2	0.70	−45	−3
200	1256.6	2.0	5	0.45	−64°	−7
400	2513.3	4.0	17	0.24	−76°	−12.4
500	3141.6	5.0	26	0.19	−79°	−14.4
900	5654.9	9.0	82	0.11	−83°	−19.0
1000	6283.2	10.0	101	0.10	−84°	−19.3

TABLE 8.2

Low frequencies	$\omega \ll 1/T$	$\phi \to 0$	$A \to 1\ (=0\ dB)$
High frequencies	$\omega \gg 1/T$	$\phi \to -90°$	$A \propto 1/\omega$
Corner frequency	$\omega = 1/T$	$\phi = -45°$	$A = 1/\sqrt{2} = 0.7\ (=-3\ dB)$

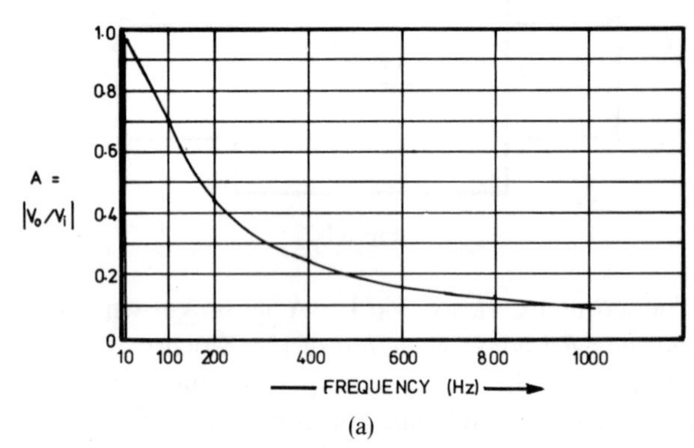

(a)

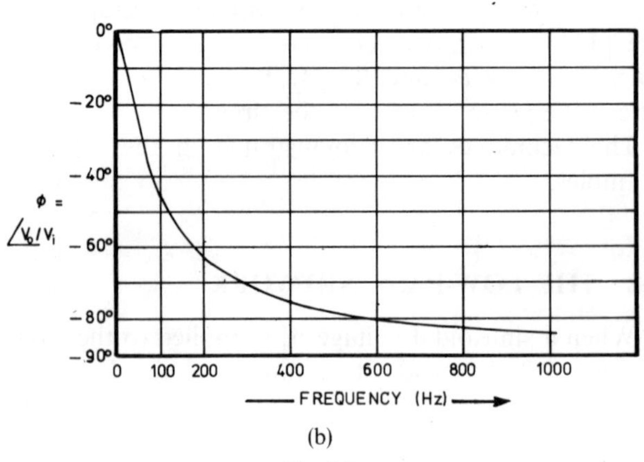

(b)

Fig. 8.3

The frequency corresponding to that value of angular frequency which is equal to the reciprocal of the time constant is known as the *Critical Frequency, Corner Frequency* or *Break Frequency.*

Table 8.2 enables asymptotic approximations to the response curves to be sketched rapidly. The low frequency asymptote for the amplitude response is a horizontal line at 0 dB. At high frequencies where $\omega T \gg 1$, equation 8.5 becomes

$$A_{dB} = -20\log_{10}(\omega T)$$

If $\omega T = 10$, $A = -20$ dB and if ω increases by a factor of

10, then $A = -20 \log_{10}100 = -40$ dB. Similarly if the frequency is doubled the gain decreases by 6 dB so that *the high frequency asymptote has a slope of −20 dB per decade or −6 dB per octave.*

The two asymptotes intersect at the corner frequency. The maximum error introduced by the approximation is 3 dB and it occurs at the corner frequency. The approximation is shown by the broken line in figure 8.4a.

Table 8.2 shows that the phase response approaches 0° at low frequencies and −90° at high frequencies. If a straight line is drawn between the points ($\phi = 0°$, $\omega T = 0.2$) and ($\phi = -90°$, $\omega T = 5$) the maximum phase error is about 11° and a straight line from ($\phi = 0$, $\omega T = 0.1$) to ($\phi = -90°$, $\omega T = 10$) results in a maximum phase error of about 6°. The approximations are shown by the dotted and broken lines respectively in figure 8.4b.

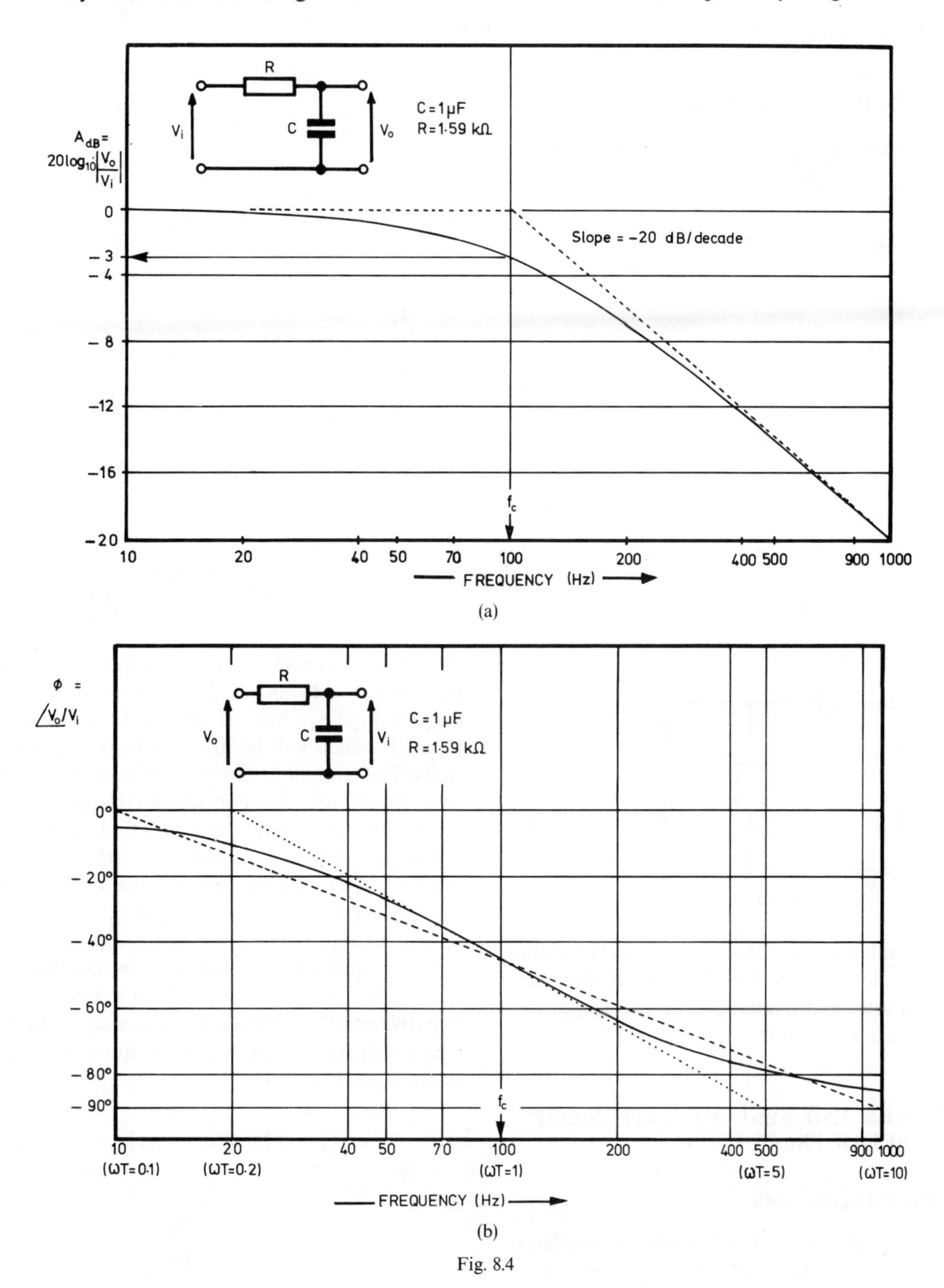

(a)

(b)

Fig. 8.4

It is common practice to indicate the corner angular frequency as $\omega_c = 1/T$ so that equations 8.2 and 8.3 become

† $$A = \frac{1}{[1+(\omega/\omega_0)^2]^{1/2}} = \frac{1}{(1+x^2)^{1/2}} \tag{8.6}$$

and

† $$\phi = \tan^{-1}(-\omega/\omega_c) = \tan^{-1} -x \tag{8.7}$$

where $x = \omega/\omega_c$ or $\omega = x\omega_c$.

8.3 THE HIGH-PASS NETWORK

The frequency response function of the network shown in figure 8.5 is

$$\frac{V_0}{V_i} = \frac{j\omega T}{1+j\omega T} = \frac{jx}{1+jx} \tag{8.8}$$

where $T = CR$ and $x = \omega T = \omega/\omega_c$

† $$A = \left|\frac{V_0}{V_i}\right| = \frac{\omega T}{[1+(\omega T)^2]^{1/2}} = \frac{x}{(1+x^2)^{1/2}} \tag{8.9}$$

and

† $$\phi = [90° - \tan^{-1}(\omega T)] = [90° - \tan^{-1} x] \tag{8.10}$$

From equation 8.9 and 8.10 the following table can be drawn up

TABLE 8.3

Low frequencies	$\omega \ll 1/T$	$\phi \to 90°$	$A \propto \omega$
High frequencies	$\omega \gg 1/T$	$\phi \to 0°$	$A \to 1$ (= 0 dB)
Corner frequency	$\omega = 1/T$	$\phi = 45°$	$A = 1/\sqrt{2}$ (= −3 dB)

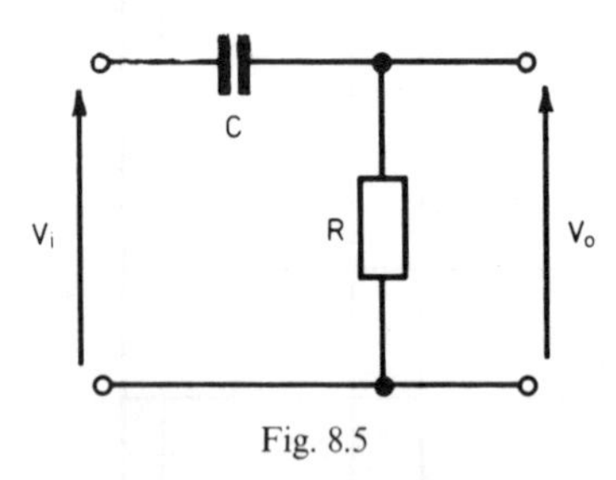

Fig. 8.5

The amplitude and phase responses for a network having $f_c = 100$ Hz are shown in figures 8.6a and b, together with the asymptotic approximation for the amplitude response, obtained from Table 8.3.

8.4 NETWORKS AND SYSTEMS WITH MORE THAN ONE BREAK FREQUENCY

8.4.1 The Phase-Lag Network

The network shown in figure 8.7, is used in feedback control systems and is known as a *phase-lag network*.

The frequency response function of the network is

$$\frac{V_0}{V_i} = \frac{R_2 + 1/j\omega C}{R_1 + R_2 + 1/j\omega C} = \frac{1+j\omega T}{1+j\omega T_1} \tag{8.11}$$

where $T_1 = (R_1 + R_2)C$ and $T = R_2 C$.

The manipulation can be simplified by writing

$$T_1 = \alpha T, \text{ where } \alpha = \left(\frac{R_1+R_2}{R_2}\right) > 1$$

Then

$$\frac{V_0}{V_i} = \frac{1+j\omega T}{1+j\omega\alpha T} = \frac{1+jx}{1+j\alpha x} \tag{8.12}$$

and

† $$A = \left|\frac{V_0}{V_i}\right| = \left(\frac{1+(\omega T)^2}{1+(\alpha\omega T)^2}\right)^{1/2} = \left(\frac{1+x^2}{1+(\alpha x)^2}\right)^{1/2} \tag{8.13}$$

† $$\phi = \angle\frac{V_0}{V_i} = \tan^{-1}(\omega T) - \tan^{-1}(\alpha\omega T) = \tan^{-1} x - \tan^{-1}(\alpha x) \tag{8.14}$$

If, in equation 8.14, we let $\phi_1 = \tan^{-1}(\omega T)$ and $\phi_2 = \tan^{-1}(\alpha\omega T)$, we can write

$$\tan\phi = \tan(\phi_1 - \phi_2) = \frac{\tan\phi_1 - \tan\phi_2}{1+\tan\phi_1\tan\phi_2} = \frac{\omega T(1-\alpha)}{1+\alpha(\omega T)^2}$$

or

† $$\phi = \tan^{-1}\left[\frac{\omega T(1-\alpha)}{1+\alpha(\omega T)^2}\right] \tag{8.15}$$

From equation 8.13 it can be seen that the low-frequency gain, when ωT and $\alpha\omega T \ll 1$, is unity and the high-frequency gain, when ωT and $\alpha\omega T \gg 1$, is $1/\alpha$ or 20 log $(1/\alpha)$ dB which will be negative since α is greater than unity. The straight line approximations are also obtained from equation 8.13 by considering the numerator and denominator separately: the term $[1+(\omega T)^2]^{1/2}$ is represented by curve (i) in figure 8.8a and the term $1/[1+(\alpha\omega T)^2]^{1/2}$, which is the denominator of equation 8.13, by curve (ii). The two curves are added on the decibel scale to give the approximate amplitude response curve.

From equation 8.14 it can be seen that the phase angle approaches zero at low and high frequencies but is negative at all intermediate frequencies. The maximum phase shift is obtained by putting $d(\tan\phi)/d(\omega T) = 0$, that is, from equation 8.15

$$\omega T(1-\alpha)\, 2\alpha\omega T = (1-\alpha)\,[1+\alpha(\omega T)^2]$$

giving

$$\omega = \frac{1}{T\sqrt{\alpha}} \tag{8.16}$$

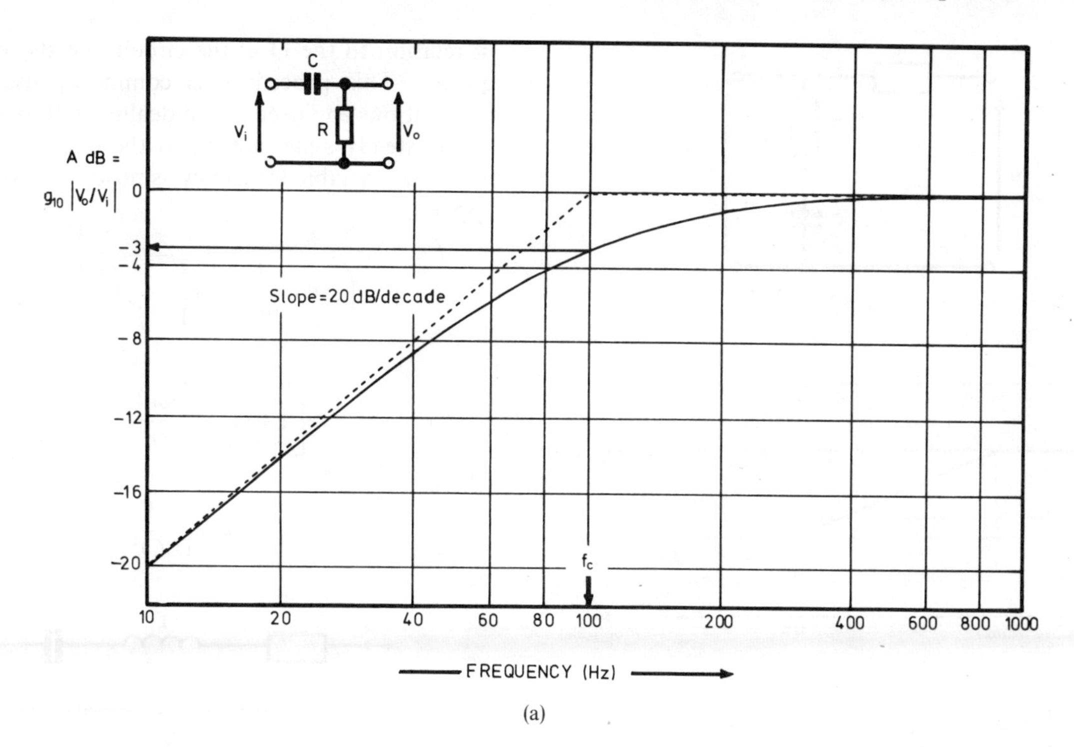

(a)

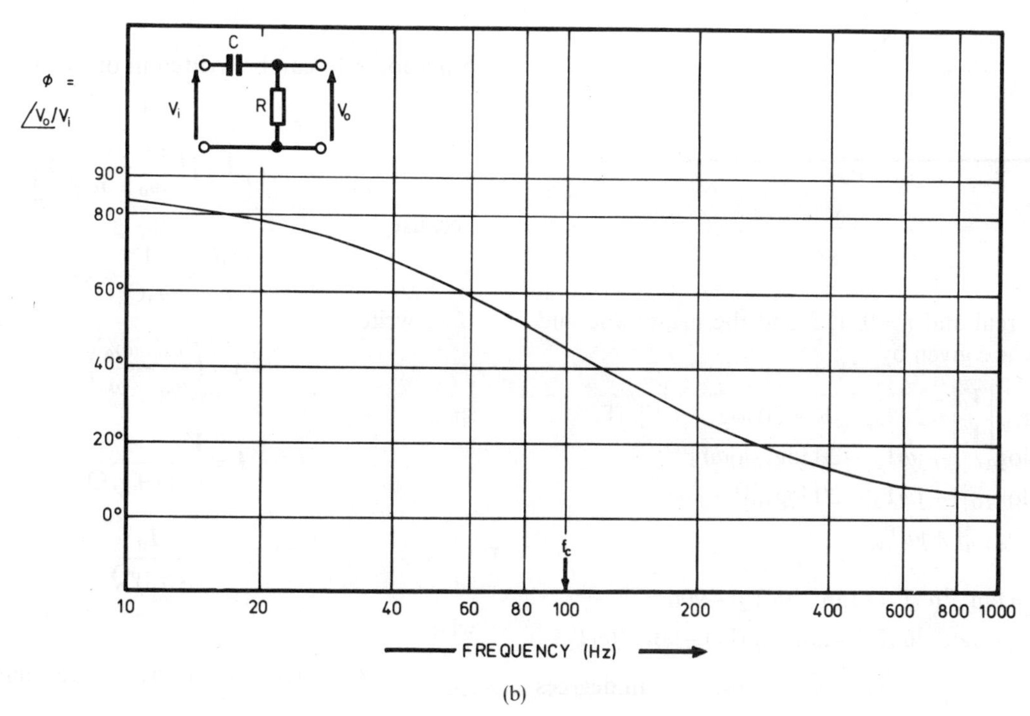

(b)

Fig. 8.6

Hence

$$\phi_{\max} = \tan^{-1}\left[\frac{1-\alpha}{2\sqrt{\alpha}}\right] \qquad (8.17)$$

which is negative since α is greater than unity. The phase response is plotted in figure 8.8b.

8.4.2 The General Case

In general, if the frequency response function is of the form

$$\frac{V_0}{V_i} = \frac{K(1+j\omega T_1)(1+j\omega T_2)}{(j\omega)^n(1+j\omega T_3)(1+j\omega T_4)(1+j\omega T_5)}$$

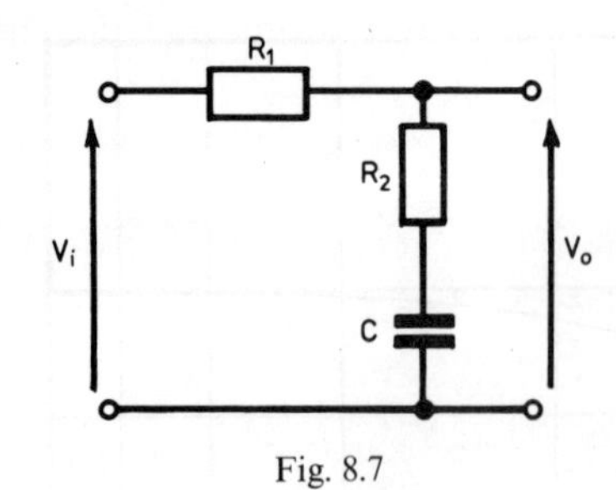

Fig. 8.7

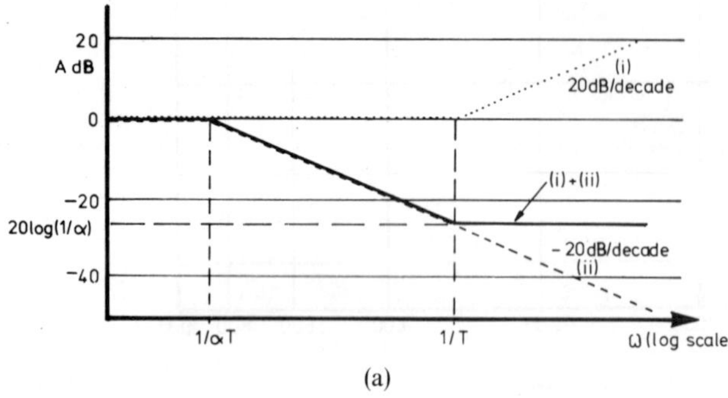

(a)

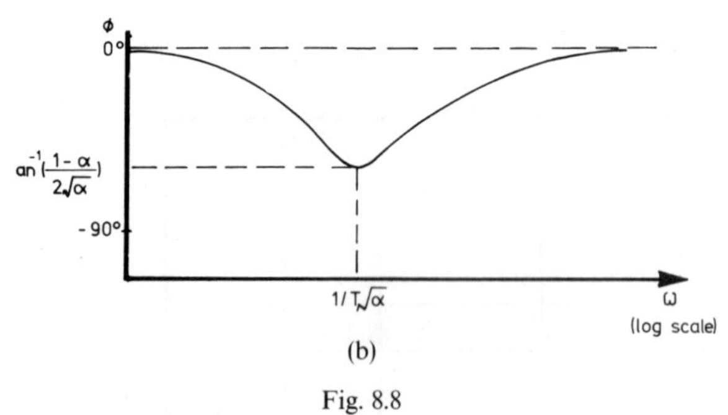

(b)

Fig. 8.8

where K is real and n = 0, 1, 2 and the magnitude and phase angle are given by

$$A_{dB} = 20\log_{10}\left|\frac{V_0}{V_i}\right| = 20\log_{10} K + 20\log_{10}|1+j\omega T_1| + 20\log_{10}|1+j\omega T_2| - 20\log_{10}|(j\omega)^n| - 20\log_{10}|1+j\omega T_3| - 20\log_{10}|1+j\omega T_4| - 20\log_{10}|1+j\omega T_5|$$

$$\phi = \underline{/V_0/V_i} = \tan^{-1}(\omega T_1) + \tan^{-1}(\omega T_2) - 90n - \tan^{-1}(\omega T_3) - \tan^{-1}(\omega T_4) - \tan^{-1}(\omega T_5)$$

in degrees

The amplitude and phase responses can be calculated from these expressions or the approximate response curves can be sketched using the asymptotic approximations.

8.5 THE SERIES LCR CIRCUIT

A rather different approach will be adopted for resonant circuits, the steady-state performance being examined in relation to the Q of the circuit and its resonant frequency. This procedure is commonly used by communications engineers when dealing with tuned circuits.

The steady-state current in the circuit of figure 8.9, when a variable-frequency sinusoidal voltage V is applied, is

$$I = \frac{V}{r + j\left(\omega L - \dfrac{1}{\omega C}\right)} = \frac{V}{r\left[1 + j\left(\dfrac{\omega L}{r} - \dfrac{1}{\omega C r}\right)\right]}$$

$$= \frac{V}{r\left[1 + j\left(\dfrac{\omega}{\omega_0}\cdot\dfrac{\omega_0 L}{r} - \dfrac{\omega_0}{\omega}\cdot\dfrac{1}{\omega_0 C r}\right)\right]} \qquad (8.18)$$

where

$$\omega_0 = \frac{1}{(LC)^{1/2}}$$

Fig. 8.9

Equation 8.18 can be written in the form

$$I = \frac{V}{r\left[1 + j\left(\dfrac{\omega}{\omega_0} - \dfrac{\omega_0}{\omega}\right)Q\right]}$$

because

$$\frac{\omega_0 L}{r} = \frac{1}{\omega_0 C r} = Q$$

If we write

$$y = \left(\frac{\omega}{\omega_0} - \frac{\omega_0}{\omega}\right)$$

then

$$I = \frac{V}{r}\cdot\frac{1}{(1 + jyQ)}$$

or

$$I = \frac{I_0}{1 + jyQ} \qquad (8.19)$$

where

$I_0 (= V/r)$ is the current at resonance.

The magnitude of the current at a frequency ω is therefore

$$|I_\omega| = \frac{|I_0|}{[1 + (yQ)^2]^{1/2}} \qquad (8.20)$$

and its phase angle with respect to the applied voltage is

$$(\phi)_\omega = \tan^{-1}(-yQ) \qquad (8.21)$$

The nature of the parameter y will now be examined in

greater detail

$$y=\left(\frac{\omega}{\omega_0}-\frac{\omega_0}{\omega}\right)=\left(\frac{\omega^2-\omega_0{}^2}{\omega_0\omega}\right)=\frac{(\omega-\omega_0)(\omega+\omega_0)}{\omega_0\omega}$$

If $\omega=(\omega_0+\delta\omega)$, $\delta\omega$ being negative if $\omega<\omega_0$, then

$$y=\frac{\delta\omega(2\omega_0+\delta\omega)}{\omega_0(\omega_0+\delta\omega)}$$

If attention is confined to frequencies in the region of the resonant frequency, we can write

$$y \doteqdot \frac{\delta\omega\, 2\omega_0}{\omega_0{}^2}$$

that is

† $$y \doteqdot \frac{2\delta\omega}{\omega_0} \tag{8.22}$$

and it is seen that y is a measure of the detuning of the circuit from the resonant frequency.

In figure 8.10a the magnitude of the current, which, for a given applied voltage is proportional to the admittance, is plotted as a function of yQ. It should be noted that although this curve is symmetrical with respect to the $|\boldsymbol{I}|$ axis when the yQ scale is linear, the corresponding current/frequency curve is not symmetrical. This can be shown by putting $\omega=2\omega_0$, giving $y\text{Q}=1.5$ Q and $\omega=\omega_0/2$,

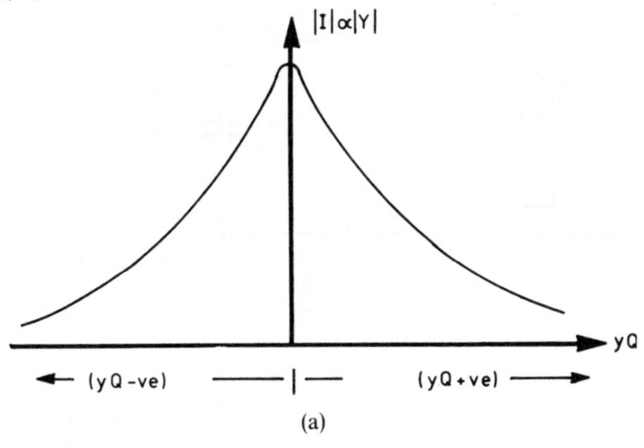

(a)

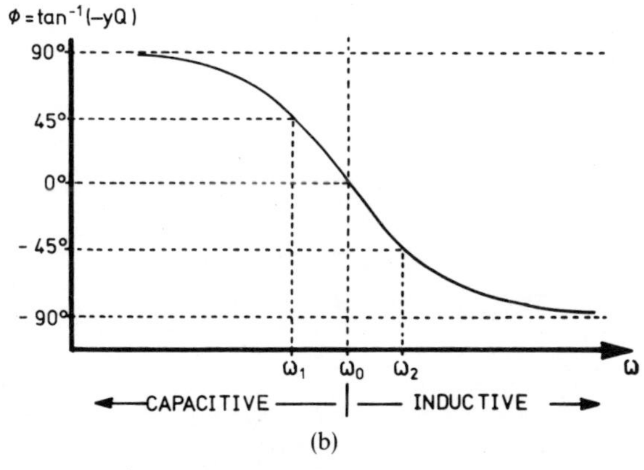

(b)

Fig. 8.10

giving $y\text{Q}=-1.5$ Q and noting that the current

$$|\boldsymbol{I}|=\frac{|\boldsymbol{I}_0|}{[1+(y\text{Q})^2]^{1/2}}$$

is the same at both frequencies, which are not symmetrical with respect to ω_0.

Figure 8.10b shows the phase of the current with respect to the applied voltage and it can be seen that at frequencies ω_1 and ω_2 the phase angles are $+45°$ and $-45°$ respectively, giving $y\text{Q}=\pm 1$.

Substituting for yQ in equation 8.20 gives $|\boldsymbol{I}|=|\boldsymbol{I}_0|/\sqrt{2}$ and these frequencies are known as the *half power points* or -3 *dB points* on the amplitude response curve. The range of frequencies between the half power points is known as the *bandwidth* of the circuit.

At the half power points $y\text{Q}=\pm 1$

Therefore

$$\frac{1}{\text{Q}}=\pm y=\left(\frac{\omega_2}{\omega_0}-\frac{\omega_0}{\omega_2}\right)=-\left(\frac{\omega_1}{\omega_0}-\frac{\omega_0}{\omega_1}\right)$$

Hence

$$\frac{\omega_2{}^2-\omega_0{}^2}{\omega_0\omega_2}=\frac{\omega_0{}^2-\omega_1{}^2}{\omega_0\omega_1} \text{ from which } \omega_0{}^2=\omega_1\omega_2.$$

But

$$\text{Q}=\frac{1}{\left(\frac{\omega_2}{\omega_0}-\frac{\omega_0}{\omega_2}\right)}=\frac{\omega_0\omega_2}{\omega_2{}^2-\omega_0{}^2}=\frac{\omega_0\omega_2}{\omega_2(\omega_2-\omega_1)}=\frac{\omega_0}{(\omega_2-\omega_1)}$$

That is

† $$\text{Q}=\frac{\text{Mid-band frequency}}{\text{Bandwidth}} \tag{8.23}$$

Thus for a given centre frequency (ω_0), the higher the Q the smaller the bandwidth and the sharper the amplitude response curve.

From equation 8.20 it follows that when

$$(y\text{Q})\gg 1,\ |\boldsymbol{I}_\omega| \doteqdot \frac{|\boldsymbol{I}_0|}{y\text{Q}}$$

which corresponds to a slope of -20 dB per decade in figure 8.10a. It must be remembered that when $(y\text{Q})\gg 1$ it is usually necessary to use the expression

$$y=\left(\frac{\omega}{\omega_0}-\frac{\omega_0}{\omega}\right)$$

and not the approximation given in equation 8.22, since the frequencies concerned may be far removed from the resonant frequency.

If, instead of the current, one is interested in the voltage across the capacitor, the symmetry exhibited by equation 8.20 no longer exists since

$$|V_c|=\frac{|I|}{\omega C}=\frac{|I_0|}{\omega C[1+(y\text{Q})^2]^{1/2}} \tag{8.24}$$

A similar analysis may be performed on the parallel circuit shown in figure 7.14a in which case dual relationships apply.

PROBLEMS

8.1. Express the following voltage ratios V_1/V_2 in decibels:
(i) 1, (ii) 2, (iii) 3, (iv) 10, (v) 30, (vi) 100, (vii) 1000, (viii) 0.5, (ix) 0.1, (x) 1/15.

8.2. Sketch the Bode diagrams for the networks shown in figure Q.2. In figure Q.2d the amplifier may be assumed to have unity gain, infinite input impedance and an output resistance of 60 kΩ.

8.3. Sketch the Bode diagram for a network having a frequency response function

$$\frac{V_o}{V_i}=\frac{200(1+0.04j\omega)}{(1+0.5j\omega)(1+0.2j\omega)j\omega}$$

8.4. A series *LCR* circuit is tuned to resonate at 2 MHz and has Q = 100, $L = 30\ \mu$H. A voltage $v = [2 \sin (4\pi\, 10^6 t) + 3 \sin (6\pi\, 10^6 t)]$ mV is applied to the circuit.

Determine (i) the values of the 2 MHz and 3 MHz current components in the circuit

(ii) the values of the 2 MHz and 3 MHz voltages across the capacitor.

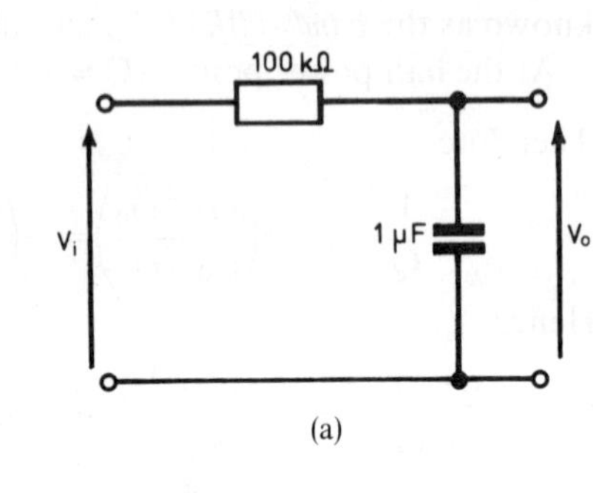

(a)

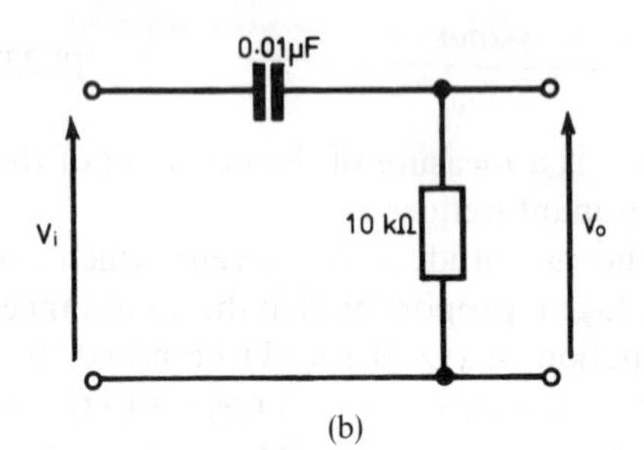

(b)

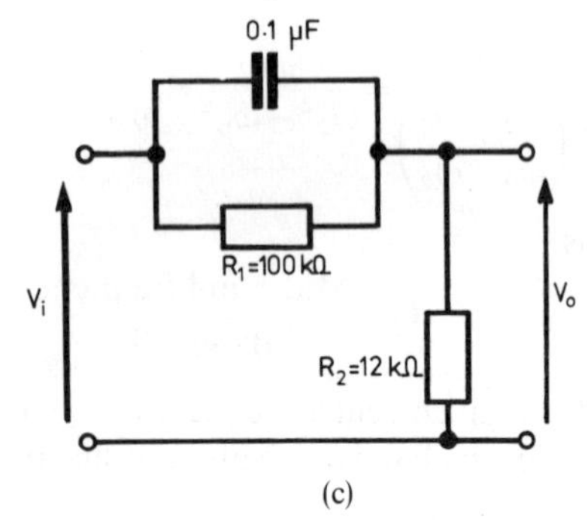

(c)

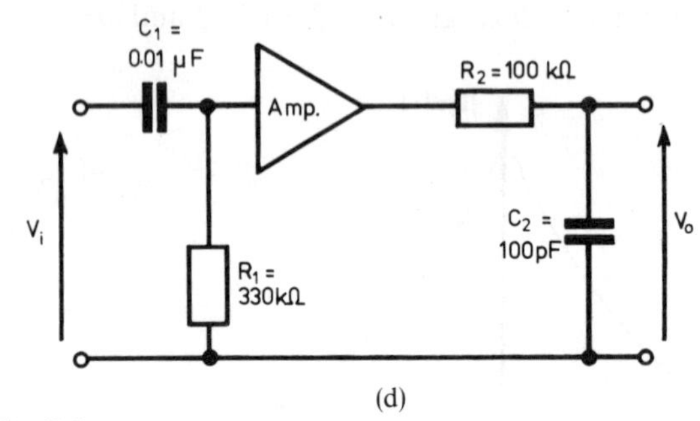

(d)

Fig. Q.2

CHAPTER NINE

Linear Two-Port Networks

9.1 INTRODUCTION

Networks having two pairs of terminals are frequently encountered in practical systems; the pairs of terminals are usually designated *input* and *output* terminals. These networks are known as *two-port* networks and may contain only passive elements, as in an attenuator, or active and passive elements, as in an integrated circuit linear amplifier; active devices such as thermionic valves and transistors operating in the linear mode can be represented by linear two-port networks.

Before studying the details of typical devices represented by two-port networks, it is useful to examine the way in which a two-port network can be characterized in terms of the voltage and current at each port, the network being considered as a 'black box' with an input port and an output port.

9.2 PARAMETERS OF LINEAR TWO-PORT NETWORKS

It is assumed that the network does not contain any *independent* sources; it is described in terms of voltages V_1, V_2, currents I_1, I_2, two of which are independent, and the parameters of the network. The directions of the voltages and currents in figure 9.1 should be noted carefully.

The procedure for determining the parameters of the linear two-port network is to select, arbitrarily, two of the variables as independent variables and to write down expressions for the two dependent variables, using superposition since the network is linear.

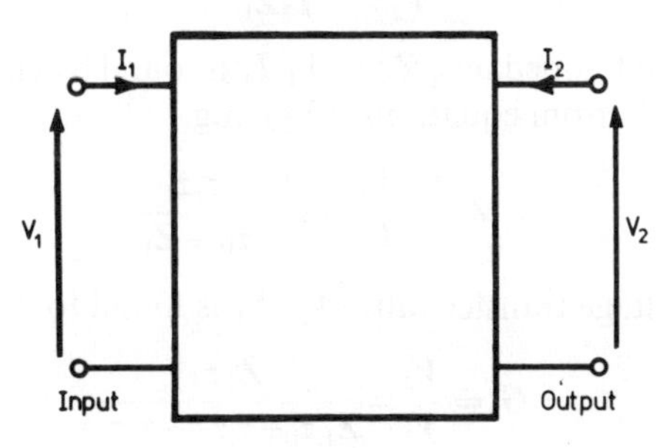

Fig. 9.1

9.2.1 Impedance (or z) Parameters

Select I_1 and I_2 as the independent variables, then

$$V_1 = f(I_1, I_2) = I_1 z_i + I_2 z_r \tag{9.1}$$

and

$$V_2 = f(I_1, I_2) = I_1 z_f + I_2 z_o \tag{9.2}$$

It is clear that the constants of proportionality in equations 9.1 and 9.2 must be impedances so that the equations are dimensionally correct. The values of these constants, known as the impedance parameters or z-parameters of the network are determined by setting $I_2 = 0$ and $I_1 = 0$ in turn which corresponds to the output and input ports respectively being open-circuited.

In equation 9.1, putting $I_2 = 0$ gives

$$z_i = \left.\frac{V_1}{I_1}\right|_{I_2=0}$$

z_i being the *input* impedance of the network when the *output* port is open circuit; z_i is known as the *open circuit input impedance.*

If $I_1 = 0$ in equation 9.1, then

$$z_r = \left.\frac{V_1}{I_2}\right|_{I_1=0}$$

The physical interpretation of this expression is that when, with the input open circuit, a current I_2 is caused to flow at the output port, energy is transferred through the network in the *reverse* direction, resulting in a voltage V_1 appearing at the input port. z_r is the ratio of the voltage V_1 at the input port to the current I_2 at the output port and is known as the *open circuit reverse transfer impedance.* Similarly if $I_2 = 0$ in equation 9.2

$$z_f = \left.\frac{V_2}{I_1}\right|_{I_2=0}$$

so that when the output is open circuit, a current I_1 flowing at the input port results in a voltage V_2 at the output port because of the transfer of energy through the network in the *forward* direction. z_f is the ratio of the voltage V_2 at the putput port to the current I_1 at the input port and is known as the *open circuit forward transfer impedance.* Finally if $I_1=0$ in equation 9.2

$$z_0=\left.\frac{V_2}{I_2}\right|_{I_1=0}$$

z_0 being the *output* impedance of the network when the *input* port is open circuit; z_0 is known as the *open circuit output impedance.*

The expressions for the z-parameters of the linear two-port network are summarized in Table 9.1.

TABLE 9.1

$z_i=\left.\frac{V_1}{I_1}\right\|_{I_2=0}$	Open circuit input impedance
$z_r=\left.\frac{V_1}{I_2}\right\|_{I_1=0}$	Open circuit reverse transfer impedance
$z_f=\left.\frac{V_2}{I_1}\right\|_{I_2=0}$	Open circuit forward transfer impedance
$z_0=\left.\frac{V_2}{I_2}\right\|_{I_1=0}$	Open circuit output impedance

Having described the networks in terms of their terminal voltages and currents and the z-parameters by means of equations 9.1 and 9.2 we now put into the 'black box' of figure 9.1 circuit elements so that the equations are satisfied.

The right hand side of equation 9.1 is the sum of two voltages I_1z_i and I_2z_r. The first term results from the input current I_1, flowing through an impedance z_i; the second term is a function of the current I_2 which does not flow in the input circuit and this term can be represented by a voltage source I_2z_r. Similar reasoning can be applied to equation 9.2, resulting in the equivalent circuit or model shown in Figure 9.2.

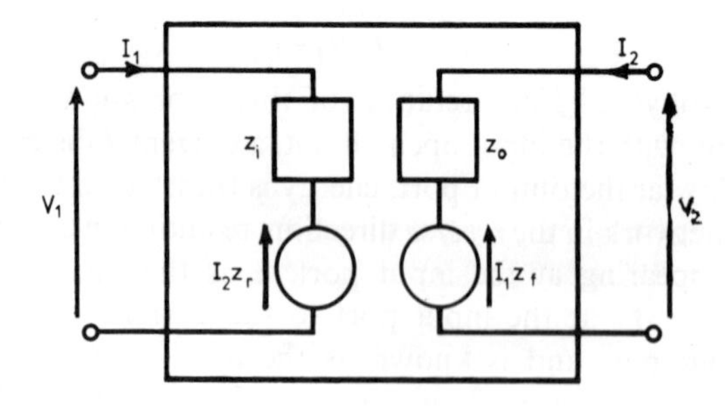

Fig. 9.2

The representation in figure 9.2 is an *equivalent* circuit and it does not follow that all practical two-port networks contain dependent voltage sources. Consider for example the passive two-port network shown in figure 9.3.

The z-parameters of this network can be determined from Table 9.1 by applying normal network analysis methods.

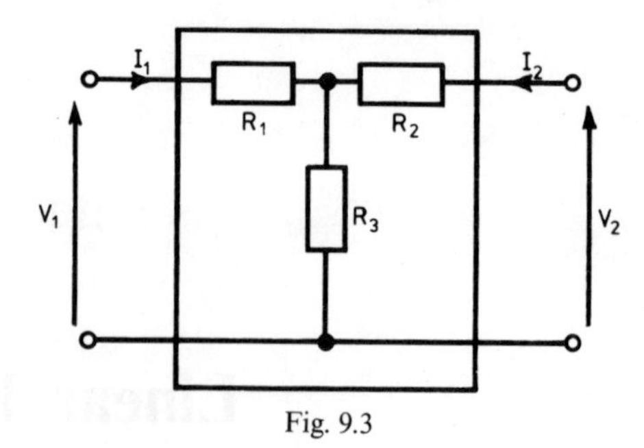

Fig. 9.3

$$z_i=\left.\frac{V_1}{I_1}\right|_{I_2=0}=R_1+R_3$$

$$z_r=\left.\frac{V_1}{I_2}\right|_{I_1=0}=R_3$$

$$z_f=\left.\frac{V_2}{I_1}\right|_{I_2=0}=R_3$$

$$z_0=\left.\frac{V_2}{I_2}\right|_{I_1=0}=R_2+R_3$$

It should be noted that $z_r=z_f$; *this is always true in the case of a linear passive network.*

The network of figure 9.3 may be represented by the equivalent circuit of figure 9.4.

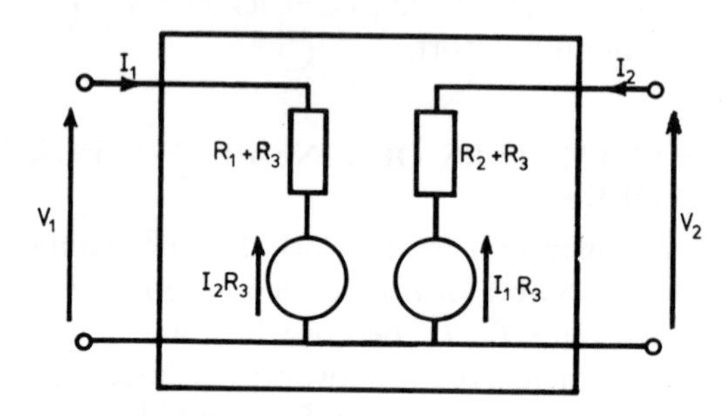

Fig. 9.4

In practice it is usual for a two-port network to be connected to an external load Z_L as shown in figure 9.5. The network equations are

$$\begin{aligned}V_1&=I_1z_i+I_2z_r\\V_2&=I_1z_f+I_2z_0\\V_2&=-I_2Z_L\end{aligned}\qquad(9.3)$$

The input impedance $Z_{in}=V_1/I_1$ is found by eliminating V_2 and I_2 from equations 9.3 giving

$$Z_{in}=\frac{V_1}{I_1}=z_i-\frac{z_rz_f}{z_0+Z_L}\qquad(9.4)$$

The voltage transfer ratio V_2/V_1 is found to be

$$G_v=\frac{V_2}{V_1}=\frac{Z_Lz_f}{Z_Lz_i+z_iz_0-z_fz_r}\qquad(9.5)$$

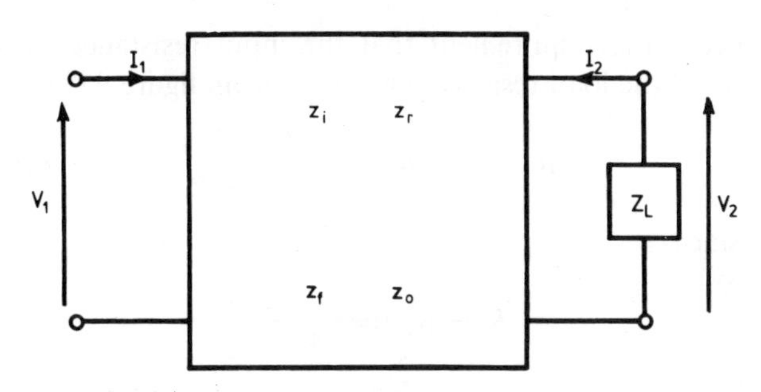

Fig. 9.5

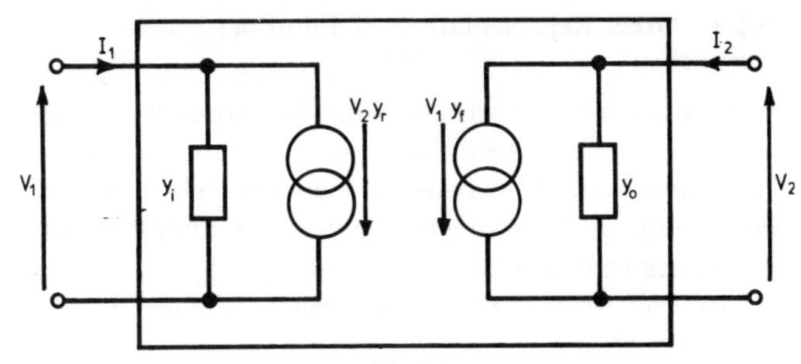

Fig. 9.6

and the current transfer ratio I_2/I_1 is

$$G_1 = \frac{I_2}{I_1} = \frac{-z_f}{z_o + Z_L} \tag{9.6}$$

From equation 9.4 it is seen that the input impedance of the network is a function of the load Z_L unless either z_r or z_f is zero. $z_f = 0$ implies zero transfer of energy in the forward direction and is therefore an impracticable condition. Putting $z_r = 0$ indicates zero transfer of energy in the reverse direction in which case the network is known as a *unilateral* network.

9.2.2 Admittance (or *y*) Parameters

If V_1 and V_2 are chosen as the independent variables, the network equations are

$$I_1 = V_1 y_i + V_2 y_r \tag{9.7}$$

and

$$I_2 = V_1 y_f + V_2 y_o \tag{9.8}$$

The *y*-parameters are defined in Table 9.2.

TABLE 9.2

$y_i = \left.\frac{I_1}{V_1}\right\vert_{V_2=0}$	Short circuit input admittance
$y_r = \left.\frac{I_1}{V_2}\right\vert_{V_1=0}$	Short circuit reverse transfer admittance
$y_f = \left.\frac{I_2}{V_1}\right\vert_{V_2=0}$	Short circuit forward transfer admittance
$y_o = \left.\frac{I_2}{V_2}\right\vert_{V_1=0}$	Short circuit output admittance

From equations 9.7 and 9.8 the circuit model can be developed, as shown in figure 9.6.

The *y*-parameters are frequently used at radio-frequencies, because many radio frequency bridges give a direct reading of admittance. The *y*-parameters of transistors for use as radio-frequency amplifiers are often given on the data sheets.

9.2.3 Hybrid (or *h*) Parameters

If I_1 and V_2 are chosen as the independent variables, the network equations are

$$V_1 = I_1 h_i + V_2 h_r \tag{9.9}$$

and

$$I_2 = I_1 h_f + V_2 h_o \tag{9.10}$$

From the equations it can be seen that h_i has the dimensions of impedance, h_r and h_f are dimensionless and h_o has the dimensions of admittance, hence the term hybrid parameters.

The *h*-parameters are defined as in Table 9.3.

TABLE 9.3

$h_i = \left.\frac{V_1}{I_1}\right\vert_{V_2=0}$	Short circuit input impedance
$h_r = \left.\frac{V_1}{V_2}\right\vert_{I_1=0}$	Open circuit reverse voltage transfer ratio
$h_f = \left.\frac{I_2}{I_1}\right\vert_{V_2=0}$	Short circuit forward current transfer ratio
$h_o = \left.\frac{I_2}{V_2}\right\vert_{I_1=0}$	Open circuit output admittance

From equations 9.9 and 9.10 the circuit model can be developed, as shown in figure 9.7.

The *h*-parameters are often used to represent the equivalent circuit of a transistor at low and medium frequencies. The *h*-parameters of the device can be obtained directly from the static characteristics.

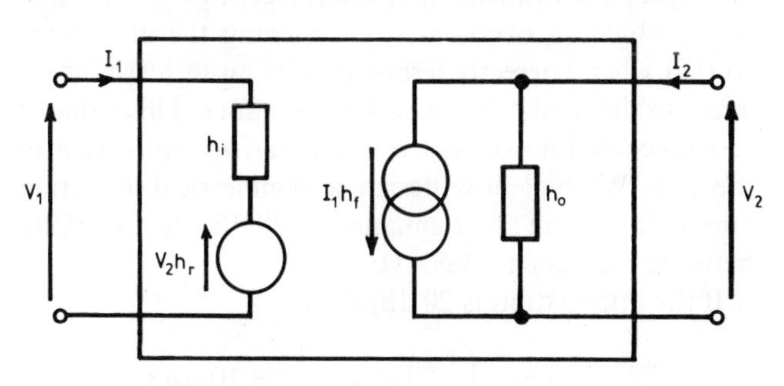

Fig. 9.7

9.2.4 Other Representations of Two-Port Networks

Two independent variables may be chosen from a set of four variables in six different ways, resulting in six sets of equations for the two-port network. Three sets of commonly used parameters have been discussed, the remaining three sets are

(i) *The Inverse Hybrid parameters*, defined by the equations

$$\begin{aligned} I_1 &= V_1 g_i + I_2 g_r \\ V_2 &= V_1 g_f + I_2 g_o \end{aligned} \qquad (9.11)$$

(ii) *The Transmission parameters*, defined by the equations

$$\begin{aligned} V_1 &= V_2 a_i + I_2 a_r \\ I_1 &= V_2 a_f + I_2 a_o \end{aligned} \qquad (9.12)$$

(iii) *The Inverse Transmission parameters*, defined by the equations

$$\begin{aligned} V_2 &= V_1 b_i + I_1 b_r \\ I_2 &= V_1 b_f + I_1 b_o \end{aligned} \qquad (9.13)$$

The transmission parameters are frequently used, in modified form, in power engineering where they are known as the ***ABCD*** parameters. In this case however the accepted convention is for the direction of I_2 to be changed, so that $A = a_i$, $B = -a_r$, $C = a_f$ and $D = -a_o$.

The conversion from one set of parameters to another may be performed using standard circuit analysis methods, most conveniently by the use of matrices.

9.3 EXAMPLES OF LINEAR TWO-PORT NETWORKS

9.3.1 The Symmetrical T Attenuator

When it is required to reduce the amplitude of the signal supplied to a load, a resistive attenuator is inserted in the transmission line between the source and the load. Typical examples are the output level control on a signal generator and the use of an attenuator in the aerial lead of a television receiver in an area of high signal strength. It is important that the insertion of the attenuator does not upset the transmission characteristics of the line; this problem is overcome by designing the attenuator so that when correctly terminated its input resistance is equal to the load or terminating resistance. This value of resistance is known as the *characteristic resistance* of the line. We will now design a symmetrical T-section attenuator giving an attenuation of 20 dB when working between resistances of 600 Ω.

If the attenuation is 20 dB, then

$$20 = 20 \log_{10}\left(\frac{V_1}{V_2}\right) \text{ giving } \frac{V_1}{V_2} = 10 = n \text{ say}$$

From the requirement that the input resistance must equal the load resistance we have, from figure 9.8

$$R_{in} = R_L = R_1 + \frac{R_2(R_1 + R_L)}{R_1 + R_2 + R_L} \qquad (9.14)$$

Since

$$R_{in} = R_L \text{ then } \frac{V_1}{V_2} = \frac{I_1}{I_2}$$

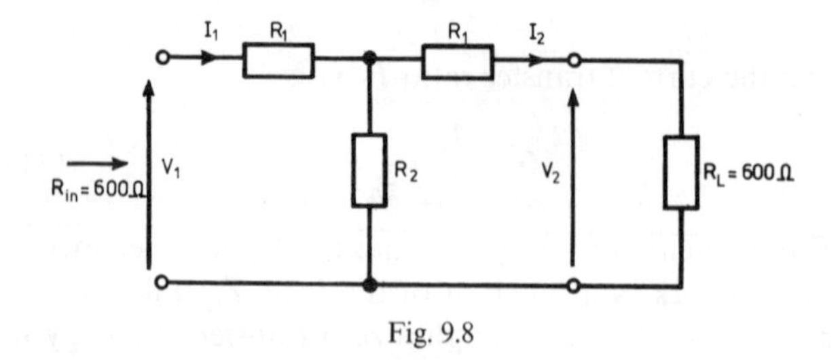

Fig. 9.8

But

$$I_2 = \frac{I_1 R_2}{R_1 + R_2 + R_L}$$

or

$$\frac{1}{n} = \frac{R_2}{R_1 + R_2 + R_L} \qquad (9.15)$$

Therefore from equation 9.14,

$$R_L = R_1 + \frac{R_1 + R_L}{n}$$

hence

$$R_1 = R_L\left(\frac{n-1}{n+1}\right) \qquad (9.16)$$

Substituting for R_1 in equation 9.15 and re-arranging the terms

$$R_2 = R_L\left(\frac{2n}{n^2 - 1}\right) \qquad (9.17)$$

Putting $n = 10$ and $R_L = 600\ \Omega$ gives

$$R_1 = 491\ \Omega \text{ and } R_2 = 121\ \Omega$$

9.3.2 The Equivalent Circuit of a Transistor

The transistor is a three-terminal active device; it is shown in figure 9.9a with the input signal applied to the base (b), the output signal taken from the collector (c), with the emitter (e) as the common point. This mode of operation is known as the *common-emitter configuration* and in the equivalent circuit shown in figure 9.9b the ***h***-parameters have an additional suffix e to denote this connection. It is also possible to operate the transistor in the *common-base* and *common-collector* configurations

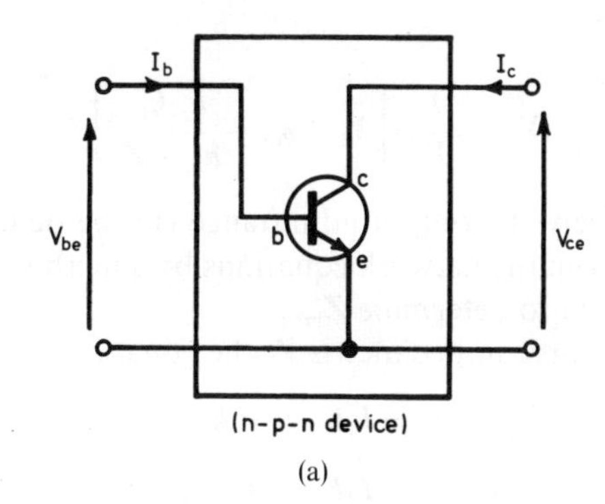

(a)

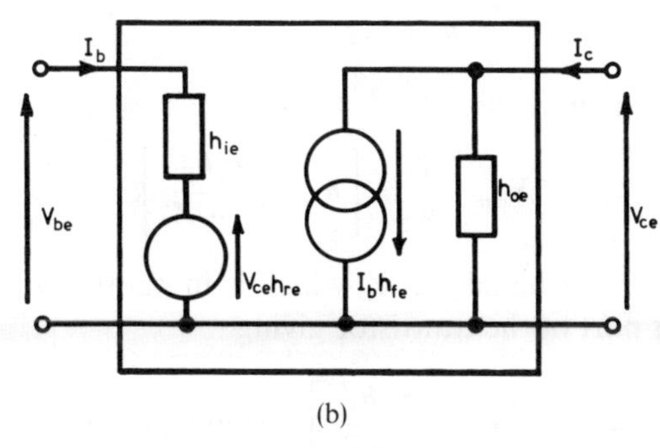

(b)

Fig. 9.9

in which case the network parameters carry additional suffices b and c respectively.

If *d.c. voltages* are applied to the transistor, *the static characteristics* of the device can be plotted; typical common-emitter characteristics are shown in figure 9.10. To denote d.c. conditions it is usual to use capital letters as suffices for the voltages and currents.

If we consider small increments on the characteristics, so that the working portion can be treated as linear, we have the conditions applying to small a.c. signals. The

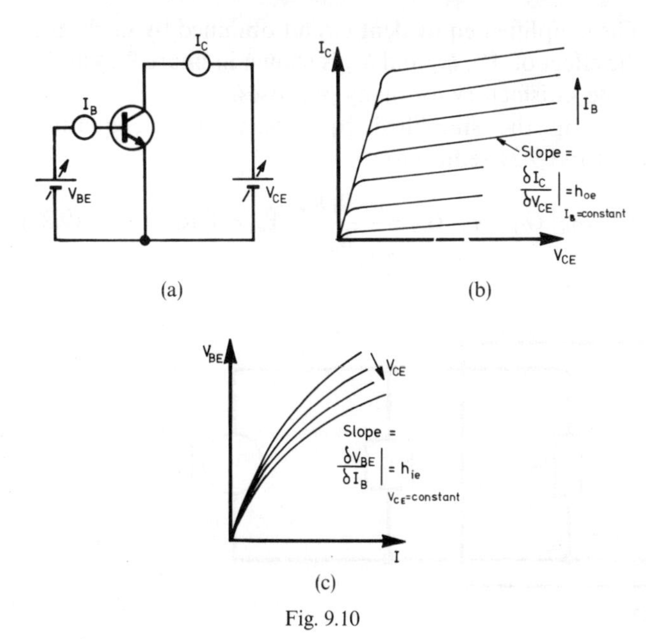

(a) (b)

(c)

Fig. 9.10

slopes of the I_C/V_{CE} and V_{BE}/I_B characteristics (for given values of I_B and V_{CE} respectively) give $\boldsymbol{h}_{oe}$ and $\boldsymbol{h}_{ie}$ directly.

From figure 9.10b,

$$\boldsymbol{h}_{fe} = \frac{\delta I_c}{\delta I_B}\bigg|_{V_{CE}=\text{const}},$$

and from figure 9.10c

$$\boldsymbol{h}_{re} = \frac{\delta V_{BE}}{\delta V_{CE}}\bigg|_{I_B=\text{const}},$$

It should be noted here that the equivalent circuits used to represent the transistor are *small-signal equivalent circuits*; they apply to the a.c. signals and not to the d.c. voltages applied to the device; the latter serve to fix the operating point which determines the values of the parameters.

Typical low-frequency values of $\boldsymbol{h}$-parameters for a transistor are:

$$\left.\begin{aligned} \boldsymbol{h}_{ie} &= 2\,\text{k}\Omega \\ \boldsymbol{h}_{re} &= 10^{-3} \\ \boldsymbol{h}_{fe} &= 10^{2} \\ \boldsymbol{h}_{oe} &= 25\,\mu\text{S} \end{aligned}\right\} \tag{9.18}$$

The values of the $\boldsymbol{h}$-parameters in equation 9.18 are real, but at high frequencies the parameters will be complex.

We now study the performance of a transistor amplifier having a complex load $\boldsymbol{Y}_L$ as represented by figure 9.11a.

It is assumed that all capacitors have zero reactance at the signal frequency and that the effect of the bias resistors R_1, R_2 is taken into account separately by

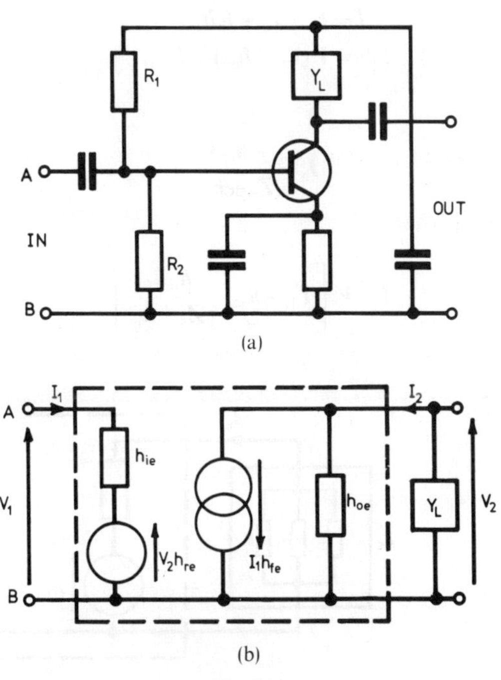

(a)

(b)

Fig. 9.11

considering them to be connected in parallel across the input AB. Under these conditions the equivalent circuit is as shown in figure 9.11b.

The network equations are

$$\left.\begin{aligned} V_1 &= I_1 h_{ie} + V_2 h_{re} \\ I_2 &= I_1 h_{fe} + V_2 h_{oe} \\ V_2 &= -\frac{I_2}{Y_L} \end{aligned}\right\} \quad (9.19)$$

From equations 9.19 the input impedance Z_{in} of the amplifier can be determined

$$Z_{in} = \frac{V_1}{I_1} = \left[h_{ie} - \frac{h_{re} h_{fe}}{h_{oe} + Y_L} \right]$$

The current gain

$$G_I = \frac{I_2}{I_1} = \frac{h_{fe}}{1 + \dfrac{h_{oe}}{Y_L}} \quad (9.20)$$

and the voltage gain

$$G_V = \frac{V_2}{V_1} = \frac{h_{fe}}{h_{re} h_{fe} - h_{ie}(h_{oe} + Y_L)}$$

The output admittance of the circuit can be determined as follows

(i) Replace the source by its internal impedance Z_s
(ii) Apply a voltage source V between the output terminals and compute the current I that this source supplies to the network: then $Y_{out} = I/V$

Z_s' includes R_1 and R_2 as shown.

$$\begin{aligned} I &= I_1 + I_2 + I_b h_{fe} \\ &= V(Y_L + h_{oe}) + I_b h_{fe} \end{aligned}$$

But

$$I_b = \frac{-h_{re} V}{Z_s' + h_{ie}}$$

Therefore

$$I = V \left[Y_L + h_{oe} - \frac{h_{ie} h_{fe}}{Z_s' + h_{ie}} \right]$$

and

$$Y_{out} = \frac{I}{V} = \left[Y_L + h_{oe} - \frac{h_{re} h_{fe}}{h_{ie} + Z_s'} \right] \quad (9.21)$$

Alternatively the output admittance can be determined directly from the network equations by a method similar to that used to determine Z_{in}.

If the source impedance is Z_s' the equations are

$$\begin{aligned} V_1 &= I_1 h_{ie} + V_2 h_{re} \\ I_2 &= I_1 h_{fe} + V_2 h_{oe} \quad (9.22) \\ V_1 &= -I_1 Z_s' \end{aligned}$$

From which

$$Y'_{out} = \frac{I_2}{V_2} = \left[h_{oe} - \frac{h_{re} h_{fe}}{h_{ie} + Z_s'} \right].$$

To this must be added Y_L which is in parallel with the output port of the transistor giving

$$Y_{out} = \left[Y_L + h_{oe} + \frac{h_{re} h_{fe}}{h_{ie} + Z_s'} \right] \quad \text{as in equation 9.21.}$$

The h-parameters of equation 9.18 will now be used in the equivalent circuit of a resistance-loadėd transistor amplifier. Typical values for the external load resistance R_L and r.m.s. short circuit collector current I_c are 5 kΩ and 1 mA respectively. Hence $I_b = I_c/h_{fe} = 0.01$ mA and $V_{ce} = 5$ V. Inserting these values in the h-parameter equivalent circuit gives those shown in figure 9.13.

From figure 9.13 it can be seen that

(i) the voltage $I_b h_{ie} \gg V_{ce} h_{re}$
(ii) $1/h_{oe} \gg R_L$

The simplified equivalent circuit obtained by neglecting the effect of V_{ce}, h_{re} and h_{oe} is shown in figure 9.14 and is quite satisfactory for many purposes.

Using the simplified equivalent circuit, equations 9.20 and 9.21 reduce to

$$Z_{in} = h_{ie}', G_I = h_{fe}', G_V = \frac{-R_L h_{fe}}{h_{ie}}, \; Y_{out} = 1/R_L \quad (9.23)$$

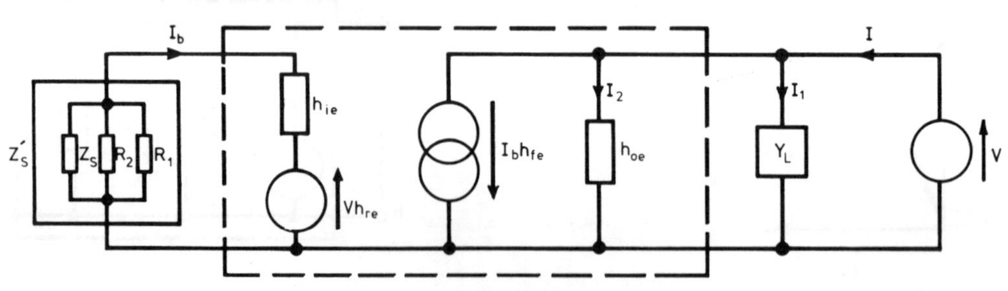

Fig. 9.12

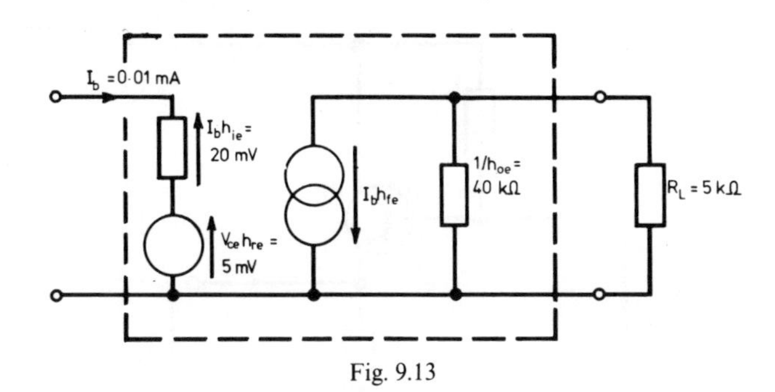

Fig. 9.13

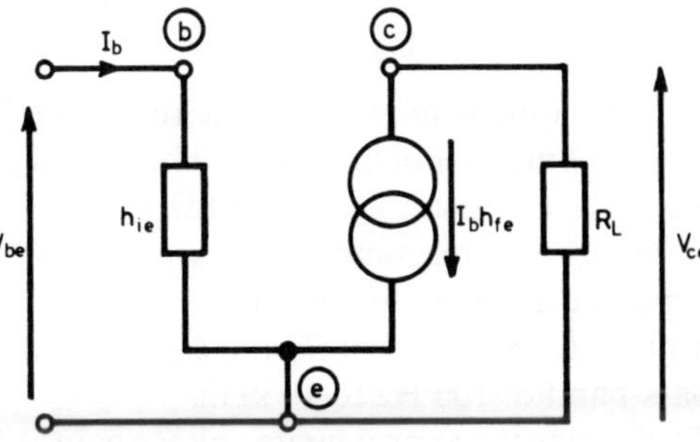

Fig. 9.14

Inserting numerical values from equation 9.18 gives

$$Z_{in} = 2\ \text{k}\Omega,\ G_I = 100,\ G_V = -250,\ Z_{out} = 5\ \text{k}\Omega,$$

It is important to note that it is not possible to determine the input impedance Z_{in} of the circuit of figure 9.11b by replacing all the sources by their internal impedances. This is because the sources $V_2 h_{fe}$ and $I_1 h_{fe}$ are *dependent* or *controlled sources*. Clearly Z_{in} is the complex ratio of the voltage across AB to the current I_1 so that we cannot put $I_1 = 0$ to remove the dependent sources.

9.4 THE INTER-RELATIONSHIP OF PARAMETERS

Situations may arise where there is a need to convert from one set of parameters to another. For example, suppose the hybrid parameters are available and we require to know the admittance parameters.

The relevant equations for the hybrid parameters are equations 9.9 and 9.10. From equation 9.9

$$I_1 = \frac{1}{h_i} V_1 - \frac{h_r}{h_i} V_2 \qquad (9.24)$$

Substituting in equation 9.10 gives

$$I_2 = \frac{h_f}{h_i} V_1 - \left(\frac{h_f h_r}{h_i} - h_O\right) V_2$$

$$= \frac{h_f}{h_i} V_1 + \frac{\Delta_h}{h_i} V_2 \qquad (9.25)$$

where $\Delta_h = (h_i h_O - h_f h_r)$.

Comparing equations 9.24 and 9.25 with equations 9.7 and 9.8 we see that

$$y_i = \frac{1}{h_i};\ y_r = -\frac{h_r}{h_i};\ y_f = \frac{h_f}{h_i};\ y_O = \frac{\Delta_h}{h_i}$$

Relationships between other sets of parameters may be derived in a similar manner; the results are summarized in Table 9.4. The transformations can also be performed conveniently using matrices.

TABLE 9.4

	Expressed in terms of					
Parameter	z		y		h	
z	z_i	z_r	$\frac{y_O}{\Delta_y}$	$-\frac{y_r}{\Delta_y}$	$\frac{\Delta_h}{h_O}$	$\frac{h_r}{h_O}$
	z_f	z_O	$-\frac{y_f}{\Delta_y}$	$\frac{y_i}{\Delta_y}$	$-\frac{h_f}{h_O}$	$\frac{1}{h_O}$
y	$\frac{z_O}{\Delta_z}$	$-\frac{z_r}{\Delta_z}$	y_i	y_r	$\frac{1}{h_i}$	$-\frac{h_r}{h_i}$
	$-\frac{z_f}{\Delta_z}$	$\frac{z_i}{\Delta_z}$	y_f	y_O	$\frac{h_f}{h_i}$	$\frac{\Delta_h}{h_i}$
h	$\frac{\Delta_z}{z_O}$	$\frac{z_r}{z_O}$	$\frac{1}{y_i}$	$-\frac{y_r}{y_i}$	h_i	h_r
	$-\frac{z_f}{z_O}$	$\frac{1}{z_O}$	$\frac{y_f}{y_i}$	$\frac{\Delta_y}{y_i}$	h_f	h_O
Δ_z	$(z_i z_O - z_f z_r)$		$\frac{1}{\Delta_y}$		$\frac{h_i}{h_O}$	
Δ_y	$\frac{1}{\Delta_z}$		$(y_i y_O - y_f y_r)$		$\frac{h_O}{h_i}$	
Δ_h	$\frac{z_i}{z_O}$		$\frac{y_O}{y_i}$		$(h_i h_O - h_f h_r)$	

PROBLEMS

9.1. Derive expressions for the h and $ABCD$ parameters of the two-port network shown in figure Q.1.

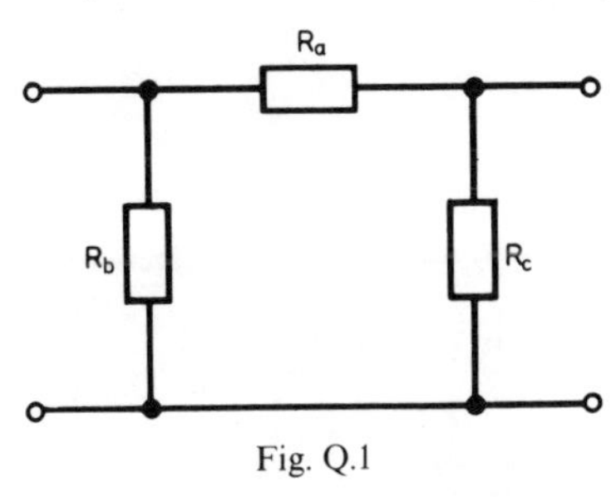

Fig. Q.1

9.2. Verify the results for the mesh/star and star/mesh transformations obtained in Section 2.11 by determining the z and y-parameters of the networks.

9.3. Design a symmetrical π-section resistive network to produce an attenuation of 25 dB when inserted in a coaxial transmission line of characteristic resistance 50 Ω.

9.4. Determine the z-parameters of the network of figure Q.4, in which resistance values are in ohms. Hence reduce the network to its simplest form.

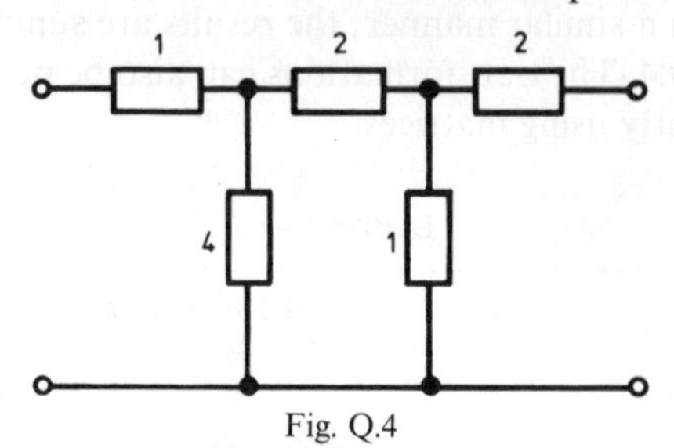

Fig. Q.4

9.5. Derive expressions for the parameters of the network shown in figure Q.5 in terms of its z-parameters and $\boldsymbol{I}_1$.

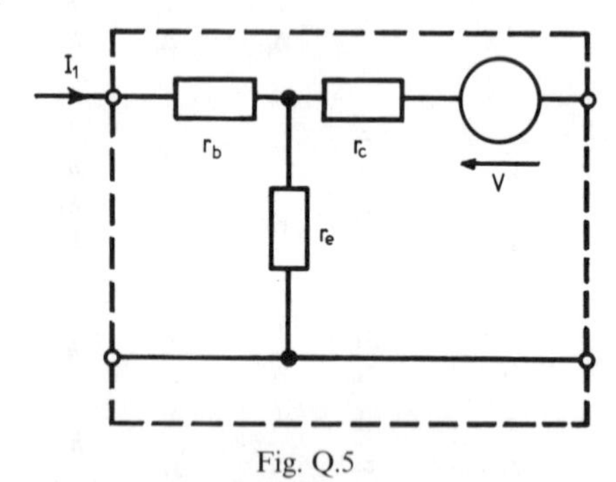

Fig. Q.5

9.6. Show that the input admittance of a two-port network, terminated by an admittance Y_L, is

$$Y_{in} = y_i - \frac{y_r y_f}{y_o + Y_L}$$

9.7. The circuit of an emitter follower amplifier driven by a 600 Ω source is shown in figure Q.7. The $\boldsymbol{h}$-parameters of the transistor are $\boldsymbol{h}_{ie} = 1.5\ \text{k}\Omega$, $\boldsymbol{h}_{fe} = 100$, $\boldsymbol{h}_{oe} = \boldsymbol{h}_{re} = 0$; $R_b = 500\ \text{k}\Omega$ and $R = 5\ \text{k}\Omega$. Determine, deriving the formulae used, the voltage gain, input resistance and output resistance of the circuit.

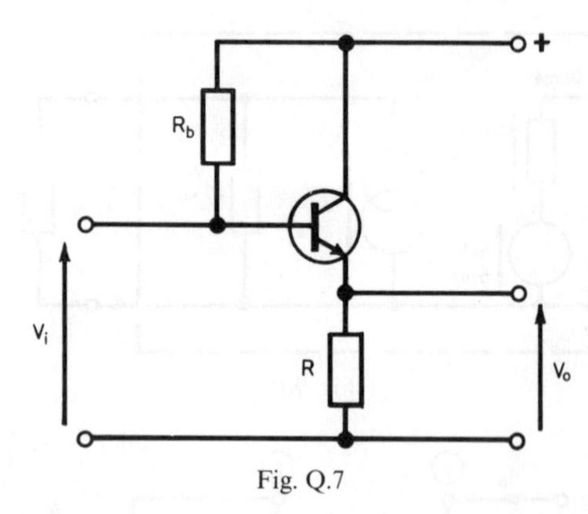

Fig. Q.7

9.8. Draw the equivalent circuit of the resistance-loaded transistor amplifier of figure Q.8. The hybrid parameters of the transistor are $\boldsymbol{h}_{ie} = 1\ \text{k}\Omega$, $\boldsymbol{h}_{re} = 0$, $\boldsymbol{h}_{fe} = 50$, $\boldsymbol{h}_{oe} = 50\ \mu\text{S}$. The reactance of the capacitors C_E and C_O may be assumed to be zero.

Calculate the values of C_1 and C_2 required to give a pass-band of 100 Hz to 10 kHz.

Determine the approximate voltage gain at 1 kHz.

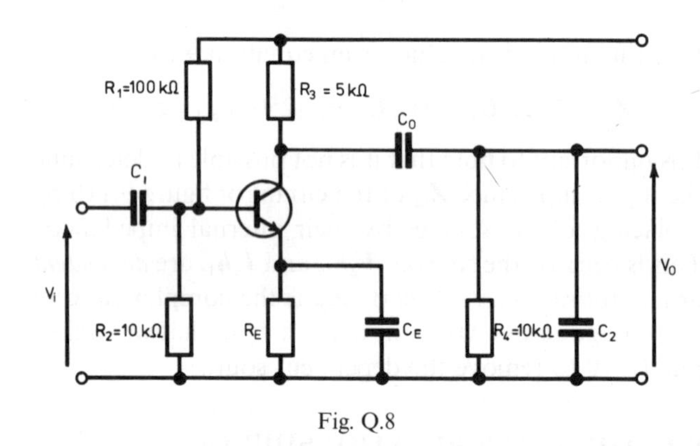

Fig. Q.8

9.9. The $\boldsymbol{y}$-parameters of an integrated circuit amplifier, measured at a frequency of 10 MHz are:
$y_i = (0.60 + \text{j}1.50)$ mS; $y_r = 0.0003$ mS; $y_f = (100 - \text{j}20)$ mS; $y_o = \text{j}0.08$ mS.
Determine the $\boldsymbol{h}$-parameters of the device.

CHAPTER TEN

Locus Diagrams

10.1 INTRODUCTION

In Chapter 8 the variation with frequency of circuit parameters such as impedance, admittance and phase angle was expressed in graphical form. This method of presentation is convenient because it enables the effect of parameter variations to be seen at a glance. It is not of course necessary that frequency is the variable and a diagram can be constructed to show the effect on, for example, the input impedance of a circuit when one of the circuit elements is varied. Typical examples occur in the study of induction motor performance and the stability of transistor circuits.

The path traced out by the end of the phasor representing the dependent variable being examined is known as the *locus* of that quantity and the complete diagram is a *locus diagram.*

When constructing locus diagrams one frequently wishes to transfer from an impedance locus to an admittance locus or vice versa; the operation of obtaining the locus of the reciprocal quantity is known as *inversion.*

The techniques employed in the development of locus diagrams are discussed and illustrated by means of examples in the following sections.

10.2 THE LOCUS DIAGRAM FOR A SIMPLE *CR* CIRCUIT

The steady state performance of the low-pass *CR* netword was examined in section 8.2 and the results expressed by separate amplitude and phase response diagrams. The information is now given in the form of a locus diagram with frequency as the variable.

From equation 8.1 we can write

$$G(j\omega)=\frac{V_0}{V_i}=\frac{1}{1+j\omega T}$$

Rationalizing

$$G(j\omega)=\frac{1}{1+(\omega T)^2}-\frac{j\omega T}{1+(\omega T)^2}$$

$$=x+jy \qquad (10.1)$$

Hence

$$x^2+y^2=x$$

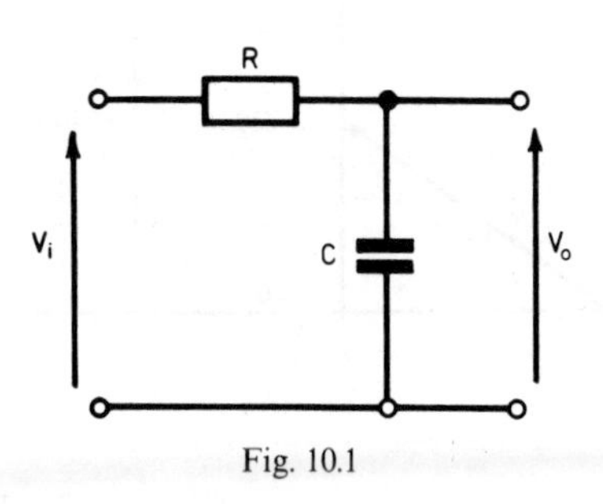

Fig. 10.1

and re-arranging the terms

$$(x-\tfrac{1}{2})^2+y^2=(\tfrac{1}{2})^2 \qquad (10.2)$$

which is the equation of a circle of radius $\frac{1}{2}$ and centre $(\frac{1}{2}, 0)$ as shown in figure 10.2. The complete circle corresponds to values of ω between minus infinity and plus infinity; at this stage, only the lower half of the circle, which corresponds to positive frequencies, is of interest.

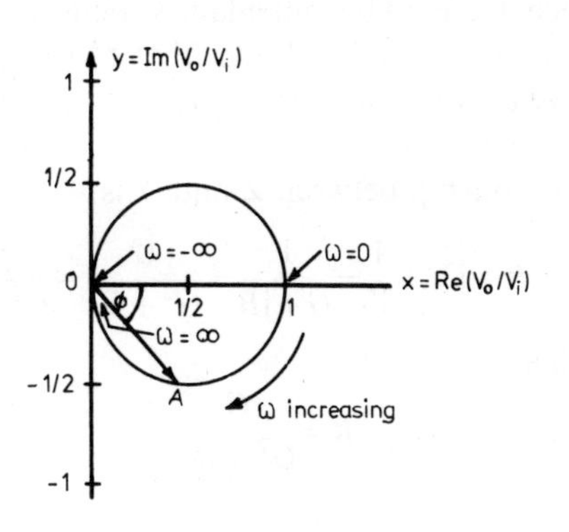

Fig. 10.2

The magnitude and phase of V_0/V_i at a particular frequency ω_1 are evaluated by measuring OA and ϕ on the diagram.

10.3 THE INVERSION OF A STRAIGHT LINE

In the circuit consisting of a variable inductor in series with a resistor, shown in figure 10.3, the locus of the

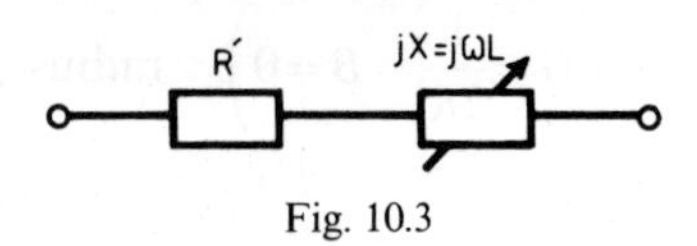

Fig. 10.3

impedance $(R'+jX)$, as the frequency is varied, is a straight line as in figure 10.4.

If, and only if, the same scale is used for both axes the magnitude of $\boldsymbol{Z}$ is determined by measuring the distance from the origin O to the point on the locus corresponding to the appropriate value of X; similarly the phase angle of $\boldsymbol{Z}$ is obtained by measuring the angle ϕ_2.

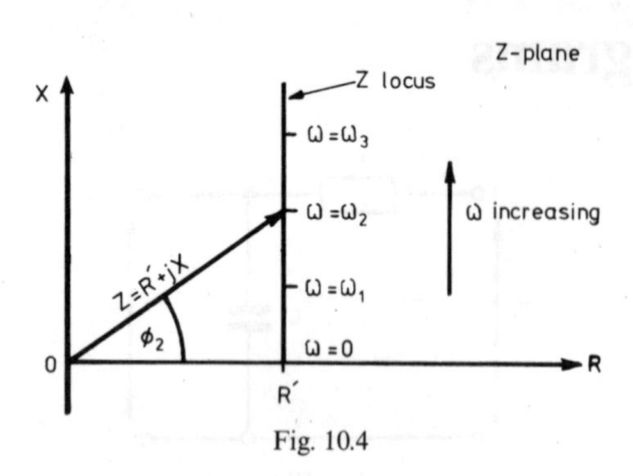

Fig. 10.4

To examine the variation of current in the circuit of figure 10.3 when a voltage of constant amplitude and variable frequency is applied, it is convenient to determine the variation of admittance. Since $\boldsymbol{I}=\boldsymbol{V}\boldsymbol{Y}$ it is necessary to change only the scale of the locus diagram to convert from admittance to current.

The problem is therefore to derive the admittance locus from the impedance locus; but $\boldsymbol{Y}=1/\boldsymbol{Z}$ and it is necessary to *invert* the impedance locus to obtain the admittance locus. The impedance locus is a straight line and it will now be shown that *the inversion of a straight line about a point results in a circle passing through the point of inversion.*

The relationship between $\boldsymbol{Z}$ and $\boldsymbol{Y}$ is

$$\boldsymbol{Z}=R+jX=\frac{1}{\boldsymbol{Y}}=\frac{1}{G+jB}=\frac{G}{G^2+B^2}-\frac{jB}{G^2+B^2}$$

from which

$$R=\frac{G}{G^2+B^2} \tag{10.3}$$

and

$$X=\frac{-B}{G^2+B^2} \tag{10.4}$$

From equation 10.3

$$G^2+B^2-\frac{G}{R}=0$$

or

$$\left(G-\frac{1}{2R}\right)^2+B^2=\left(\frac{1}{2R}\right)^2 \tag{10.5}$$

Equation 10.5 represents a circle on the $\boldsymbol{Y}$-plane,

$$\text{Centre}\left(G=\frac{1}{2R},\quad B=0\right),\quad \text{radius }\frac{1}{2R}.$$

This circle is the admittance locus, shown in figure 10.5, when R is constant and X is varied from $-\infty$ to $+\infty$. When X is positive (full line) the Y locus is in the lower half of the plane and when X is negative (broken line) the Y locus is in the upper half of the plane.

From equation 10.4:

$$G^2+B^2+\frac{B}{X}=0$$

or

$$G^2+\left(B+\frac{1}{2X}\right)^2=\left(\frac{1}{2X}\right)^2 \tag{10.6}$$

Equation 10.6 represents a circle in the $\boldsymbol{Y}$-plane,

† $$\text{Centre}\left(G=0,\ B=-\frac{1}{2X}\right)$$

$$\text{Radius }\frac{1}{2X}$$

This circle is the admittance locus of a series RX circuit when R is varied and X remains constant. The corresponding $\boldsymbol{Z}$ and $\boldsymbol{Y}$ loci are shown in figure 10.6.

The left hand side of the plane corresponds to negative values of R (broken lines).

In figures 10.5 and 10.6 E_1, E_2 and E_3 are the inverted points corresponding to D_1, D_2 and D_3 respectively.

† If $\boldsymbol{Z}=|\boldsymbol{Z}|\angle\phi$, then $\boldsymbol{Y}=\dfrac{1}{\boldsymbol{Z}}=\dfrac{1}{|\boldsymbol{Z}|}\angle-\phi$

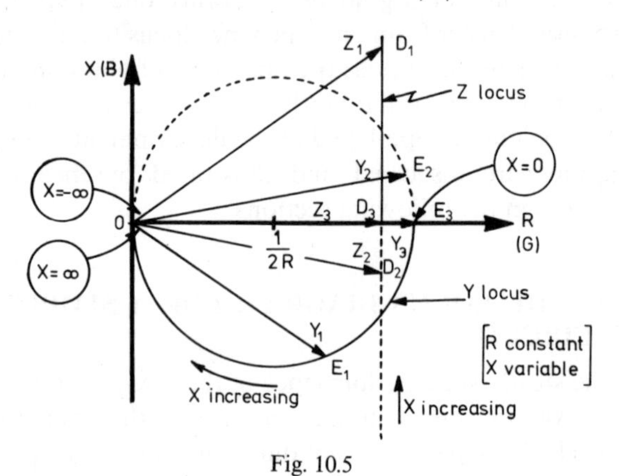

Fig. 10.5

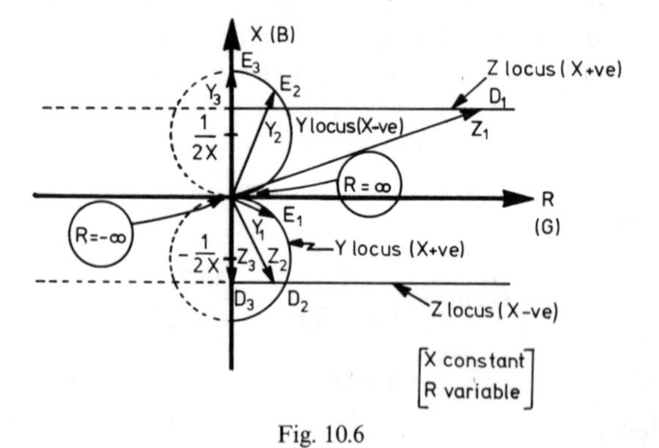

Fig. 10.6

Taking into account the scale factor k, we have

$$Y = \frac{k}{|Z|} \underline{/-\phi}.$$

The scale factor is chosen so that the locus resulting from the inversion fits conveniently onto the sheet of paper being used, bearing in mind that the *shortest* Z phasor results in the *longest* Y phasor since $|Y| = 1/|Z|$. In figure 10.5 for example, the admittance scale is chosen so that a circle of radius $1/2R$ S fits conveniently onto the page.

If a circle is inverted **about a point on its circumference** *a straight line is produced*; this is the converse of the original statement.

10.4 THE INVERSION OF A CIRCLE ABOUT A POINT NOT ON ITS CIRCUMFERENCE

If, in the circuit of figure 10.7, it is required to determine the variation of input admittance Y_{AB} as X_1 is varied from $-\infty$ to $+\infty$, one proceeds as follows

(i) Plot the Z_1 locus; this is a straight line as shown in figure 10.8

(ii) Invert the Z_1 locus about O to give the Y_1 locus; this produces a circle, centre ($G = 1/2R_1, B = 0$) and radius $1/2R_1$ as represented by equation 10.5.

(iii) To obtain the Y_{AB} locus it is necessary to add the constant admittance Y_2 to the Y_1 locus. This operation is most conveniently performed by moving the origin from O to O′ where $OO' = Y_2$. The circular locus, with reference to O′ is now the $Y_{AB} = (Y_1 + Y_2)$ locus; that is, values of Y_{AB} are measured from O′ and not from O.

This is illustrated by considering a particular value of $X_1 = X_1'$, giving Z_1' which when inverted gives Y_1'. The corresponding input admittance Y_{AB}' is also shown in figure 10.8.

Now suppose that the input impedance $Z_{AB} = 1/Y_{AB}$ is required. It is necessary to invert the circular admittance locus about O′ which is not on its circumference. It will now be shown that *if a circle is inverted* **about a point not on its circumference** *another circle is produced.* This may be done using complex variable theory; it may also be done geometrically and the latter method is used here.

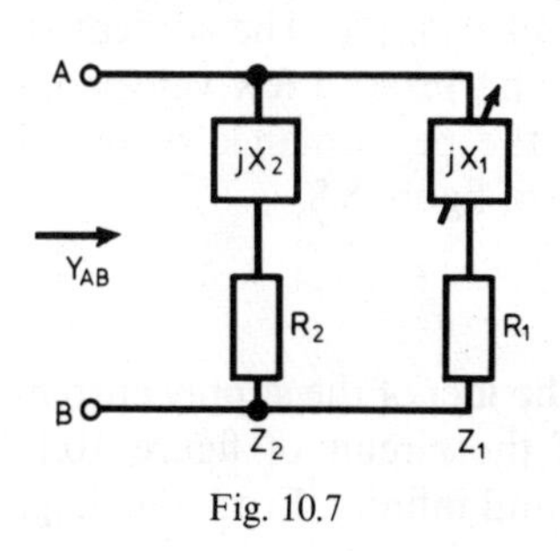

Fig. 10.7

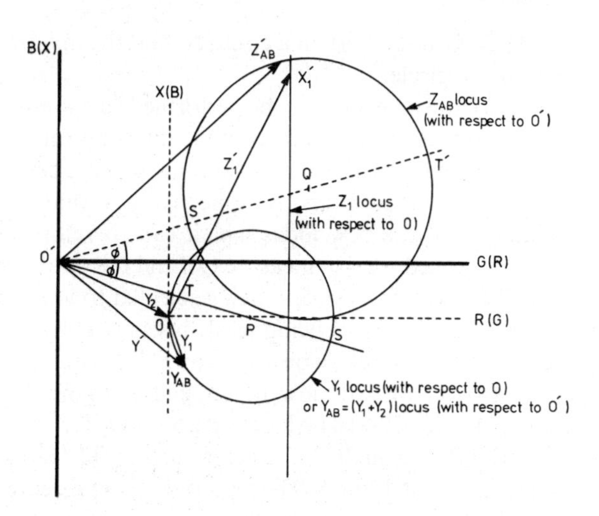

Fig. 10.8

The circle, centre P, in figure 10.9 is to be inverted about O, which does not lie on the circumference of the circle.

Draw chords OAB and ODC from O such that they make angles $+\phi$ and $-\phi$ respectively with the horizontal axis.

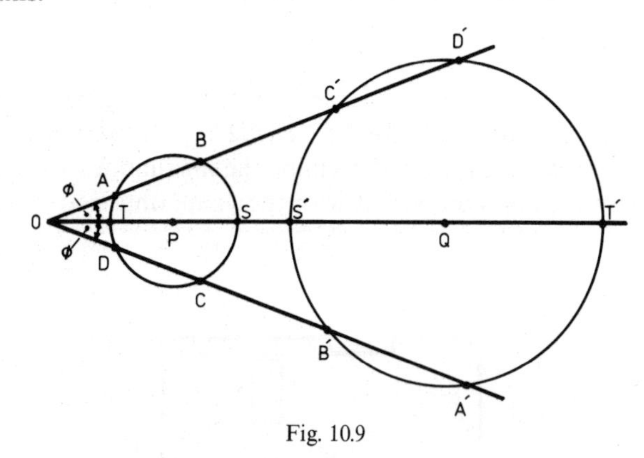

Fig. 10.9

Since ABCD lie on a circle, by Theorem 56:

$$OA.OB = OC.OD \tag{10.7}$$

Now invert these points about O giving A′, B′, C′ and D′ such that $OA' = k/OA$, $OB' = k/OB$, $OC' = k/OB$ and $OD' = k/OB$ where k is the constant of inversion.

Then $OA'.OB' = \dfrac{k^2}{OA.OB}$ and $OC'.OD' = \dfrac{k^2}{OC.OD}$

Therefore

$$(OA'.OB')(OA.OB) = (OC'.OD')(OC.OD)$$

But $(OA.OB) = (OC.OD)$ from equation 10.7

Therefore

$$OA'.OB' = OC'.OD'$$

Hence A′, B′, C′ and D′ lie on a circle, so that the inverted locus is also a circle.

In practice the inversion can be performed very simply. Points T and S, at the extremities of the diameter formed by the line from the point of inversion through the centre of the circle, invert to T′ and S′ respectively so that T′S′ is a diameter of the new locus which can therefore be drawn. The procedure is to measure OT and OS, evaluate OT′ = k/OT and OS′ = k/OS, k being selected to suit the size of the sheet of paper being used; bisect S′T′ to give Q, the centre of the circle to be drawn on S′T′ as diameter.

This construction will now be applied to figure 10.8 where the $\boldsymbol{Y}_{AB}$ locus is to be inverted about O′.

Draw O′TPS through P, the centre of the $\boldsymbol{Y}_{AB}$ circle, cutting the circle at T and S. The admittances represented by O′T and O′S have phase angles $-\phi$ so that the corresponding impedances O′T′ and O′S′ have phase angles $+\phi$; that is, it is necessary to reflect across the horizontal axis and make O′T′ = k/O′T and O′S′ = k/O′S. Bisect S′T′ to give point Q, the centre of the $\boldsymbol{Z}_{AB}$ locus which has a diameter S′T′.

10.5 WORKED EXAMPLES

Example

Construct the locus diagram for the phase lag network shown in figure 10.10 for $R_1 = 18$ kΩ, $R_2 = 2$ kΩ, $C = 100$ μF. From the diagram determine the maximum value of phase lag and compare it with the value obtained from equation 8.17.

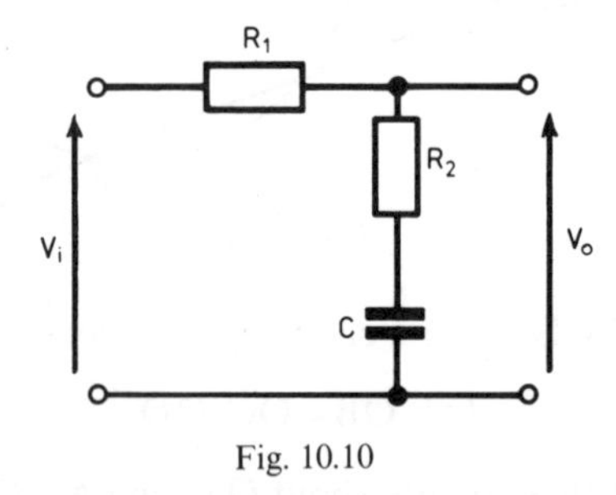

Fig. 10.10

Solution

The frequency response function of the network is, from equation 8.12

$$\boldsymbol{G}(j\omega) = \frac{V_0}{V_i} = \frac{1 + j\omega T}{1 + j\omega\alpha T}$$

where $T = CR_2$ and $\alpha = \dfrac{R_1 + R_2}{R_2}$

Putting $V_0/V_i = x + jy$ and rationalizing

$$x = \frac{1 + \alpha\omega^2 T^2}{1 + (\alpha\omega T)^2} = \frac{1/\alpha[\alpha + (\alpha\omega T)^2]}{1 + (\alpha\omega T)^2} \quad (10.8)$$

$$y = \frac{\omega T(1 - \alpha)}{1 + (\alpha\omega T)^2} + \frac{(\alpha\omega T)[1/\alpha - 1]}{1 + (\alpha\omega T)^2} \quad (10.9)$$

From equation 10.8

$$(\alpha\omega T) = \left(\frac{1 - x}{x - 1/\alpha}\right)^{1/2}$$

and substituting in equation 10.9 and rearranging the terms gives

$$\left[x - \left(\frac{\alpha + 1}{2\alpha}\right)\right]^2 + y^2 = \left(\frac{\alpha - 1}{2\alpha}\right)^2 \quad (10.10)$$

which is the equation of a circle, centre $(\alpha + 1)/2\alpha$, 0 and radius $[(\alpha - 1)/2\alpha]$.

In this case $\alpha = (R_1 + R_2)/R_2 = 10$, so that the centre of the circle is (0.55, 0) and the radius is 0.45 as shown in figure 10.11.

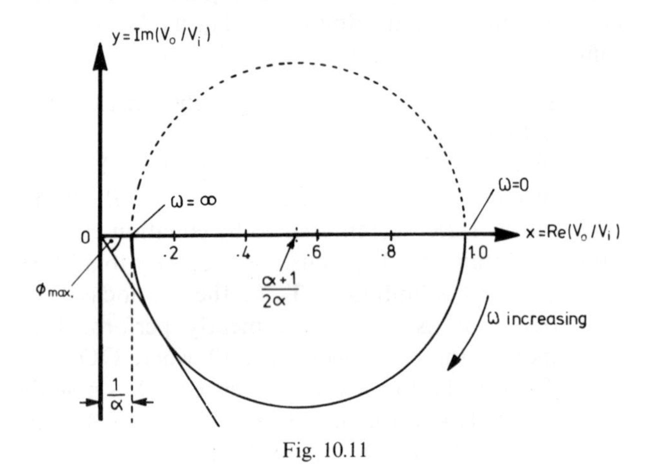

Fig. 10.11

For positive values of ω only the lower half of the circle is required. The maximum value of phase lag ϕ_{max} is obtained by drawing the tangent to the semicircle from O; the measured value of ϕ_{max} is 55° which agrees with the value obtained by putting $\alpha = 10$ in equation 8.17.

It will be seen that the centre and radius of the circle are functions of α and do not depend on the actual values of the circuit elements.

However the location of any particular value of ω on the locus is a function of the values of the circuit elements since the expressions for the amplitude and phase angle of $\boldsymbol{G}(j\omega)$ contain α and T. The student should draw the locus to scale and insert a few values of ω on the circle and compare the performance of the circuit with the Bode diagram of figure 8.8.

Example

Construct the loci of the supply current and the input impedance of the circuit of figure 10.12 as R_1 varies between 2.5Ω and infinity. From the diagram, determine

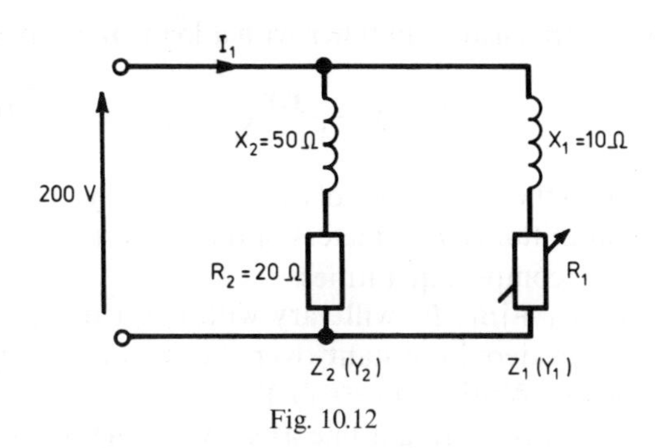

Fig. 10.12

the current and the input impedance when $R_1=30\,\Omega$ and check the result by calculation.

Solution

The procedure for constructing the locus is set out in step by step form below; the student should carry out the steps using the scales suggested.

(i) Draw the $\boldsymbol{Z}_1$ locus, use a scale of 1 in $=10\,\Omega$ *for both axes.*

(ii) Invert the $\boldsymbol{Z}_1$ locus about O to obtain the $\boldsymbol{Y}_1$ locus. Use a scale of 1 in $=0.02$ S *for both axes.* Note that the radius of the circle is $1/2X_1$.

Mark the points on the $\boldsymbol{Y}_1$ locus corresponding to the limits of R_1, that is, $R_1=2.5\,\Omega$, $R_1=\infty$.

(iii) Obtain the $Y_{in}=(Y_1+Y_2)$ locus by shifting the origin from O to O′ where O′O$=Y_2$

$$Y_2=\frac{1}{\boldsymbol{Z}_2}=\frac{1}{20+\mathrm{j}50}=(0.007-\mathrm{j}0.017)\ \mathrm{S}$$

Therefore O′O$=(0.007-\mathrm{j}0.017)$ S *to the same scale as* $\boldsymbol{Y}_1$.

(iv) To obtain the current locus the relationship $\boldsymbol{I}=V\boldsymbol{Y}$ is used; here $V=200$ V so the current scale is 1 in $=200\times$ the admittance scale; that is 1 in $=(200\times0.02)=4$ A.

The current locus is the same as the Y_{in} locus, only the scale being changed.

(v) To plot the reference scale. Draw the 'image' of the $\boldsymbol{Z}_1$ locus, this is marked 'R_1 scale' on figure 10.13. If it is now required to obtain the value of the supply current when $R_1=30\,\Omega$ (P′ on the reference scale), use a ruler to determine the point Q where OP′ [NOT O′P′] intersects the Y_1 locus. Measuring O′Q and $\angle$HO′Q gives $\boldsymbol{I}=9.0\angle-36°$ A. which is in good agreement with the value obtained by putting $R_1=30\,\Omega$ in figure 10.12 and calculating $\boldsymbol{I}$.

(vi) To obtain the locus of the input impedance it is necessary to invert the Y locus about O′.

Draw O′TS from O′ through the centre of the Y locus, cutting the locus at T and S.

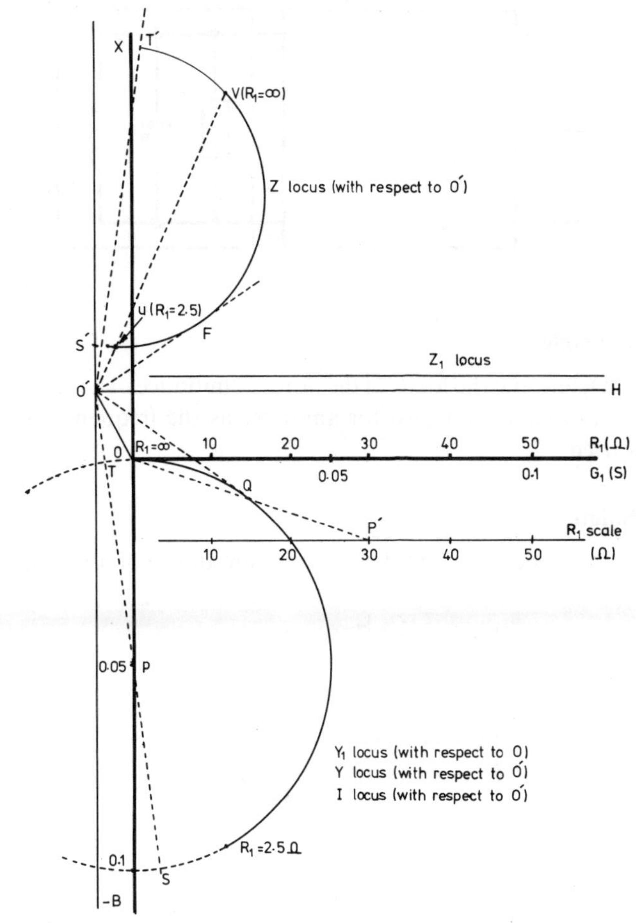

Fig. 10.13

$$\mathrm{O'T}=0.8\ \mathrm{in}=(0.8\times0.02)\ \mathrm{S}=0.016\ \mathrm{S}$$

$$\mathrm{O'S}=5.8\ \mathrm{in}=(5.8\times0.02)\ \mathrm{S}=0.116\ \mathrm{S}$$

Invert these quantities (see figure 10.8)

$$\frac{1}{\mathrm{O'T}}\rightarrow\mathrm{O'T'}=\frac{1}{0.016}\,\Omega=62.5\,\Omega$$

$$\frac{1}{\mathrm{O'S}}\rightarrow\mathrm{O'S'}=\frac{1}{0.116}\,\Omega=8.6\,\Omega$$

The maximum value of resistance is 62.5 Ω and a suitable scale for the diagram to fit onto a sheet of A4 size paper is 1 in $=15\,\Omega$.

(vii) Draw a circle on S′T′ as diameter; this circle is the locus of the input impedance.

(viii) The limits of the locus are determined by 'reflecting' the lines from O′ to $R_1=2.5\,\Omega$ and O′ to $R_1=\infty$ on the Y locus across the horizontal axis O′H to intersect the $\boldsymbol{Z}$ locus at U and V respectively.

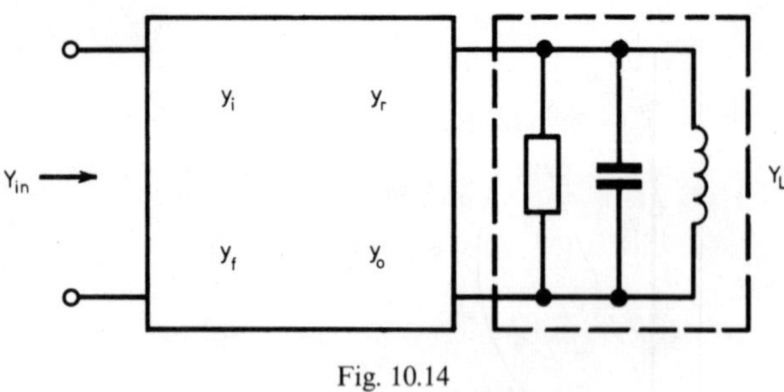

Fig. 10.14

Example

Determine the locus of the input admittance of a tuned radio-frequency transistor amplifier as the frequency is varied.

Solution

It can be shown that the input admittance of a radio-frequency transistor amplifier with a load Y_L is given by

$$Y_{in} = y_i - \frac{y_r y_f}{y_o + Y_L} \tag{10.11}$$

where Y_L is the admittance of the load and y_i, y_r, y_f and y_o are the admittance parameters of the transistor and are, in general, complex quantities.

If $Y_L = G_L + jB_L$, B_L will vary with frequency and G_L can be considered constant over the working range of frequencies. Writing $Y_2 = y_o + Y_L = (g_o + G_L) + j(b_o + B_L)$ the Y_2 locus is a straight line as shown in figure 10.15a.

Inverting the Y_2 locus gives $Z_2 = 1/Y_2$ and equation 10.11 may be written

$$Y_{in} = y_i + (-y_r y_f) Z_2 \tag{10.12}$$

The Z_2 locus is a circle as shown in figure 10.15a.

It is now necessary to multiply the Z_2 locus by $(-y_r y_f) = D\angle\phi$ say. This operation involves a change of scale by a factor D and rotation through an angle ϕ, giving the locus shown in figure 10.15b. y_i is now added by shifting the origin from O to O′ such that O′O $= y_i$ giving the Y_{in} locus shown in figure 10.15c.

This example shows how the locus of a quantity represented by quite a complicated expression can be determined. This particular problem is important in the examination of the stability of radio-frequency amplifiers. From figure 10.15c it can be seen that if g_c is less than the radius of the Y_{in} locus, it is possible for Y_{in} to have a negative real component. This corresponds to the input resistance of the amplifier being negative, a condition that may lead to instability.

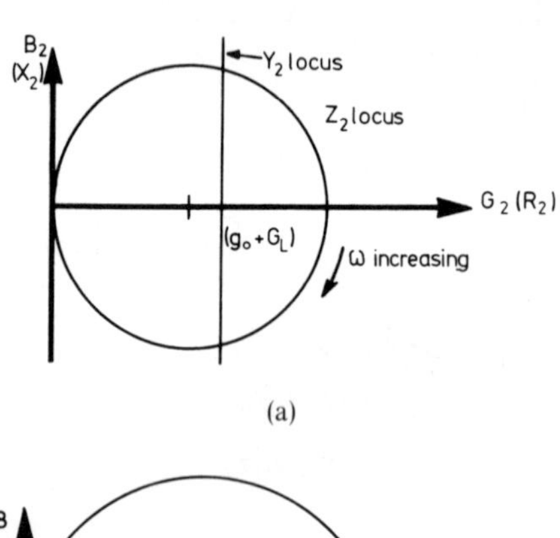

(a)

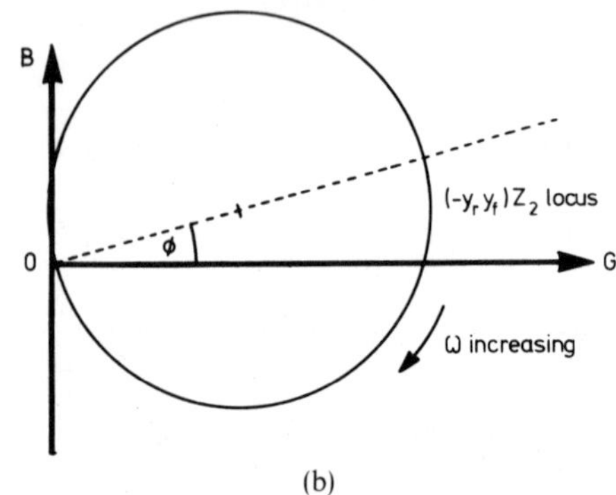

(b)

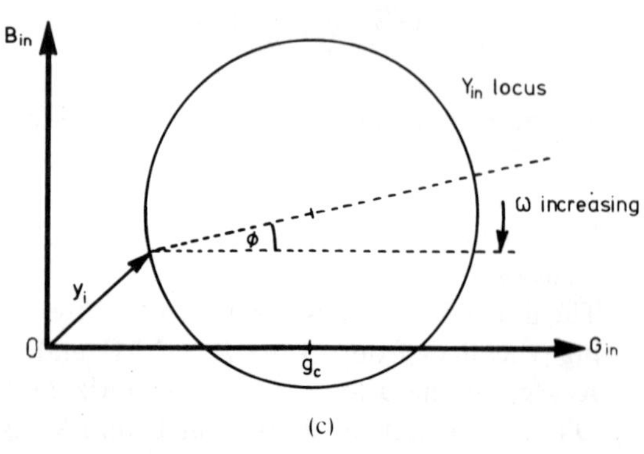

(c)

Fig. 10.15

PROBLEMS

10.1. Construct the locus of the output voltage V_0 when a voltage V_i of constant-amplitude and variable frequency is applied to the phase advance network of figure Q.1. Determine the maximum value of the phase angle and compare it with the result obtained in problem 8.2c.

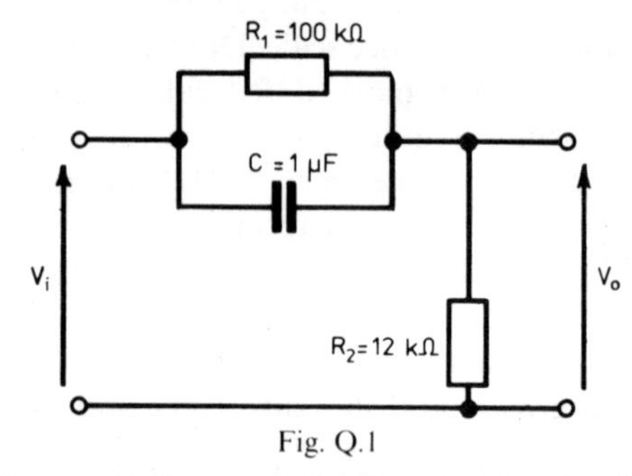

Fig. Q.1

10.2. The approximate equivalent circuit of an induction motor is shown in figure Q.2; the resistance R represents the effect of the external mechanical load on the motor.

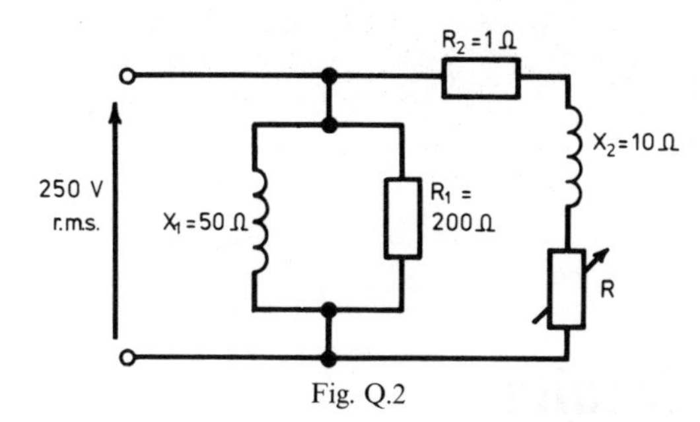

Fig. Q.2

Construct the input admittance locus of the equivalent circuit over the range $R=0$ (locked rotor condition) to $R=\infty$ (no-load condition), explaining each step in the construction and indicating clearly the scales used.

From the locus diagram determine:

(i) the value of the supply current and its phase angle with respect to the supply voltage when $R=10\ \Omega$ (full-load condition)

(ii) the highest power factor at which the motor operates

(iii) the power input to the motor when the power factor is at its maximum value.

10.3. Show that, for the network of figure Q.3, $V_0/V_i=$

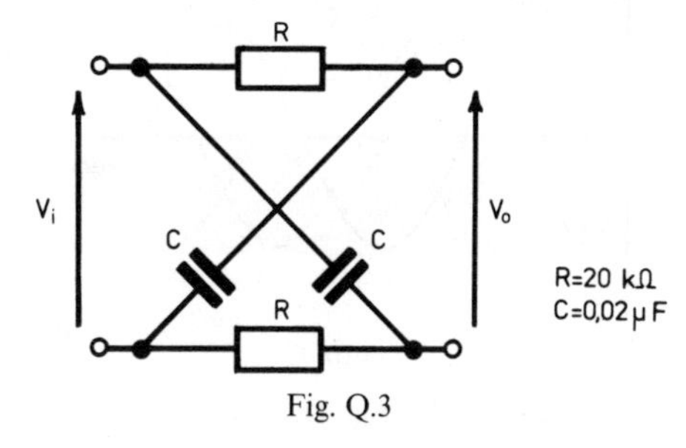

Fig. Q.3

$(1-j\omega T)/(1+j\omega T)$ where $T=CR$. Hence, or otherwise, plot the locus of V_0 when V_i is a constant-amplitude, variable-frequency voltage. From the locus determine the frequencies at which the phase shift is $-30°$, $-90°$, $-120°$.

Why is the network called an 'all-pass' network?

10.4. A constant-amplitude voltage of frequency $f=500/\pi$ Hz is applied to the circuit of figure Q.4.

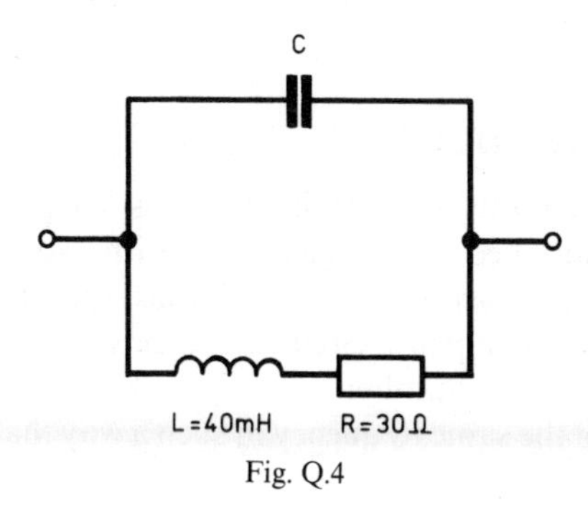

Fig. Q.4

(i) Draw the locus of the admittance of the circuit as C is varied and from the diagram show that the admittance is a minimum when $C=16\ \mu F$.

(ii) Draw the locus diagram of the admittance of the circuit as R is varied, hence show that if $C=12.5\ \mu F$ the magnitude of the admittance is independent of the value of R.

CHAPTER ELEVEN

Three-Phase Circuits

11.1 INTRODUCTION

The a.c. circuits studied in previous chapters are, in general, supplied by a single source with two conductors connecting the source to the circuit; such circuits are known as *single-phase* circuits. It is possible however to interconnect a number of single-phase circuits and sources of the same frequency in such a way that there are well-defined phase relationships between the sources. These are known as *polyphase* circuits or systems.

Polyphase systems are more complicated than single-phase systems but have a number of advantages, particularly in high power installations. The advantages of polyphase systems include the following

(i) Less conductor material is required to transmit a given amount of power over a given distance when a polyphase system is used
(ii) A polyphase winding in a motor or generator makes more efficient use of the available winding space than a single-phase winding. In other words, for a given frame size, a polyphase machine produces greater output.
(iii) Polyphase machines produce a steady output, whereas single-phase machines produce a pulsating output.
(iv) Polyphase generators may be connected in parallel to provide higher power more easily than single-phase generators.

The most widely used polyphase system is *the three-phase system*; the complexity resulting from a greater number of phases is not compensated for by the resulting small increase in efficiency.

11.2 THE GENERATION OF A THREE-PHASE SUPPLY

A three-phase supply consists essentially of three single-phase systems displaced in time phase from each other by one-third of a period, that is by 120°. The principle of three-phase generation may be understood by considering an armature having three coils aa′, bb′ and cc′ wound in the same sense and spaced 120° as shown in figure 11.1a. When the armature is rotated at a constant angular velocity ω rad/sec in a uniform magnetic field sinusoidal voltages are developed across the coils as shown in figure 11.1b.

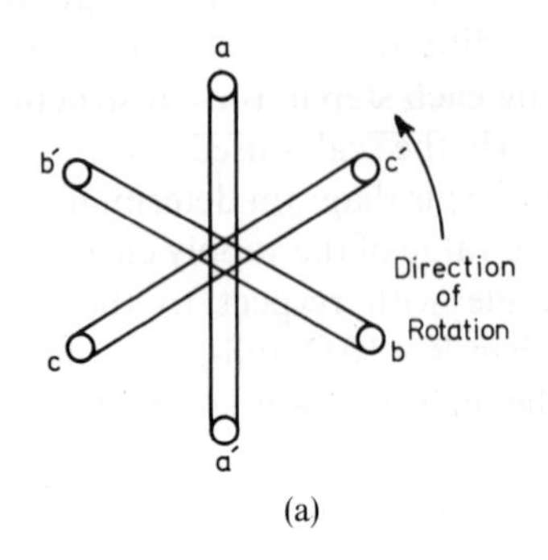

(a)

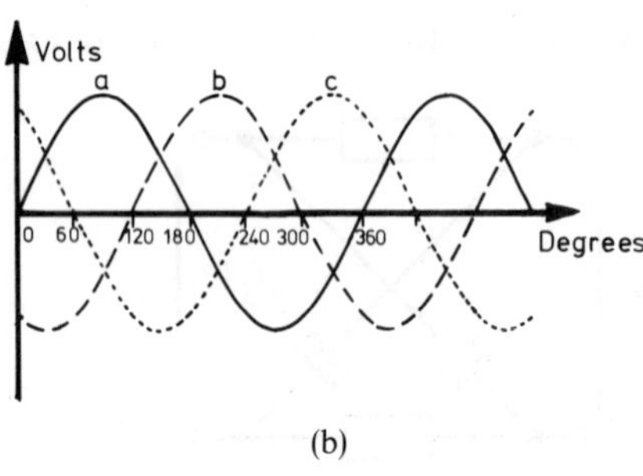

(b)

Fig. 11.1

The order in which the voltages reach their maximum values is known as the *phase sequence*. In this case the phase sequence is abc, but in practical systems the phases are usually referred to as the Red, Yellow and Blue phases in which case the phase sequence could be RYB.

11.3 METHODS OF CONNECTION OF THREE-PHASE SUPPLIES

The three coils aa′, bb′ and cc′ of figure 11.1a may be connected as shown in figure 11.2a. This method of connection is known as the *Star Connection or Y-Connection; the common point n is known as the Neutral-Point.*

The phasor diagram of the star-connected generator is shown in figure 11.2b; the voltages across the coils V_{an}, V_{bn} and V_{cn} are known as the *Phase Voltages* and the

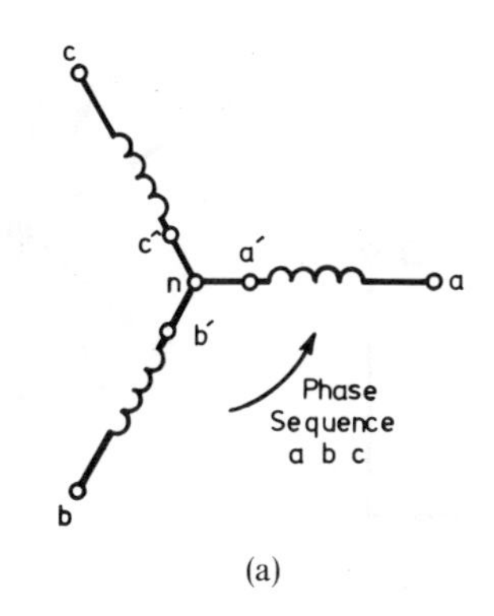

(a)

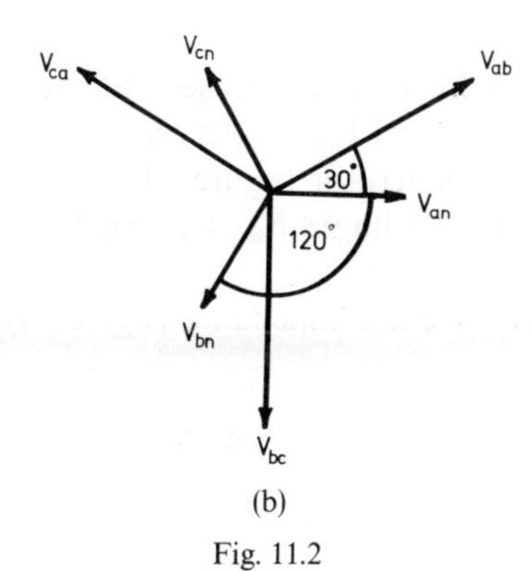

(b)

Fig. 11.2

voltages between the outer ends of the coils $\boldsymbol{V}_{ab}$, $\boldsymbol{V}_{bc}$ and $\boldsymbol{V}_{ca}$ are known as the *Line Voltages.*

The line voltages can be expressed in terms of the phase voltages

$$\left.\begin{aligned} \boldsymbol{V}_{ab} &= \boldsymbol{V}_{an} - \boldsymbol{V}_{bn} \\ \boldsymbol{V}_{bc} &= \boldsymbol{V}_{bn} - \boldsymbol{V}_{cn} \\ \boldsymbol{V}_{ca} &= \boldsymbol{V}_{cn} - \boldsymbol{V}_{an} \end{aligned}\right\} \qquad (11.1)$$

If the three coils are identical, as is usual in practice,

$$|\boldsymbol{V}_{an}| = |\boldsymbol{V}_{bn}| = |\boldsymbol{V}_{cn}| = V_p$$

and taking aa′ as the reference in figure 11.2 we can write

$$\left.\begin{aligned} \boldsymbol{V}_{an} &= V_p \angle 0^\circ \\ \boldsymbol{V}_{bn} &= V_p \angle -120^\circ \\ \boldsymbol{V}_{cn} &= V_p \angle -240^\circ \end{aligned}\right\} \qquad (11.2)$$

From the geometry of figure 11.2b it is seen that

$$\left.\begin{aligned} \boldsymbol{V}_{ab} &= V_p \sqrt{3} \angle 30^\circ \\ \boldsymbol{V}_{bc} &= V_p \sqrt{3} \angle -90^\circ \\ \boldsymbol{V}_{ca} &= V_p \sqrt{3} \angle -210^\circ \end{aligned}\right\} \qquad (11.3)$$

That is the line voltages

$$|\boldsymbol{V}_{ab}| = |\boldsymbol{V}_{bc}| = |\boldsymbol{V}_{ca}| = V_L = \sqrt{3}\, V_p$$

So that *in the star-connected generator, Line Voltage* $= \sqrt{3} \times$ *Phase Voltage.*

It is also possible to express the phase voltages in rectangular co-ordinates

$$\left.\begin{aligned} \boldsymbol{V}_{an} &= V_p(1 + j0) \\ \boldsymbol{V}_{bn} &= V_p[\cos(-120^\circ) + j\sin(-120^\circ)] \\ &= V_p[-\tfrac{1}{2} - j\sqrt{3}/2] \\ \boldsymbol{V}_{cn} &= V_p[\cos(-240^\circ) + j\sin(-240^\circ)] \\ &= V_p[-\tfrac{1}{2} + j\sqrt{3}/2] \end{aligned}\right\} \qquad (11.4)$$

From these expressions it is apparent that the vector sum

† $$\boldsymbol{V}_{an} + \boldsymbol{V}_{bn} + \boldsymbol{V}_{cn} = 0;$$

and it is possible to represent the voltages as a closed triangle instead of from a common origin as in figure 11.2b.

Similarly for the line voltages

$$\begin{aligned} \boldsymbol{V}_{ab} &= V_p \sqrt{3}[\cos 30^\circ + j\sin 30^\circ] \\ &= V_p[\tfrac{3}{2} + j\sqrt{3}/2] \end{aligned}$$

$$\left.\begin{aligned} \boldsymbol{V}_{bc} &= V_p \sqrt{3}[\cos(-90^\circ) + j\sin(-90^\circ)] \\ &= V_p[0 - j\sqrt{3}] \\ \boldsymbol{V}_{ca} &= V_p \sqrt{3}[\cos(-210^\circ) + j\sin(-210^\circ)] \\ &= V_p[-\tfrac{3}{2} + j\sqrt{3}/2] \end{aligned}\right\} \qquad (11.5)$$

The vector sum of the line voltages is also zero, that is

† $$\boldsymbol{V}_{ab} + \boldsymbol{V}_{bc} + \boldsymbol{V}_{ca} = 0$$

An alternative method of connecting a three-phase supply is shown in figure 11.3a; this is known as the *Delta or Mesh Connection* and the corresponding phasor diagram is shown in figure 11.3b.

The voltages can be expressed in polar and rectangular co-ordinates

$$\left.\begin{aligned} \boldsymbol{V}_{ab} &= V_p \angle 0^\circ = V_p[1 + j0] \\ \boldsymbol{V}_{bc} &= V_p \angle -120^\circ = V_p[-\tfrac{1}{2} - j\sqrt{3}/2] \\ \boldsymbol{V}_{ca} &= V_p \angle -240^\circ = V_p[-\tfrac{1}{2} + j\sqrt{3}/2] \end{aligned}\right\} \qquad (11.6)$$

As for the star-connection, the vector sum of the voltages

† $$\boldsymbol{V}_{ab} + \boldsymbol{V}_{bc} + \boldsymbol{V}_{ca} = 0$$

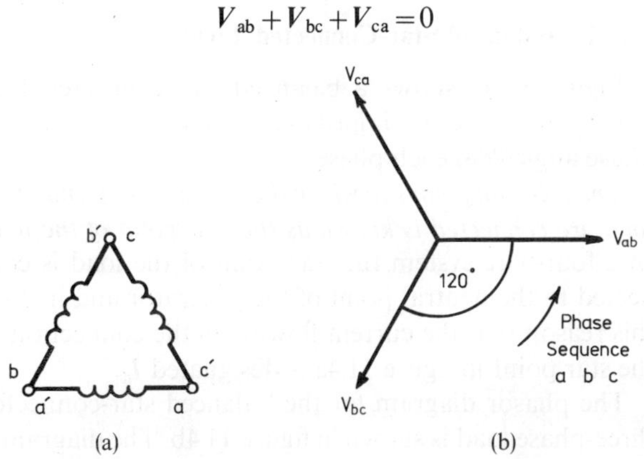

Fig. 11.3

and the voltages may be represented by a closed triangle.
† *The phase and line voltages are identical in the delta-connected system, that is* $V_L = V_P$.

Inspection of equations 11.4, 11.5 and 11.6 shows that the expressions for the three-phase voltages in rectangular co-ordinates are rather cumbersome and when dealing with more complicated three-phase problems it is convenient to introduce *the operator 'a' which corresponds to a rotation of* 120° *in an anticlockwise direction* so that in equation 11.6

$$V_{ab} = V_p$$
$$V_{bc} = a^2 V_p$$
$$V_{ca} = a V_p$$

Here, however, all quantities will be expressed in rectangular coordinates to avoid the confusion of an additional operator.

With the star-connection a four-wire system is possible, whereas only three wires are available with the delta connection.

At this stage we are concerned only with problems in which the generated voltages are equal in magnitude and spaced by 120°. The supply is known as a symmetrical supply and it is advisable to use these three voltages as the starting point in the solution of three-phase circuit problems.

11.4 BALANCED THREE-PHASE LOADS

The purpose of the generator is to provide power for use in loads connected to the system and the remainder of this section of the work is concerned with the calculation of voltages, currents and power associated with the load and methods of measuring the power dissipated in the load.

The load may be connected either in the star connection or the delta-connection. *When the impedances in all three phases are identical the load is said to be balanced.*

11.4.1 Balanced Star-Connected Load

Figure 11.4a shows a balanced star-connected load having an inductive impedance of magnitude $|Z|$ and phase angle ϕ in each phase.

The common point s to which the impedances forming the load are connected is known as the star point of the load. In a four-wire system the star point of the load is connected to the neutral point of the generator and it is for this reason that the current flowing in the connection to the star point in figure 11.4a is designated I_n.

The phasor diagram for the balanced star-connected three-phase load is shown in figure 11.4b. The diagram is constructed by starting with the phase voltages V_{as},

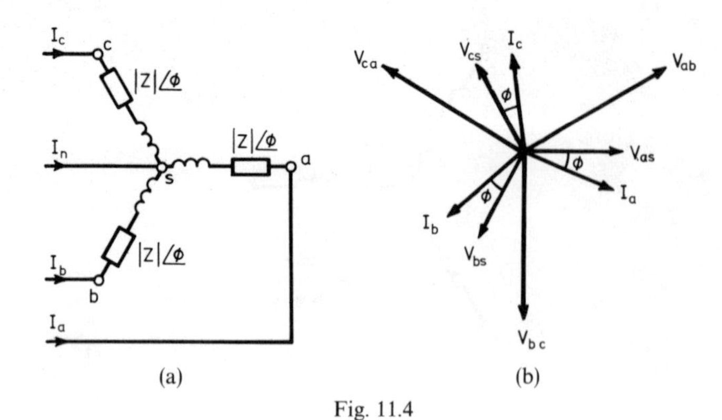

Fig. 11.4

V_{bs} and V_{cs} which, in this case, are the same as the voltages V_{an}, V_{bn} and V_{cn} on the phasor diagram for the star-connected generator (figure 11.2). From the phase voltages, the line voltages V_{ab}, V_{bc} and V_{ca} can be determined using equation 11.1.

The current in each impedance is given by

$$\left.\begin{aligned} I_a &= \frac{V_{as}}{Z} \\ I_b &= \frac{V_{bs}}{Z} \\ I_c &= \frac{V_{cs}}{Z} \end{aligned}\right\} \quad (11.7)$$

It is necessary for all the quantities in equation 11.7 to be expressed in complex form. Referring to figures 11.4a and b and substituting for Z and the voltages we have

$$\left.\begin{aligned} I_a &= \frac{V_P}{|Z|} \angle{-\phi} \\ I_b &= \frac{V_P}{|Z|} \angle{-(120^\circ + \phi)} \\ I_c &= \frac{V_P}{|Z|} \angle{-(240^\circ + \phi)} \end{aligned}\right\} \quad (11.8)$$

If Kirchhoff's Current Law is applied at the star point one obtains

$$I_a + I_b + I_c + I_n = 0$$

but from equation 11.7

$$(I_a + I_b + I_c) = \frac{1}{Z}[V_{as} + V_{bs} + V_{cs}]$$

and since s is connected to n,

$$V_{as} = V_{an}, \; V_{bs} = V_{bn} \quad \text{and} \quad V_{cs} = V_{cn};$$

But it has already been shown that

$$(V_{an} + V_{bn} + V_{cn}) = 0$$

hence

$$(V_{as} + V_{bs} + V_{cs}) = 0$$

from which it follows that

$$(\boldsymbol{I}_a + \boldsymbol{I}_b + \boldsymbol{I}_c) = 0$$

in which case $\boldsymbol{I}_n = 0$.

It is seen therefore that *in a* **balanced** *star-connected load the current in the neutral conductor is zero.*

It is apparent that the line current is the same as the phase current and that the magnitude of all these currents is the same, that is

† $$|\boldsymbol{I}_a| = |\boldsymbol{I}_b| = |\boldsymbol{I}_c| = I_L = I_P \quad (11.9)$$

It has already been shown in equation 11.3 that for this connection

† $$|\boldsymbol{V}_{ab}| = |\boldsymbol{V}_{bc}| = |\boldsymbol{V}_{ca}| = V_L = \sqrt{3}\, V_p \quad (11.10)$$

11.4.2 Balanced Delta-Connected Load

When the three impedances $|\boldsymbol{Z}|\angle\phi$ are delta-connected as shown in figure 11.5a the line voltage is the same as the phase voltage giving

† $$|\boldsymbol{V}_{ab}| = |\boldsymbol{V}_{bc}| = |\boldsymbol{V}_{ca}| = V_p = V_L \quad (11.11)$$

The phasor diagram for the balanced delta-connected three-phase load is shown in figure 11.5b. The diagram is constructed by starting with the line voltages $\boldsymbol{V}_{ab}$, $\boldsymbol{V}_{bc}$ and $\boldsymbol{V}_{ca}$ which are also the phase voltages.

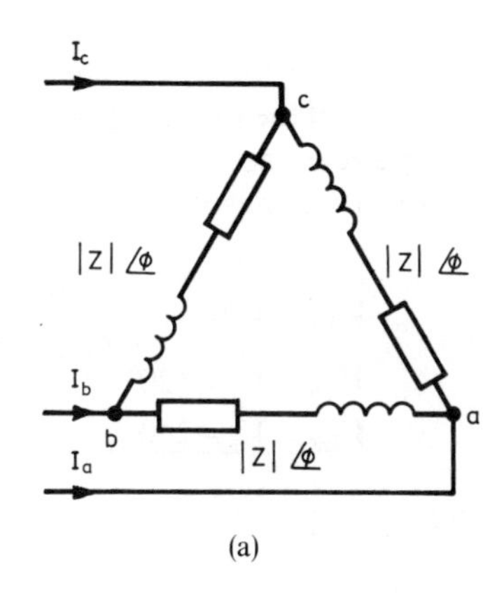

(a)

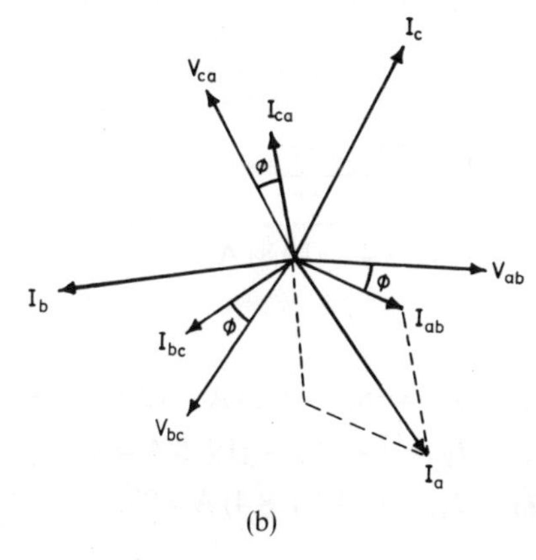

(b)

Fig. 11.5

The current in each impedance is given by

$$\left.\begin{aligned} \boldsymbol{I}_{ab} &= \frac{\boldsymbol{V}_{ab}}{\boldsymbol{Z}} \\ \boldsymbol{I}_{bc} &= \frac{\boldsymbol{V}_{bc}}{\boldsymbol{Z}} \\ \boldsymbol{I}_{ca} &= \frac{\boldsymbol{V}_{ca}}{\boldsymbol{Z}} \end{aligned}\right\} \quad (11.12)$$

It is necessary for all the quantities in equation 11.12 to be expressed in complex form so that

$$\left.\begin{aligned} \boldsymbol{I}_{ab} &= \frac{V_L}{|\boldsymbol{Z}|}\angle{-\phi} \\ \boldsymbol{I}_{bc} &= \frac{V_L}{|\boldsymbol{Z}|}\angle{-(120^\circ + \phi)} \\ \boldsymbol{I}_{ca} &= \frac{V_L}{|\boldsymbol{Z}|}\angle{-(240^\circ + \phi)} \end{aligned}\right\} \quad (11.13)$$

The line currents are given by

$$\left.\begin{aligned} \boldsymbol{I}_a &= \boldsymbol{I}_{ab} - \boldsymbol{I}_{ca} \\ \boldsymbol{I}_b &= \boldsymbol{I}_{bc} - \boldsymbol{I}_{ab} \\ \boldsymbol{I}_c &= \boldsymbol{I}_{ca} - \boldsymbol{I}_{bc} \end{aligned}\right\} \quad (11.14)$$

From the geometry of figure 11.5b it can be seen that $\boldsymbol{I}_a$, $\boldsymbol{I}_b$ and $\boldsymbol{I}_c$ are 120° apart and that

† $$|\boldsymbol{I}_a| = |\boldsymbol{I}_b| = |\boldsymbol{I}_c| = I_L = \sqrt{3}\, I_p \quad (11.15)$$

11.4.3 Equivalence of Star-Connected and Delta-Connected Balanced Loads

The star-mesh transformation was developed in section 2.11 and the results given in equations 2.35 and 2.39. In the star-connected network of figure 2.22a the resistors R_1, R_2 and R_3 are replaced by equal complex impedances $\boldsymbol{Z}_s$, and putting $R_1 = R_2 = R_3 = \boldsymbol{Z}_s$ in equation 2.39 gives the equivalent delta-connected impedances $\boldsymbol{Z}_D = 3\boldsymbol{Z}_S$, resulting in the equivalent circuits shown in figure 11.6. Because the two circuits are equivalent they will dissipate the same amount of power.

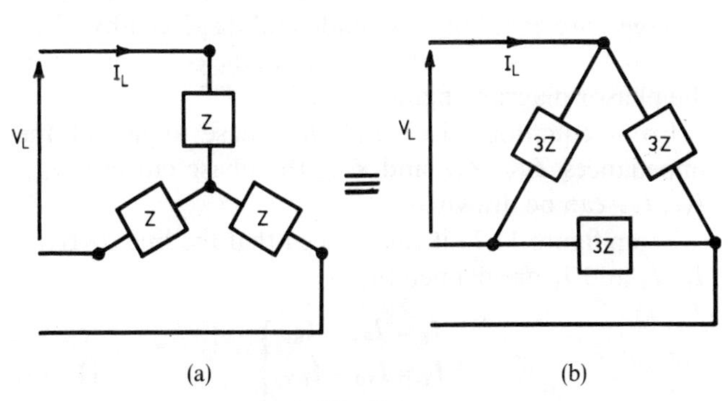

(a) (b)

Fig. 11.6

11.5 UNBALANCED THREE-PHASE LOADS

Under normal operating conditions the power systems engineer is able to maintain a fairly good balance between the loads on the three phases of large three-phase distribution systems. It is likely however that the loads on individual feeders may be unbalanced in which case the circuit relationships discussed in the previous sections do not apply. The power engineer represents the unbalanced three-phase system by a combination of three sets of components which themselves form three balanced systems; this technique is known as *Symmetrical Component analysis.* It is however possible to deal with many unbalanced three-phase circuits by the direct application of Kirchhoff's Laws and, although the method can be rather tedious, it will be used here. It is usually advisable to construct a phasor diagram as the solution of the problem proceeds.

11.5.1 Unbalanced Delta-Connected Load

An unbalanced delta-connected load is shown in figure 11.7a. The impedances are defined by

$$\left.\begin{aligned} \boldsymbol{Z}_{RY} &= Z_1 \angle\phi_1 \\ \boldsymbol{Z}_{YB} &= Z_2 \angle\phi_2 \\ \boldsymbol{Z}_{BR} &= Z_3 \angle\phi_3 \end{aligned}\right\} \qquad (11.16)$$

and the phase sequence is RYB.

Because the load is unbalanced the currents in the three phases, and therefore the line currents, are not equal in magnitude. The phase angle between the phase voltage and the phase current is determined by the load impedance connected in that phase.

The magnitudes of the phase currents are given by

$$\left.\begin{aligned} |\boldsymbol{I}_{RY}| &= \frac{|\boldsymbol{V}_{RY}|}{Z_1} \\ |\boldsymbol{I}_{YB}| &= \frac{|\boldsymbol{V}_{YB}|}{Z_2} \\ |\boldsymbol{I}_{BR}| &= \frac{|\boldsymbol{V}_{BR}|}{Z_3} \end{aligned}\right\} \qquad (11.17)$$

The line voltages, which are identical with the phase voltages, are equal in magnitude and displaced by 120°, and are taken as the starting point in the construction of the phasor diagram, figure 11.7b.

From equation 11.17 and the phase angles of the impedances $\boldsymbol{Z}_{RY}$, $\boldsymbol{Z}_{YB}$ and $\boldsymbol{Z}_{BR}$, the phase currents $\boldsymbol{I}_{RY}$, $\boldsymbol{I}_{YB}$, $\boldsymbol{I}_{BR}$ can be drawn.

From figure 11.7a it can be seen that the line currents $\boldsymbol{I}_R$, $\boldsymbol{I}_Y$ and $\boldsymbol{I}_B$ are defined by

$$\left.\begin{aligned} \boldsymbol{I}_R &= \boldsymbol{I}_{RY} - \boldsymbol{I}_{BR} \\ \boldsymbol{I}_Y &= \boldsymbol{I}_{YB} - \boldsymbol{I}_{RY} \\ \boldsymbol{I}_B &= \boldsymbol{I}_{BR} - \mathrm{I}_{YB} \end{aligned}\right\} \qquad (11.18)$$

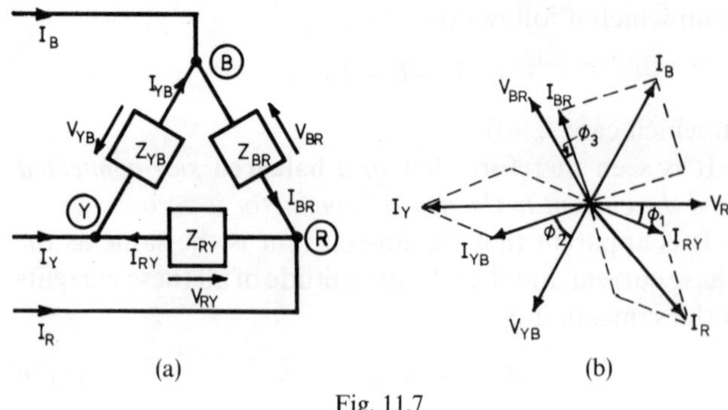

Fig. 11.7

The currents in equation 11.18 *must be expressed in complex form.*

Application of Kirchhoff's Current Law shows that even though the load is unbalanced

† $$\boldsymbol{I}_R + \boldsymbol{I}_Y + \boldsymbol{I}_B = 0$$

Example

The currents in the RY, YB and BR branches of a delta-connected load are respectively 15 A at power factor 0.7 leading, 10 A at unity power factor and 20 A at power factor 0.8 lagging. Determine the current in each line. The phase sequence is RYB.

Solution

The circuit diagram of the load is shown in figure 11.8a.

Taking $\boldsymbol{V}_{RY}$ as the reference, the line (=phase) voltages can be drawn on the phasor diagram and may be expressed as

$$\begin{aligned} \boldsymbol{V}_{RY} &= V\angle 0^\circ \\ \boldsymbol{V}_{YB} &= V\angle -120^\circ \\ \boldsymbol{V}_{BR} &= V\angle -240^\circ \end{aligned}$$

The phase currents are:

$$\begin{aligned} \boldsymbol{I}_{RY} &= 15\angle 45^\circ = (10.6 + \mathrm{j}10.6)\ \mathrm{A} \\ \boldsymbol{I}_{YB} &= 10\angle 0^\circ . 1\angle -120^\circ \\ &= 10\angle -120^\circ = (-5 - \mathrm{j}8.66)\ \mathrm{A} \\ \boldsymbol{I}_{BR} &= 20\angle -37^\circ . 1\angle -240^\circ \\ &= 20\angle -277^\circ = 20\angle 83^\circ \\ &= (2.4 + \mathrm{j}19.8)\ \mathrm{A} \end{aligned}$$

Now

$$\begin{aligned} \boldsymbol{I}_R &= \boldsymbol{I}_{RY} - \boldsymbol{I}_{BR} = (8.2 - \mathrm{j}9.2)\ \mathrm{A} = 12.3\angle -48^\circ\ \mathrm{A} \\ \boldsymbol{I}_Y &= \boldsymbol{I}_{YB} - \boldsymbol{I}_{RY} = (-15.6 - \mathrm{j}19.2)\ \mathrm{A} = 24.8\angle -129^\circ\ \mathrm{A} \\ \boldsymbol{I}_B &= \boldsymbol{I}_{BR} - \boldsymbol{I}_{YB} = (7.4 + \mathrm{j}28.4)\ \mathrm{A} = 29.4\angle 75^\circ\ \mathrm{A} \end{aligned}$$

[Check $\boldsymbol{I}_R + \boldsymbol{I}_Y + \boldsymbol{I}_B = 0$]

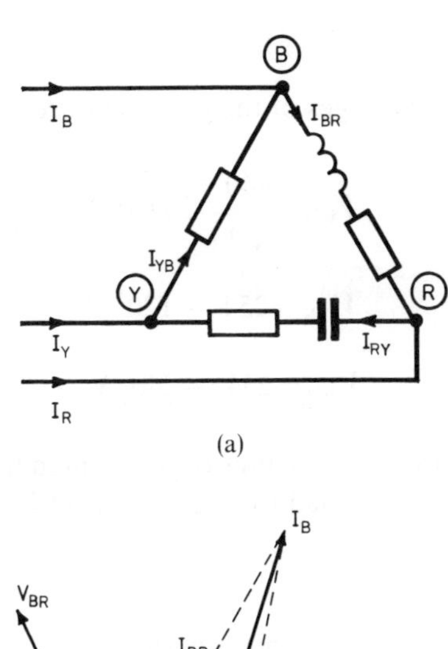

(a)

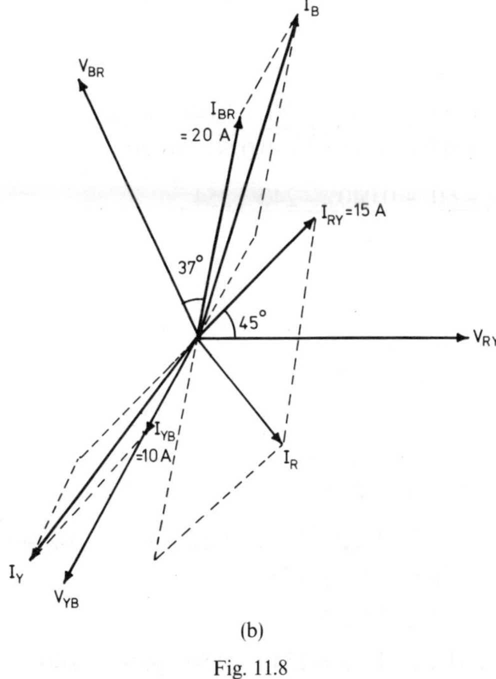

(b)

Fig. 11.8

11.5.2 Unbalanced Star-Connected Load

Whereas the delta-connected three-phase load is connected to the source by three wires, the star-connected three-phase load may form part of either a three-wire or four-wire system, depending upon whether or not there is a neutral connection.

The following general points should be noted

(i) The phase voltages are unequal in magnitude and are not spaced 120° apart on the phasor diagram.

(ii) In a four-wire system a current flows in the neutral conductor and its value is given by

$$\boldsymbol{I}_N = -(\boldsymbol{I}_R + \boldsymbol{I}_Y + \boldsymbol{I}_B) \tag{11.19}$$

(iii) The star point S of the load is not at the same potential as the neutral point in a three-wire system.

An expression for the voltage between the star point of the load and the neutral point of the system will now be derived.

Figure 11.9a represents a star-connected unbalanced load fed from a symmetrical star-connected source. It is assumed that the lines connecting the source to the load are loss-free, except that the neutral conductor has an impedance $\boldsymbol{Z}_N$ ($=\infty$ for a three-wire system).

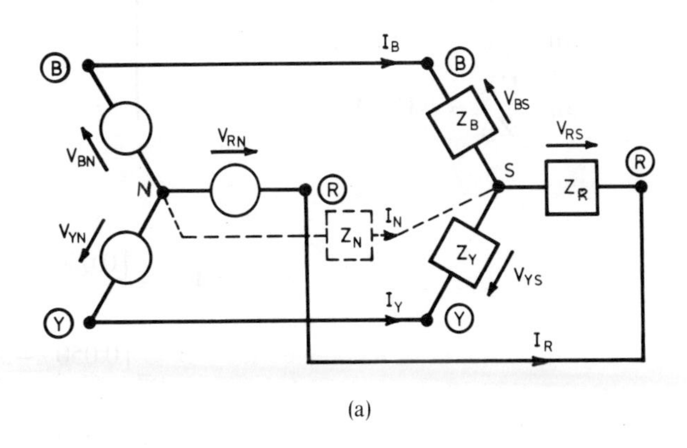

(a)

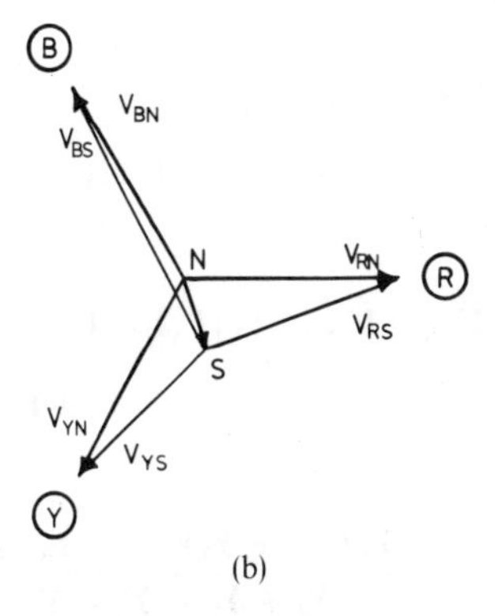

(b)

Fig. 11.9

For the generator we have

$$\boldsymbol{V}_{RN} + \boldsymbol{V}_{YN} + \boldsymbol{V}_{BN} = 0 \tag{11.20}$$

The voltages are shown on the phasor diagram of figure 11.9b.

In general the star point of the load is not at the same potential as the neutral point, but because there are no voltage drops in the R, Y and B lines the extremities of the source and load voltages will be coincident as shown in the phasor diagram.

From the diagram of Figure 11.9b

$$\left.\begin{aligned} \boldsymbol{V}_{RS} &= \boldsymbol{V}_{RN} - \boldsymbol{V}_{SN} \\ \boldsymbol{V}_{YS} &= \boldsymbol{V}_{YN} - \boldsymbol{V}_{SN} \\ \boldsymbol{V}_{BS} &= \boldsymbol{V}_{BN} - \boldsymbol{V}_{SN} \end{aligned}\right\} \tag{11.21}$$

But

$$\left.\begin{aligned} I_R &= \frac{V_{RS}}{Z_R} = V_{RS}\,Y_R = Y_R(V_{RN} - V_{SN}) \\ I_Y &= \frac{V_{YS}}{Z_Y} = V_{YS}\,Y_Y = Y_Y(V_{YN} - V_{SN}) \\ I_B &= \frac{V_{BS}}{Z_B} = V_{BS}\,Y_B = Y_B(V_{BN} - V_{SN}) \\ &\text{and} \\ I_N &= \frac{V_{NS}}{Z_N} = -V_{SN}\,Y_N \end{aligned}\right\} \quad (11.22)$$

By Kirchhoff's Current Law

$$I_N + I_R + I_Y + I_B = 0$$

Hence

$$-V_{SN}Y_N + Y_R(V_{RN} - V_{SN}) + Y_Y(V_{YN} - V_{SN}) + Y_B(V_{BN} - V_{SN}) = 0$$

giving

$$V_{SN} = \frac{Y_R V_{RN} + Y_Y V_{YN} + Y_B V_{BN}}{Y_R + Y_Y + Y_B + Y_N} \quad (11.23)$$

V_{SN} having been determined, it is possible to calculate the phase voltages and currents from equations 11.21 and 11.22.

The same method can be used for a star-connected load without a neutral conductor by putting $I_N = 0$ and $Y_N = 0$.

Example

A star-connected generator with earthed neutral produces a symmetrical three-phase supply with a line voltage of 440 V. It is connected to an unbalanced three-wire star-connected load having impedances

$$Z_R = 20\,\underline{/30^\circ}\ \Omega,\ Z_Y = 30\,\underline{/-60^\circ}\ \Omega \text{ and } Z_B = 25\,\underline{/0^\circ}\ \Omega.$$

The phase sequence is RYB.

Calculate the voltage between the star point of the load and earth, the line currents and the voltage across each load impedance.

Solution

The phase voltages of the generator are

$$V_{RN} = \frac{440}{\sqrt{3}} = 254\,\underline{/0^\circ}\ \text{V}$$

$$V_{YN} = 254\,\underline{/-120^\circ}\ \text{V}$$

$$V_{BN} = 254\,\underline{/-240^\circ}\ \text{V}$$

These are shown on the phasor diagram in figure 11.10b. V_{SN} can be determined from equation 11.23.

$$V_{SN} = \frac{[0.050\,\underline{/-30^\circ}\,.\,1\,\underline{/0^\circ} + 0.033\,\underline{/60^\circ}\,.\,1\,\underline{/-120^\circ} + 0.040\,\underline{/0^\circ}\,.\,1\,\underline{/-240^\circ}]\,254}{(0.043 - j0.025) + (0.0165 + j0.028) + 0.040}\ \text{V}$$

$$= \frac{[0.050\,\underline{/-30^\circ} + 0.033\,\underline{/-60^\circ} + 0.040\,\underline{/-240^\circ}]\,254}{0.1}\ \text{V}$$

$$= 25.4\,(4 - j2)\ \text{V} = 112\,\underline{/-26^\circ}\ \text{V}$$

From equation 11.21

$$\begin{aligned} V_{RS} &= (V_{RN} - V_{SN}) = 254\,(1 - 0.4 + j0.2) \\ &= 254\,(0.6 + j0.2) \\ &= 161\,\underline{/18^\circ}\ \text{V} \end{aligned}$$

$$\begin{aligned} V_{YS} &= (V_{YN} - V_{SN}) = 254\,(-0.50 - j0.87 - 0.40 + j0.20) \\ &= 254\,(-0.9 - j0.67) \\ &= 285\,\underline{/-143^\circ}\ \text{V} \end{aligned}$$

$$\begin{aligned} V_{BS} &= (V_{BN} - V_{SN}) = 254\,(-0.50 + j0.87 - 0.40 + j0.20) \\ &= 254\,(-0.9 + j1.07) \\ &= 355\,\underline{/130^\circ}\ \text{V} \end{aligned}$$

The line currents I_R, I_Y and I_B are determined from equation 11.22

$$I_R = V_{RS}\,Y_R = (161\,\underline{/18^\circ}\,.\,0{,}050\,\underline{/-30^\circ}) = 8.1\,\underline{/-12^\circ}\ \text{A}$$

$$I_Y = V_{YS}\,Y_Y = (285\,\underline{/-143^\circ}\,.\,0.033\,\underline{/60^\circ}) = 9.4\,\underline{/-83^\circ}\ \text{A}$$

$$I_B = V_{BS}\,Y_B = (355\,\underline{/130^\circ}\,.\,0.040\,\underline{/0^\circ}) = 14.2\,\underline{/130^\circ}\ \text{A}$$

11.6 THE MEASUREMENT OF POWER IN THREE-PHASE CIRCUITS

The total power dissipated in a three-phase load is

$$P = (V_R I_R \cos\phi_R + V_Y I_Y \cos\phi_Y + V_B I_B \cos\phi_B)$$

where V, I and ϕ have the significance indicated in figure 11.11.

For a *balanced* load it follows that

$$P = 3\,VI\cos\phi$$

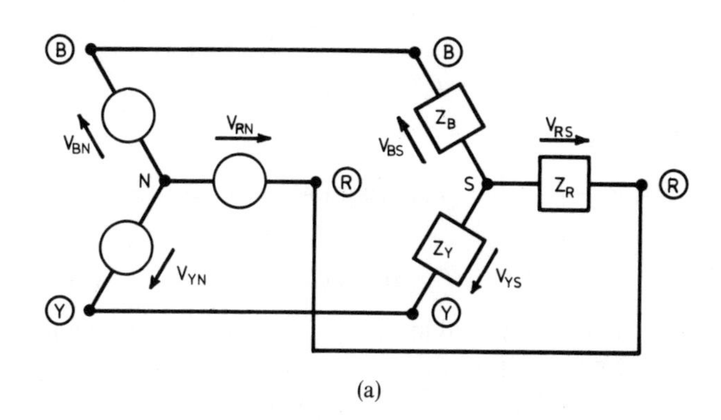

(a)

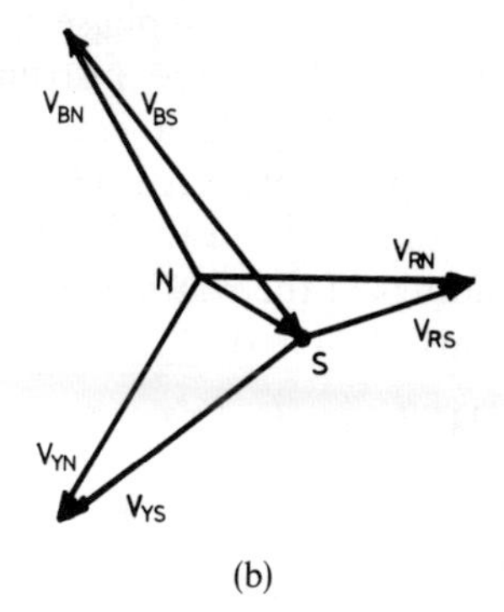

(b)

Fig. 11.10

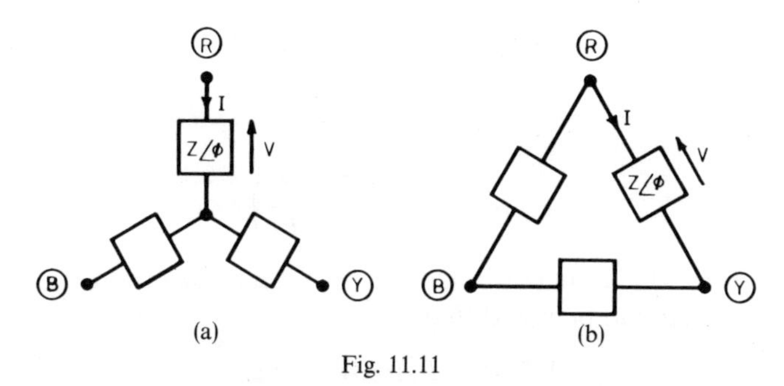

(a) (b)

Fig. 11.11

In the delta connection $V=V_L=V_P$ and $I=I_P=I_L/\sqrt{3}$

Hence

$$P=3V_PI_P\cos\phi$$
$$=\sqrt{3}\,V_LI_L\cos\phi$$

and for the star connection

$$V=V_P=\frac{V_L}{\sqrt{3}} \quad \text{and} \quad I=I_P=I_L$$

Hence

$$P=3V_PI_P\cos\phi$$
$$=\sqrt{3}\,V_LI_L\cos\phi$$

For a balanced load therefore it is possible to measure the total power dissipated in the load by using a single wattmeter in one phase and multiplying the reading by three.

For an unbalanced load one wattmeter per phase can be used, the total power dissipated in the load being the sum of the three wattmeter readings. The method of connection for a four-wire system is shown in figure 11.12.

For a three-wire system (star- or delta-connected) it is possible to measure the power in the load by means of two-wattmeters.

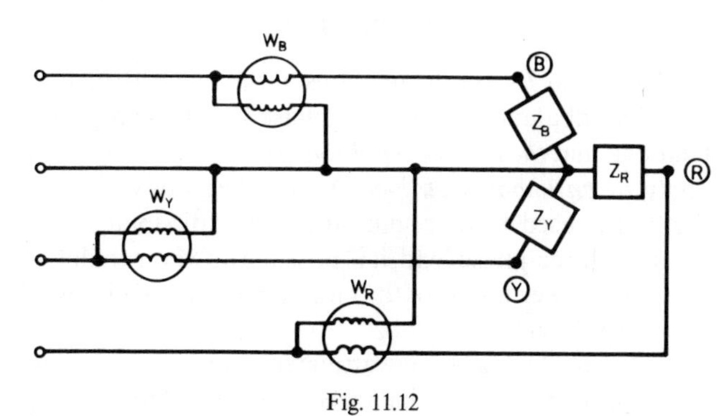

Fig. 11.12

11.6.1 The Two-Wattmeter Method of Three-Phase Power Measurement

Figure 11.13 shows an unbalanced, three-phase *three-wire load* with two wattmeters W_1 and W_2 connected to measure the total power dissipated in the load.

The instantaneous power dissipated in the load is

$$p=v_Ri_R+v_Yi_Y+v_Bi_B$$

But, because the system is a three-wire system

$$i_R+i_Y+i_B=0$$

Hence

$$i_R=-(i_Y+i_B)$$

and

$$p=-v_R(i_Y+i_B)+v_Yi_Y+v_Bi_B$$
$$=i_B(v_B-v_R)+i_Y(v_Y-v_R)$$
$$=i_Bv_{BR}+i_Yv_{YR}$$

Now i_Bv_{BR} is the instantaneous power p_1 measured by wattmeter W_1 and i_Yv_{YR} is the instantaneous power p_2 measured by wattmeter W_2 so that $p=p_1+p_2$.

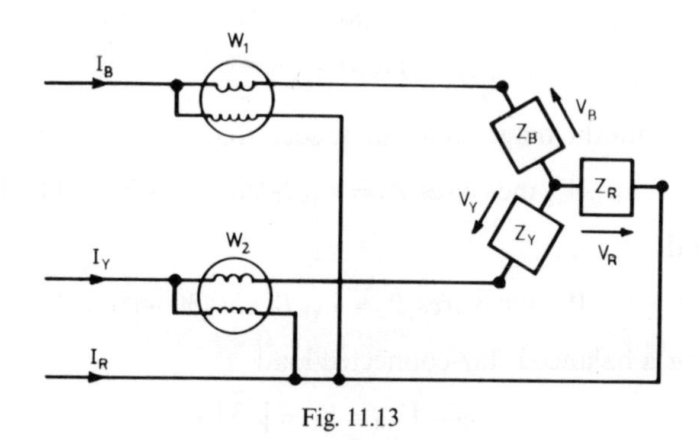

Fig. 11.13

The indication of a wattmeter is proportional to

$$\frac{1}{T}\int_0^T vi\mathrm{d}t = \frac{1}{T}\int_0^T p\,\mathrm{d}t$$

which is the average power. Hence the average power P dissipated in the load is

$$P = P_1 + P_2$$

where P_1 and P_2 are the readings of the two wattmeters.

In an unbalanced load each phase has its own power factor so that *the normal definition of power factor does not apply to an unbalanced load.* When the two-wattmeter method is used to determine the power dissipated in a *balanced* three-phase load, it is possible however to determine the power factor of the circuit from the readings of the wattmeters.

In figure 11.14a two wattmeters are connected to measure the power in a balanced three-wire load having a phase angle ϕ; the phasor diagram is given in figure 11.14b.

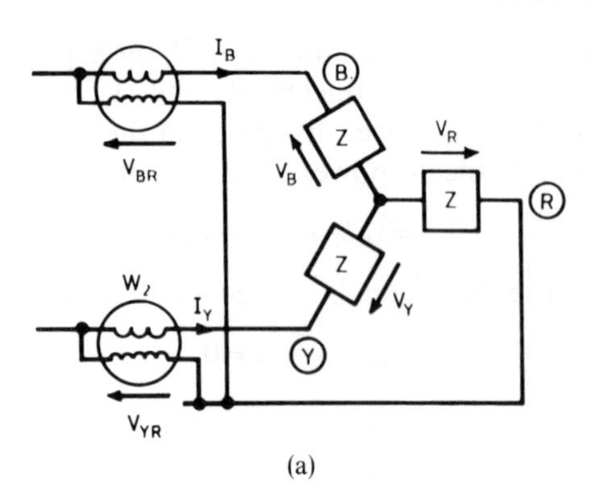

(a)

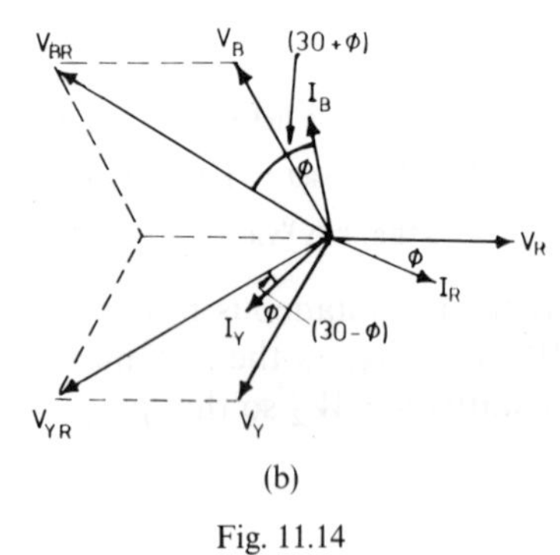

(b)

Fig. 11.14

From the diagram it can be seen that

$$W_1 \text{ measures } P_1 = V_{BR} I_B \cos(30+\phi) \tag{11.24}$$

and

$$W_2 \text{ measures } P_2 = V_{YR} I_Y \cos(30-\phi) \tag{11.25}$$

For a balanced star-connected load

$$V_{BR} = V_{YR} = V_L = \sqrt{3}\,V_P$$

and

$$I_B = I_Y = I_L = I_P$$

Therefore

$$P = P_1 + P_2 = \sqrt{3}\,.\,V_p I_p\,[\cos(30^\circ+\phi) - \cos(30-\phi)]$$

† $$P = 3V_p I_p \cos\phi \tag{11.26}$$

(for a delta-connected load $V_L = V_p$ and $I_L = \sqrt{3}I_p$ giving the same overall result).

It can be seen from the phasor diagram that if either of the wattmeter currents differs in phase by more than 90° from its associated voltage the instrument will read backwards and its voltage coil connections must be reversed; thus if ϕ is greater than 60°, W_1 reads backwards and the total power in the load is the difference between the readings of the wattmeters.

From equations 11.24 and 11.25

$$P_1 + P_2 = 3V_p I_p \cos\phi$$

$$P_1 - P_2 = \sqrt{3}\,V_p I_p\,[\cos(30+\phi) - \cos(30-\phi)]$$

$$= -\sqrt{3}\,V_p I_p \sin\phi$$

Hence

$$\frac{P_1 - P_2}{P_1 + P_2} = \frac{-\tan\phi}{\sqrt{3}}$$

or

$$\tan\phi = \sqrt{3}\left(\frac{P_2 - P_1}{P_2 + P_1}\right) \tag{11.27}$$

from which the power factor $\cos\phi$ can be determined.

It should be noted that

† $$\sqrt{3}(P_2 - P_1) = 3V_p I_p \sin\phi$$

which is known as the *reactive power* in the load.

PROBLEMS

11.1. Determine the line currents, the voltage across each impedance and the power dissipated in an unbalanced star-connected load supplied from a symmetrical three-phase, three wire, 440 V system. The branch impedances of the load are $\mathbf{Z}_R = 20\angle 45^\circ\ \Omega$, $\mathbf{Z}_Y = 10\angle -30^\circ\ \Omega$, $\mathbf{Z}_B = 20\angle 30^\circ\ \Omega$.

Draw a phasor diagram showing all voltages and currents. The phase sequence is RYB.

11.2. If the impedances in problem 11.1 are now connected in mesh so that $\mathbf{Z}_{RY} = 20\angle 45^\circ\ \Omega$, $\mathbf{Z}_{YB} = 10\angle -30^\circ\ \Omega$, $\mathbf{Z}_{BR} = 20\angle 30^\circ\ \Omega$, determine the line and phase currents and the power dissipated.

Draw a phasor diagram.

11.3. In the circuit of figure Q.3, $R_1 = 3\Omega$, $R_2 = 3\Omega$, $X_L = 3\Omega$, $X_C = 4\Omega$; the line voltage is 440 V and the phase sequence RYB. Calculate the current in each line and draw a phasor diagram showing the line and phase voltages and currents.

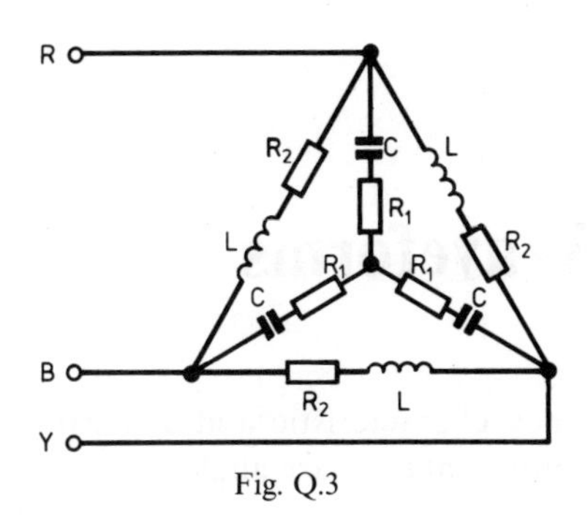

Fig. Q.3

11.4. Two wattmeters are connected as shown in figure Q.4 to measure the power dissipated in a balanced, star-connected inductive load. If $|E_R| = |E_Y| = |E_B| = 250$ V, $R = 60\ \Omega$, $X_L = 80\ \Omega$ and the phase sequence is RYB determine, with the aid of a phasor diagram, the readings of the wattmeters. For what value of X_L would one of the wattmeters

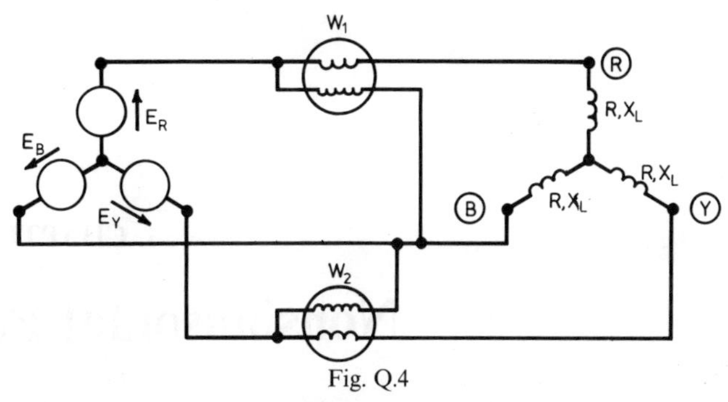

Fig. Q.4

indicate zero power and what would be the reading of the other wattmeter under these circumstances?

11.5. A 440 V balanced, three-phase system supplies a mesh-connected induction motor taking 6 kW at a lagging power factor of 0.8. In addition a 4 kW unity power factor load is connected between the R and B lines. The total power is measured by two wattmeters whose current coils are connected in the R and Y lines. The phase sequence is RYB. Determine, graphically or otherwise, the readings of the two wattmeters.

CHAPTER TWELVE

Nonsinusoidal Periodic Waveforms

12.1 THE FOURIER SERIES

Nonsinusoidal periodic waves encountered in electrical engineering can be represented by the sum of a number of sine and/or cosine terms together with, in some instances, a constant term. The Fourier Series mathematical expression for a nonsinusoidal periodic wave is of the form

$$f(t)=\frac{a_0}{2}+a_1 \cos \omega t+a_2 \cos 2\omega t+\cdots+a_n \cos n\omega t$$
$$+b_1 \sin \omega t+b_2 \sin 2\omega t+\cdots+b_n \sin n\omega t \qquad (12.1)$$

where

$$\left.\begin{aligned} a_n &=\frac{1}{\pi}\int_0^{2\pi} f(t)\,.\cos n\omega t\,.\,d(\omega t) \\ b_n &=\frac{1}{\pi}\int_0^{2\pi} f(t)\,.\sin n\omega t\,.\,d(\omega t) \end{aligned}\right\} \qquad (12.2)$$

The value of

$$\frac{a_0}{2}=\frac{1}{2\pi}\int_0^{2\pi} f(t)\,.\,d(\omega t) \qquad (12.3)$$

is known as *the average or d.c. value* of the wave.

Equation 12.1 can also be written in the form

$$f(t)=\frac{a_0}{2}+c_1 \cos(\omega t-\phi_1)+c_2 \cos(2\omega t-\phi_2)$$
$$+\cdots+c_n \cos(n\omega t+\phi_n) \qquad (12.4)$$

where

$$c_n=(a_n{}^2+b_n{}^2)^{1/2} \text{ and } \phi_n=\tan^{-1}\left(\frac{b_n}{a_n}\right) \qquad (12.5)$$

$c_1 \cos(\omega t-\phi_1)$ is known as the *fundamental* component and $c_n \cos(n\omega t-\phi_n)$ is the *nth harmonic* component of the wave.

It should be noted that if a nonsinusoidal waveform is shifted by an angle ϕ, along the ωt axis, its fundamental is shifted by ϕ and its nth harmonic component is shifted by $n\phi$. This fact is of importance when considering the characteristics of networks through which nonsinusoidal signals are transmitted. If the signal is to pass undistorted, the network must have a horizontal amplitude/frequency characteristic and a linear (though not necessarily horizontal) phase angle/frequency characteristic.

Equation 12.4 is frequently expressed in the form

$$f(t)=\frac{a_0}{2}+\sum_{n=1}^{n=\infty} c_n \cos(n\omega t-\phi_n) \qquad (12.6)$$

The Fourier series can also be expressed in exponential form.

Putting the sine and cosine terms of equation 12.1 in exponential form gives

$$f(t)=\frac{a_0}{2}+\sum_{n=1}^{\infty}\left[a_n\left\{\frac{e^{jn\omega t}+e^{-jn\omega t}}{2}\right\}-jb_n\left\{\frac{e^{jn\omega t}-e^{-jn\omega t}}{2}\right\}\right]$$
$$=\frac{a_0}{2}+\sum_{n=1}^{\infty}\left[\left(\frac{a_n-jb_n}{2}\right)e^{jn\omega t}+\left(\frac{a_n+jb_n}{2}\right)e^{-jn\omega t}\right] \qquad (12.7)$$

It can be seen from equation 12.2 that if the sign of n is changed, the sign of a_n is unchanged but that of b_n changes. Hence equation 12.7 can be written

$$f(t)=\frac{a_0}{2}+\sum_{n=1}^{\infty}\left(\frac{a_n-jb_n}{2}\right)e^{jn\omega t}+\sum_{n=-1}^{-\infty}\left(\frac{a_n-jb_n}{2}\right)e^{jn\omega t}$$
$$=\sum_{n=-\infty}^{\infty}\left(\frac{a_n-jb_n}{2}\right)e^{jn\omega t}$$
$$=\sum_{n=-\infty}^{\infty} C_n\, e^{jn\omega t} \qquad (12.8)$$

which is the exponential form of the Fourier Series. for $n=0$, $f(t)=C_0$ which corresponds to the term $a_0/2$ in the trigonometric form of the Fourier Series.

When a nonsinusoidal periodic wave is applied to a linear circuit each of the sinusoidal terms can be treated separately by the standard techniques of circuit analysis; the individual responses are then combined by Superposition to give the resultant response.

12.2 A GRAPHICAL METHOD OF ANALYSIS OF A NONSINUSOIDAL PERIODIC WAVEFORM

The function to be analyzed into its harmonics is often available as a trace on an XY recorder chart or as a photograph of the trace on a cathode ray tube. In such cases the Fourier coefficients of equation 12.2 can be evaluated by graphical integration.

The procedure can be explained by considering the nonsinusoidal periodic waveform shown in figure 12.1.

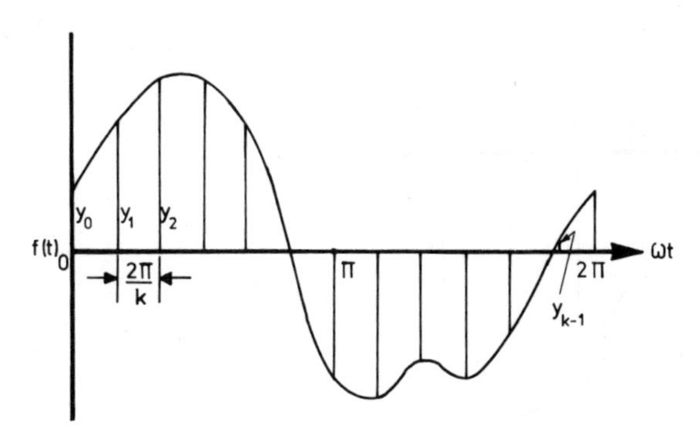

Fig. 12.1

(i) The range $0-2\pi$ is divided so that k ordinates can be drawn at equal intervals of $2\pi/k$. The larger the number of ordinates, the greater the accuracy obtainable. In general, to determine the nth harmonic with reasonable accuracy a value of $k \nless 2(n+1)$ is required.

(ii) The height of each ordinate $y_0, y_1 \ldots y_{k-1}$ is measured.

Then, from equation 12.3

$$\frac{a_0}{2}=\frac{1}{k}\left[y_0+y_1+y_2+\cdots+y_{k-1}\right] \qquad (12.9)$$

and, from equation 12.2

$$a_n = 2\,[\text{Average height of } (f(t)\cos n\omega t) \text{ curve}]$$

$$\doteqdot \frac{2}{k}\left[y_0 \cos 0 + y_1 \cos\left(\frac{n2\pi}{k}\right) + y_2 \cos\left(\frac{n4\pi}{k}\right) + \cdots y_{k-1}\cos\left(\frac{n2\pi(k-1)}{k}\right)\right]$$

$$=\frac{2}{k}\sum_{p=0}^{p=k-1} y_p \cos\left(\frac{np2\pi}{k}\right) \qquad (12.10)$$

Similarly

$$b_n=\frac{2}{k}\sum_{p=0}^{p=k-1} y_p \sin\left(\frac{np2\pi}{k}\right) \qquad (12.11)$$

The method of computing the coefficients is shown in the following example, in which the Fourier Series for the waveform shown in figure 12.2 is obtained, up to and including the third harmonic.

The ordinates are measured at 30° intervals over a range of 0° to 360° (giving $k=12$). a_0 is determined from equation 12.9, a_1, a_2 and a_3 from equation 12.10 and b_1, b_2 and b_3 from equation 12.11. The values are given in Table 12.1 and, using these values, the Fourier Series representing the waveform shown in figure 12.2 is $f(t)=0.5 + 2.5 \sin\theta + 0.71 \cos 2\theta + 0.71 \sin 2\theta + 0.25 \cos 3\theta + 0.43 \sin 3\theta$ which, from equation 12.4 may be written in the form

$$f(t)=0.5+2.5\sin\theta + (0.71^2+0.71^2)^{1/2}\cos\left[2\theta-\tan^{-1}\left(\frac{0.71}{0.71}\right)\right] + (0.25^2+0.43^2)^{1/2}\cos\left[3\theta-\tan^{-1}\left(\frac{0.43}{0.25}\right)\right]$$

$$=0.5+2.5\sin\theta+\cos(2\theta-\pi/4)+0.5\cos(3\theta-\pi/3) \qquad (12.12)$$

$$=0.5+2.5\sin\theta+\sin(2\theta+\pi/4)+0.5\sin(3\theta+\pi/6) \qquad (12.13)$$

12.3 THE RMS VALUE OF A NONSINUSOIDAL PERIODIC WAVEFORM

The r.m.s. value of a sinusoidal waveform has been shown to be

$$\text{r.m.s.}=\left[\frac{1}{T}\int_0^T f^2(t)\,.\,dt\right]^{1/2}$$

Extending this idea to a nonsinusoidal periodic wave of the form

$$v=V_0+V_{m1}\cos(\omega t-\phi_1)+V_{m2}\cos(2\omega t-\phi_2) + \cdots + V_{mn}\cos(n\omega t-\phi_n)$$

gives the r.m.s. value of the wave as

$$v=\left[\frac{1}{T}\int_0^T \{V_0+V_{m1}\cos(\omega t-\phi_1) + \cdots + V_{mn}\cos(n\omega t-\phi_n\}^2\,dt)\right]^{1/2} \qquad (12.14)$$

$$=\left[\frac{1}{T}\int_0^T \{V_0{}^2+V_{m1}^2\cos^2(\omega t-\phi) + \cdots V_{mn}^2\cos^2(n\omega t-\phi_n) + (\text{terms containing the product of two cosine terms of unequal frequencies})\}^2\,dt\right]^{1/2}$$

Now the average value of $\cos^2(\omega t-\phi)$ is $\frac{1}{2}$ and the integral of the products of terms of unlike frequencies over a complete cycle of the lower of the two frequencies is zero, hence the r.m.s. value of v is

$$V=\left(V_0{}^2+\frac{V_{m1}^2}{2}+\frac{V_{m2}^2}{2}+\cdots+\frac{V_{mn}^2}{2}\right)^{1/2} \qquad (12.15)$$

where $V_{m1} \ldots V_{mn}$ are the peak values of the fundamental and harmonic components. If the r.m.s. values of the

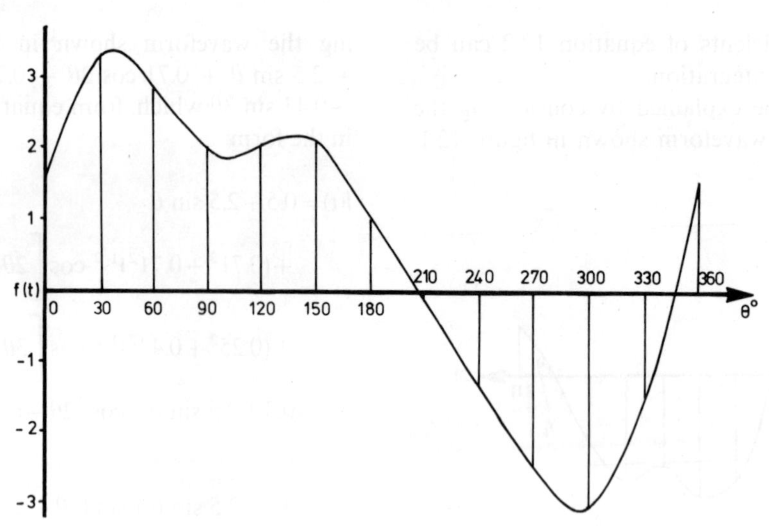

Fig. 12.2

TABLE 12.1

$\theta°$	y	$\cos\theta$	$y\cos\theta$	$\sin\theta$	$y\sin\theta$	$\cos 2\theta$	$y\cos 2\theta$	$\sin 2\theta$	$y\sin 2\theta$	$\cos 3\theta$	$y\cos 3\theta$	$\sin 3\theta$	$y\sin 3\theta$
0	1.46	1	1.46	0	0.00	1	1.46	0	0	1	1.46	0	0
30	3.15	0.866	2.73	0.5	1.57	0.5	1.57	0.866	2.73	0	0	1	3.15
60	2.67	0.5	1.34	0.866	2.31	−0.5	−1.34	0.866	2.32	−1	−2.67	0	0
90	1.86	0	0	1	1.86	−1	−1.86	0	0	0	0	−1	−1.86
120	1.95	−0.5	−0.97	0.866	1.69	−0.5	−0.97	−0.866	−1.69	1	1.95	0	0
150	1.92	−0.866	−1.67	0.5	0.96	0.5	0.96	−0.866	−1.67	0	0	1	1.92
180	0.96	−1.0	−0.96	0	0	1	0.96	0	0	−1	−0.96	0	0
210	−0.22	−0.866	0.19	−0.5	0.11	0.5	−0.11	0.866	−0.19	0	0	−1	0.22
240	−1.16	−0.5	0.58	−0.866	1.00	−0.5	0.58	0.866	−1	1	−1.16	0	0
270	−2.27	0	0	−1.00	2.27	−1	2.27	0	0	0	0	1	−2.27
300	−2.88	0.5	−1.44	−0.866	2.50	−0.5	1.44	−0.866	2.49	−1	2.88	0	0
330	−1.44	0.866	−1.25	−0.5	0.72	0.5	−0.72	−0.866	1.25	0	0	−1	1.44
Sum	6.00		0		14.99		4.24		4.24		1.53		2.60
	$\frac{a_0}{2}=\frac{6}{12}$				$b_1=\frac{2\times 14.99}{12}$		$a_2=\frac{2\times 4.24}{12}$		$b_2=\frac{2\times 4.24}{12}$		$a_3=\frac{2\times 1.53}{12}$		$b_3=\frac{2\times 2.60}{12}$
	$a_0=0.5$		$a_1=0$		$b_1=2.5$		$a_2=0.71$		$b_2=0.71$		$a_3=0.25$		$b_3=0.43$

fundamental and harmonic components are used, equation 12.15 becomes

$$V=(V_0{}^2+V_1{}^2+V_2{}^2+\cdots+V_n{}^2)^{1/2} \qquad (12.16)$$

The r.m.s. value of the waveform analysed in the previous section is therefore

$$\left(0.5^2+\frac{2.5^2}{2}+\frac{1^2}{2}+\frac{0.5^2}{2}\right)^{1/2}=2.0$$

12.4 POWER DUE TO NONSINUSOIDAL VOLTAGES AND CURRENTS

The average power dissipated in a circuit is

$$P=\frac{1}{T}\int_0^T vi\mathrm{d}t$$

For nonsinusoidal periodic waves v and i have the form

$$v=V_0+V_{m1}\cos(\omega t-\phi_1)+\cdots+V_{mn}\cos(n\omega t-\phi_n)$$
$$i=I_0+I_{m1}\cos(\omega t-\theta_1)+\cdots+I_{mn}\cos(n\omega t-\theta_n)$$

Hence the average power is

$$P=\frac{1}{T}\int_0^T [V_0+V_{m1}\cos(\omega t-\phi_1)+\cdots V_{mn}\cos(n\omega t-\phi_n)]$$
$$[I_0+I_{m1}\cos(\omega t-\theta_1)+\cdots+I_{mn}\cos(n\omega t-\theta_n)]\,\mathrm{d}t$$

$$P=\frac{1}{T}\int_0^T [V_0I_0+V_{m1}I_{m1}\cos(\omega t-\phi_1)\cos(\omega t-\theta_1)$$
$$+\cdots V_{mn}I_{mn}\cos(n\omega t-\phi_n)\cos(n\omega t-\theta_n)$$
$$+(\text{terms consisting of the products of terms of unequal frequencies})]\,\mathrm{d}t \qquad (12.17)$$

The integral of the products of terms of unequal frequencies over a complete cycle of the lower of the two frequencies is zero; the products of terms of the same frequency can be evaluated

$$\frac{1}{T}\int_0^T V_{mn}I_{mn}\cos(n\omega t-\phi_n)\cos(n\omega t-\theta_n)\,dt$$

$$=\frac{1}{T}\int_0^T \frac{1}{2}V_{mn}I_{mn}[\cos(\phi_n-\theta_n)-\cos(2n\omega t-\theta_n-\phi_n)]dt$$

$$=\frac{1}{2}V_{mn}I_{mn}\left[\cos(\phi_n-\theta_n)-\frac{1}{T}\int_0^T\cos(2n\omega t-\theta_n-\phi_n)dt\right]$$

$$=\frac{1}{2}V_{mn}I_{mn}\cos(\phi_n-\theta_n)$$

since the average value of $\cos(2n\omega t-\theta_n-\phi_n)$ over a complete cycle is zero.
Hence

$$P=V_0I_0+\tfrac{1}{2}V_{m1}I_{m1}\cos(\phi_1-\theta_1)+\cdots+\tfrac{1}{2}V_{mn}I_{mn}\cos(\phi_n-\theta_n)\qquad(12.18)$$

and if r.m.s. values of voltage and current are used

$$P=V_0I_0+V_1I_1\cos(\phi_1-\theta_1)+\cdots+V_nI_n\cos(\phi_n-\theta_n)\qquad(12.19)$$

It should be noted that no average power results from components of voltage and current of different frequencies.

Example

Determine the power in a circuit in which the voltage and current are

$$v=[5+10\sin(\omega t-30^\circ)+4\sin(2\omega t-40^\circ)]\text{V}$$
$$i=[20-5\cos(\omega t+20^\circ)+15\sin(2\omega t-70^\circ)]\text{ mA}$$

Solution

It is convenient to convert the cosine term of the current wave to a sine term

$$i=[20+5\sin(\omega t-70^\circ)+15\sin(2\omega t-70^\circ)]\text{ mA}$$

Applying equation 12.18, the power in the circuit is

$$P=[(5\times 20\times 10^{-3})+\tfrac{1}{2}(10\times 5\times 10^{-3})\cos 40^\circ+\tfrac{1}{2}(4\times 15\times 10^{-3})\cos 30^\circ]\text{ W}$$
$$=0.100+0.019+0.026)\text{ W}$$
$$=145\text{ mW}$$

12.5 THE EFFECT OF NONSINUSOIDAL PERIODIC WAVEFORMS IN REACTIVE CIRCUITS

12.5.1 Inductive Circuits

An expression will now be derived for the waveform of the current when a nonsinusoidal voltage is applied to an inductor of inductance L.

Let

$$v=V_{m1}\cos(\omega t-\phi_1)+V_{m2}\cos(2\omega t-\phi_2)+\cdots+V_{mn}\cos(n\omega t-\phi_n)\qquad(12.20)$$

The reactance of the inductor at the fundamental frequency is ωL and at the nth harmonic frequency it is $n\omega L$; hence the expression for the current is, by Superposition

$$i=\frac{V_{m1}}{\omega L}\cos(\omega t-\phi_1-\pi/2)+\frac{V_{m2}}{2\omega L}\cos(2\omega t-\phi_2-\pi/2)+\cdots+\frac{V_{mn}}{n\omega L}\cos(n\omega t-\phi_n-\pi/2)\qquad(12.21)$$

From equations 12.20 and 12.21 it is seen that

(1) The harmonics are *less prominent* in the current wave than in the voltage wave; for example the ratio (nth harmonic/fundamental) in the voltage wave is V_{mn}/V_{m1} and in the current wave the corresponding ratio is V_{mn}/nV_{m1}.
(2) The *shape* of the voltage and current waveforms is different due to the fact that each harmonic component has been shifted in phase by $\pi/2$, or one quarter of a cycle at the harmonic frequency, and that the complex wave as a whole has not been shifted $\phi=\pi/2$ along the ωt axis.

If the circuit also contains resistance r in series with the inductance the nth harmonic in the current wave is

$$i_n=\frac{V_{mn}}{[r^2+(n\omega L)^2]^{1/2}}\cos\left[n\omega t-\phi_n-\tan^{-1}\frac{n\omega L}{r}\right]$$

12.5.2 Capacitive Circuits

When the nonsinusoidal periodic voltage waveform defined by equation 12.20 is applied to a capacitor of capacitance C, the expression for the current is

$$i=V_{m1}\omega C\cos(\omega t-\phi_1+\pi/2)+2V_{m2}\omega C\cos(2\omega t-\phi_2+\pi/2)+\cdots+nV_{mn}\omega C\cos(n\omega t-\phi_n+\pi/2)\qquad(12.22)$$

From equations 12.20 and 12.22 it is seen that the harmonics are *more prominent* in the current wave than in the voltage wave; for example, the ratio (nth harmonic/fundamental) in the voltage wave is V_{mn}/V_{m1} and in the current wave the corresponding ratio is nV_{mn}/V_{m1}.

Example

An alternating voltage defined by $v=50\cos(1000t+30^\circ)+20\cos(3000t-60^\circ)V$ is applied to a $2\,\mu$F capacitor. Derive an expression for the current and determine the r.m.s. values of the voltage and current.

Solution

The expression for the current is, from equation 12.22,

$$i = 50.1000.2.10^{-6} \cos(1000t + 30^\circ + 90^\circ)$$
$$+ 3.20.1000.2.10^{-6} \cos(3000t - 60^\circ + 90^\circ) \text{ A}$$
$$= 100 \cos(1000t + 120^\circ) + 120 \cos(3000t + 30^\circ) \text{ mA}$$

The r.m.s. value of the voltage is

$$V = \left(\frac{50^2}{2} + \frac{20^2}{2}\right)^{1/2} = 38 \text{ V}$$

and the r.m.s. value of the current is

$$I = \left(\frac{100^2}{2} + \frac{120^2}{2}\right)^{1/2} = 110 \text{ mA}$$

It should be noted that when dealing with nonsinusoidal waveforms the capacitance cannot be determined from the r.m.s. voltage and current.

12.5.3 Series

When the nonsinusoidal voltage wave defined by equation 12.20 is applied to a circuit consisting of inductance, capacitance and resistance in series, the values of the inductance and capacitance may be such that $n\omega L = 1/n\omega C$. Under these conditions series resonance occurs at the nth harmonic frequency; the impedance at this frequency is small and therefore the amplitude of the nth harmonic in the current wave is large. The nth harmonic component in the current wave is

$$i_n = \frac{V_{mn}}{[r^2 + (n\omega L - 1/n\omega C)^2]^{1/2}} \cos\left(n\omega t - \phi_n - \tan^{-1}\left\{\frac{n\omega L - 1/n\omega C}{r}\right\}\right)$$

and if series resonance occurs at the nth harmonic

$$i_n = \frac{V_{mn}}{r} \cos(n\omega t - \phi_n) \qquad (12.23)$$

If r is small $I_{mn} = V_{mn}/r$ is large, so that large nth harmonic components of voltage may appear across the inductor and capacitor.

Example

A length of cable of capacitance 1000 pF is connected to a radio-frequency voltage generator of e.m.f.

$$v = [2 \sin(2\pi.10^6 t) + 0.5 \sin(4\pi.10^6 t)] \text{ V}$$

and source impedance equivalent to 3 Ω in series with 6.3 μH.

Obtain an expression for the voltage across the cable.

Solution

Reactance of cable at $\omega = 2\pi.10^6$ ($f = 1$ MHz) = 159.2 Ω
Reactance of cable at $\omega = 4\pi.10^6$ ($f = 2$ MHz) = 79.6 Ω
Source impedance at 1 MHz = (3 + j39.6) Ω
Source impedance at 2 MHz = (3 + j79.2) Ω

The 1 MHz component of voltage across the cable is given by

$$\left[\frac{\text{1 MHz e.m.f.} \times \text{Reactance of cable at 1 MHz}}{\text{Impedance of circuit at 1 MHz}}\right]$$

$$= \frac{2 \times -\text{j}159.2}{3 + \text{j}(39.6 - 159.2)} = \frac{2 \times 159.2 \angle -90^\circ}{119.6 \angle -88.6^\circ}$$

$$= 2.66 \angle -1.4^\circ \text{ V}$$

and the 2 MHz component of voltage across the cable is given by

$$\left[\frac{\text{2 MHz e.m.f.} \times \text{Reactance of cable at 2 MHz}}{\text{Impedance of circuit at 2 MHz}}\right]$$

$$= \frac{0.5 \times -\text{j}79.6}{3 - \text{j}0.4} = \frac{0.5 \times 79.6 \angle -90^\circ}{3.0 \angle -7.6^\circ}$$

$$= 13.15 \angle -82.4^\circ \text{ V}$$

The voltage across the cable is therefore

$$v_c = 2.66 \sin(2\pi.10^6 t - 1.4^\circ) + 13.15 \sin(4\pi.10^6 t - 82.4^\circ) \text{ V}$$

It should be noted that a large second harmonic voltage appears across the capacitor because the series resonant frequency of the generator source impedance and the capacitive reactance of the cable is close to the second harmonic frequency.

12.6 THE HARMONIC ANALYSIS OF WAVEFORMS

We have studied the procedure for evaluating the Fourier coefficients from experimental data in section 12.2 and will now deal briefly with the methods of determining the Fourier coefficients of some frequently encountered non-sinusoidal periodic waves whose form can conveniently be expressed analytically.

The labour involved in calculating the coefficients of the terms in a Fourier Series can, in some cases, be reduced if the waveform is examined for symmetry. Waves with certain types of symmetry have some terms missing from their Fourier Series.

The properties of some types of symmetrical waveforms are stated below; mathematical proofs are not given since the topic is normally covered in the mathematics lectures appropriate to an Electrical Engineering course at this level.

12.6.1 Even Symmetry

A function $f(t)$ is said to possess even symmetry when $f(t)=f-(t)$; in such a case the function is symmetrical about the $f(t)$ axis.

Some examples of functions with even symmetry, also known as *even functions*, are shown in figure 12.3.

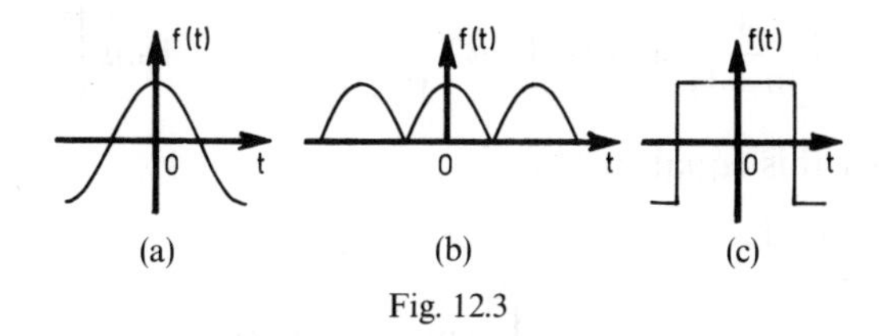

Fig. 12.3

The cosine wave is an even function, since $\cos \phi = \cos(-\phi)$, whereas the sine wave is not an even function; it is not possible therefore for the Fourier Series of an even function to contain sine terms.

The Fourier Series of a function possessing Even Symmetry (an Even Function) contains only cosine terms, and possibly a constant.

12.6.2 Odd Symmetry

A function $f(t)$ is said to possess odd symmetry when $f(t)=-f(-t)$; an odd function is skew-symmetrical about the $f(t)$ axis; as shown by the examples in figure 12.4.

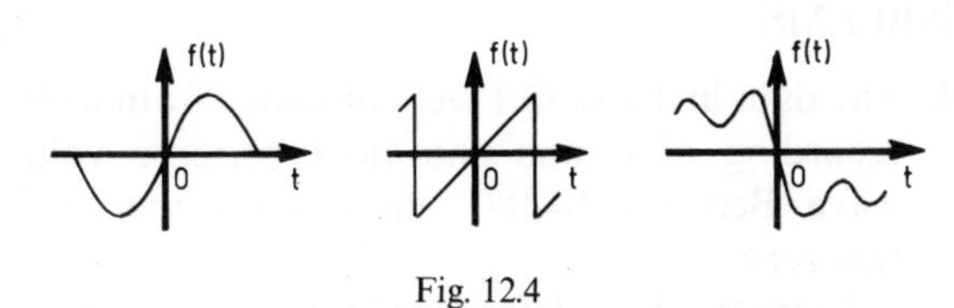

Fig. 12.4

The Fourier Series of a function possessing Odd Symmetry (an Odd Function) contains only sine terms.

12.6.3 Other Forms of Symmetry

The Fourier Series of a function $f(t)$ for which $f(t)=-f(t\pm T/2)$, where T is the period of the function, contains only odd harmonics.

Examples of this type of symmetry are shown in figure 12.5.

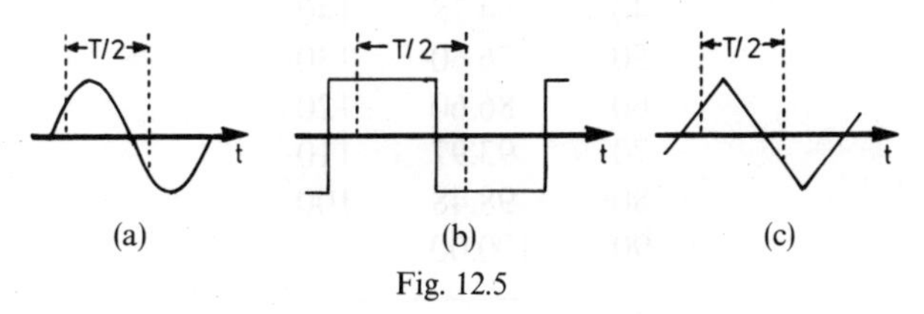

Fig. 12.5

The Fourier Series of a function $f(t)$ for which $f(t)=f(t\pm T/2)$ contains only even harmonics. Examples of this type of symmetry are shown in figure 12.6.

Work can sometimes be reduced by integrating over only part of a cycle; this is usually apparent from the symmetry of the waveform. It is also of interest to note that a function which is neither even nor odd can be made into either an even function or an odd function by shifting the axis.

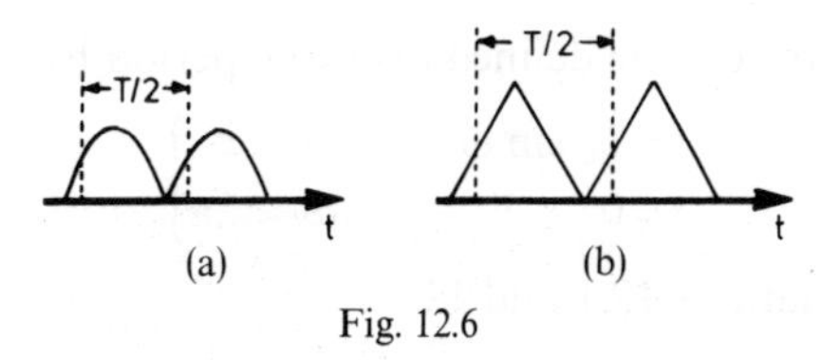

Fig. 12.6

12.6.4 The Square Wave

The wave may be defined over one period by

$$\left.\begin{aligned} v &= V : 0<\omega t<\pi \\ v &= -V : \pi<\omega t<2\pi \end{aligned}\right\} \qquad (12.24)$$

From figure 12.7 it may be seen that the wave possesses both odd symmetry and half-wave symmetry; its Fourier series will therefore contain only odd harmonics and only sine terms. It is necessary therefore to calculate only the coefficients $b_1, b_3, b_5 \ldots$ as defined by equations 12.1 and 12.2.

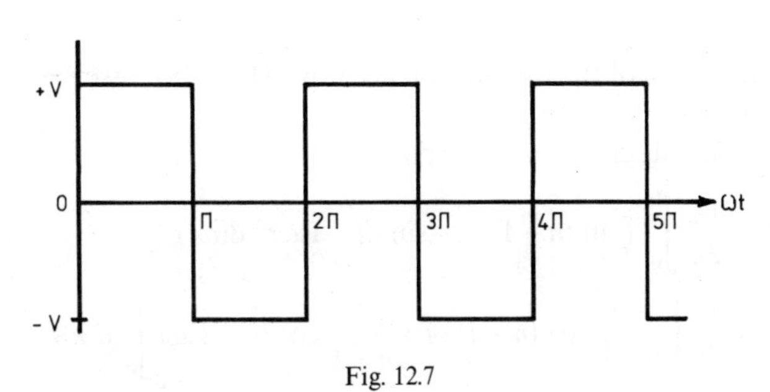

Fig. 12.7

The series will be of the form

$$f(t)=b_1 \sin \omega t+b_3 \sin 3\omega t+b_5 \sin 5\omega t \ldots$$

From equation 12.2

$$b_n=\frac{1}{\pi}\int_0^{2\pi} f(t) \,.\, \sin n\omega t \,.\, d(\omega t)$$

$$=\frac{V}{\pi}\int_0^{\pi} \sin n\omega t.d(\omega t)-\frac{V}{\pi}\int_{\pi}^{2\pi} \sin n\omega t.d(\omega t)$$

$$=\frac{V}{\pi}\left[\frac{-\cos n\omega t}{n}\right]_0^{\pi}-\frac{V}{\pi}\left[\frac{-\cos n\omega t}{n}\right]_{\pi}^{2\pi}$$

$$=\frac{V}{n\pi}[1-2\cos n\pi+\cos 2n\pi]$$

Putting $n=1, 3, 5, 7$ gives

† $$b_1=\frac{4V}{\pi},\ b_3=\frac{4V}{3\pi},\ b_5=\frac{4V}{5\pi}\text{ and } b_7=\frac{4V}{7\pi}$$

The Fourier Series for the square wave is therefore

$$v=\frac{4V}{\pi}[\sin\omega t+\tfrac{1}{3}\sin 3\omega t+\tfrac{1}{5}\sin 5\omega t+\cdots] \quad (12.25)$$

12.6.5 The Half-Wave Rectified Sine Wave

The wave can be defined over one period by

$$\left.\begin{array}{ll} i=I_m\sin\omega t: & 0<\omega t<\pi \\ i=0 & :\pi<\omega t<2\pi \end{array}\right\} \quad (12.26)$$

From equations 12.1 and 12.2

$$i=\frac{a_0}{2}+a_1\cos\omega t+\cdots a_n\cos n\omega t$$

$$+b_1\sin\omega t+\cdots b_n\sin n\omega t$$

where

$$a_n=\frac{1}{\pi}\int_0^\pi I_m\sin\omega t.\cos n\omega t.d(\omega t)$$

$$b_n=\frac{1}{\pi}\int_0^\pi I_m\sin\omega t.\sin n\omega t.d(\omega t)$$

$$\frac{a_0}{2}=\frac{1}{2\pi}\int_0^\pi I_m\sin\omega t\,.\,d\,.(\omega t)$$

The limits of the integration are now 0 to π, because $i=0$ between π and 2π.

The integrals can be expanded

$$a_n=\frac{I_m}{2\pi}\int_0^\pi[\sin(n+1)\omega t-\sin(n-1)\omega t]\,d(\omega t)$$

$$=\frac{I_m}{2\pi}\left[\frac{-1}{n+1}\cos(n+1)\omega t+\frac{1}{n-1}\cos(n-1)\omega t\right]_0^\pi \text{ if } n\neq 1$$

$$=\frac{I_m}{2\pi}\left[\frac{1}{n+1}\{1-\cos(n+1)\pi\}-\frac{1}{n-1}\{1-\cos(n-1)\pi\}\right]$$

Now if n is odd and not equal to 1, then $(n+1)$ and $(n-1)$ are even, in which case $a_n=0$.

When $n=1$:

$$a_1=\frac{I_m}{2\pi}\int_0^\pi\sin 2\omega t.d(\omega t)=0$$

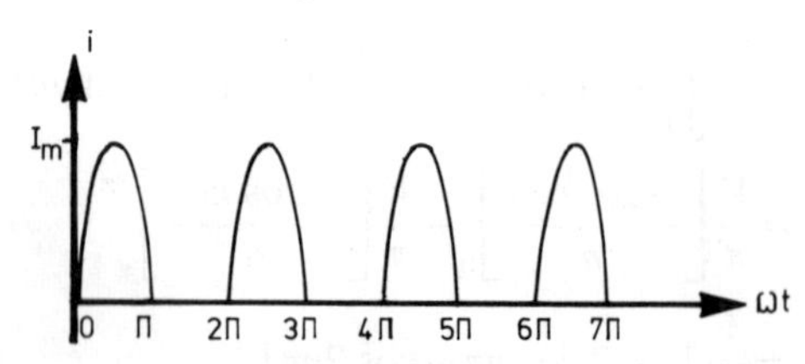

Fig. 12.8

If n is even, $(n+1)$ and $(n-1)$ are odd, in which case

$$a_n=\frac{I_m}{\pi}\left(\frac{1}{(n+1)}-\frac{1}{(n-1)}\right)=\frac{-2I_m}{(n^2-1)\pi}$$

so that

$$a_2=\frac{-2I_m}{3\pi},\ a_4=\frac{-2I_m}{15\pi},\ a_6=\frac{-2I_m}{35\pi}\text{ etc.}$$

$$b_n=\frac{I_m}{2\pi}\int_0^\pi[\cos(n-1)\omega t-\cos(n+1)\omega t]\,d(\omega t)$$

$$=\frac{I_m}{2\pi}\left[\frac{1}{(n-1)}\sin(n-1)\omega t-\frac{1}{(n+1)}\sin(n+1)\omega t\right]_0^\pi$$

if $n\neq 1$ this equals 0

When $n=1$;

$$b_1=\frac{I_m}{\pi}\int_0^\pi\sin^2\omega t\,.\,d(\omega t)$$

$$=\frac{I_m}{2}$$

Hence the Fourier Series for the half-wave rectified sine wave is

† $$i=\frac{I_m}{\pi}\left[1+\frac{\pi}{2}\sin\omega t-\frac{2}{3}\cos 2\omega t\right.$$

$$\left.-\frac{2}{15}\cos 4\omega t-\frac{2}{35}\cos 6\omega t-\cdots\right] \quad (12.27)$$

PROBLEMS

12.1. The data in Table Q.1 were obtained from a chart recording of a non-sinusoidal periodic voltage wave. Between $\theta=180°$ and $\theta=360°$ the voltage was zero.

From the data, determine by a graphical method the Fourier Coefficients for the waveform.

TABLE Q.1

θ^0	v	θ^0
0	0	180
10	17.36	170
20	34.20	160
30	50.00	150
40	64.28	140
50	76.60	130
60	86.60	120
70	93.97	110
80	98.48	100
90	100.00	

12.2. A voltage $v=5\sin\omega t$ V is applied, from a constant voltage source, to a non-linear resistor having a characteristic described by the current/voltage relationship $i=(2v^2+0.6v^3)$ mA.
Determine (i) the r.m.s. value of the current, (ii) the power dissipated in the resistor.

12.3. Derive the Fourier Series for the waveforms shown in figure Q.3a and b.

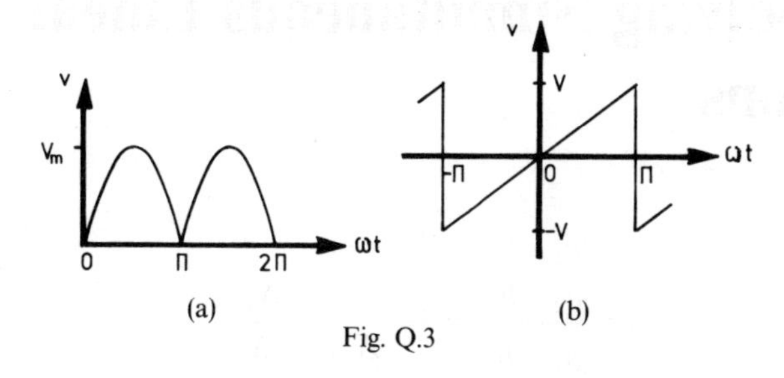

Fig. Q.3

12.4. The voltage from a full-wave rectifier is smoothed by the LC network shown in figure Q.4, R_L is the

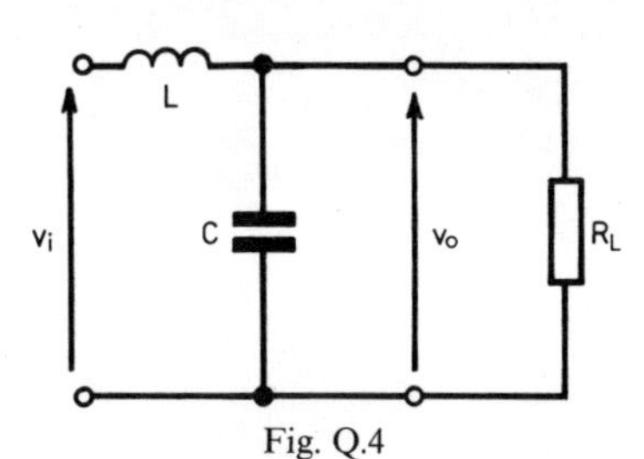

Fig. Q.4

effective load resistance. The input to the smoothing network is

$$v_i=25\left[\tfrac{1}{2}-\tfrac{1}{3}\cos 2\omega t-\tfrac{1}{15}\cos 4\omega t-\tfrac{1}{35}\cos 6\omega t\right] V$$

where $\omega=314$ rad/s.

If $R_L=200\,\Omega$, $C=200\,\mu$F and $L=2$H and its resistance may be neglected, derive an expression for the voltage v_0 across the load R_L.

12.5. Derive the Fourier Series for the current waveform in the thyristor of problem 6.8. What would be the reading of a moving-coil ammeter connected in series with the thyristor?

APPENDIX ONE

The Use of Determinants For Solving Simultaneous Linear Equations

The determinant provides a convenient method for solving simultaneous linear equations. The subject is normally dealt with fully in mathematics courses associated with first year degree and higher diploma and certificate courses, but to enable those students who have not previously encountered determinants to apply the method intelligently, a brief treatment is given in this Appendix.

Consider the following two simultaneous equations

$$\left.\begin{aligned} a_1x+b_1y&=c_1 \\ a_2x+b_2y&=c_2 \end{aligned}\right\} \qquad \begin{aligned}&(A1.1)\\&(A1.2)\end{aligned}$$

in which x and y are the unknowns.

The solution of these equations is

$$x=\frac{(c_1b_2-c_2b_1)}{(a_1b_2-a_2b_1)} \qquad (A1.3)$$

$$y=\frac{(a_1c_2-a_2c_1)}{(a_1b_2-a_2b_1)} \qquad (A1.4)$$

The use of determinants enables the solution to be expressed in a systematic and more easily memorized manner.

$$\begin{matrix} & & \text{Column 1} & \text{Column 2} & \\ \text{The array of coefficients } \Delta & = & a_1 & b_1 & \text{Row 1} \\ & & a_2 & b_2 & \text{Row 2} \end{matrix}$$

is called a determinant and its expanded value is $(a_1b_2-a_2b_1)$.

Note that in order to expand the determinant the *upper left* element is multiplied by the *lower right* element and from this is subtracted the product of the *upper right* and *lower left* elements.

A determinant is always a square array having the same number of rows as columns. The order of the determinant is equal to the number of rows.

The solution of equations A1.1 and A1.2 can be expressed in determinant form as follows.

$$x=\frac{\begin{vmatrix} c_1 & b_1 \\ c_2 & b_2 \end{vmatrix}}{\begin{vmatrix} a_1 & b_1 \\ a_2 & b_2 \end{vmatrix}}=\frac{\begin{vmatrix} c_1 & b_1 \\ c_2 & b_2 \end{vmatrix}}{\Delta}=\frac{\Delta_1}{\Delta} \qquad (A1.5)$$

$$y=\frac{\begin{vmatrix} a_1 & c_1 \\ a_2 & c_2 \end{vmatrix}}{\begin{vmatrix} a_1 & b_1 \\ a_2 & b_2 \end{vmatrix}}=\frac{\begin{vmatrix} a_1 & c_1 \\ a_2 & c_2 \end{vmatrix}}{\Delta}=\frac{\Delta_2}{\Delta} \qquad (A1.6)$$

where Δ is the determinant containing the coefficients on the left hand sides of the equations.

The determinant Δ_1 in the numerator of the expression for x is obtained by replacing the column in which the x coefficients were located in Δ by the constants on the right hand sides of the original equations; similarly the determinant Δ_2 in the numerator of the expression for y is obtained by replacing the column in which the y coefficients were located in Δ by the constants on the right hand sides of the original equations.

Example

Solve, for x and y

$$4x+2y=8$$
$$3x+5y=13$$

Solution

$$x=\frac{\begin{vmatrix} 8 & 2 \\ 13 & 5 \end{vmatrix}}{\begin{vmatrix} 4 & 2 \\ 3 & 5 \end{vmatrix}}=\frac{40-26}{20-6}=1$$

$$y=\frac{\begin{vmatrix} 4 & 8 \\ 3 & 13 \end{vmatrix}}{\begin{vmatrix} 4 & 2 \\ 3 & 5 \end{vmatrix}}=\frac{52-24}{20-6}=2$$

It should be noted that if two rows or columns are interchanged, the sign of the determinant is changed

$$\begin{vmatrix} a_1 & b_1 \\ a_2 & b_2 \end{vmatrix}=-\begin{vmatrix} a_2 & b_2 \\ a_1 & b_1 \end{vmatrix}=-\begin{vmatrix} b_1 & a_1 \\ b_2 & a_2 \end{vmatrix}$$

If there are three simultaneous equations to be solved it is necessary to evaluate third-order determinants of the form

$$\Delta=\begin{vmatrix} a_1 & b_1 & c_1 \\ a_2 & b_2 & c_2 \\ a_3 & b_3 & c_3 \end{vmatrix} \qquad \text{(A1.7)}$$

This determinant can be expanded by converting it into three second-order determinants. If the row and column containing a particular element are omitted the remaining elements form a determinant of lower order known as the *minor* of that element.

Expanding A1.7 into three minors gives

$$\Delta=a_1\begin{vmatrix} b_2 & c_2 \\ b_3 & c_3 \end{vmatrix}-a_2\begin{vmatrix} b_1 & c_1 \\ b_3 & c_3 \end{vmatrix}+a_3\begin{vmatrix} b_1 & c_1 \\ b_2 & c_2 \end{vmatrix} \qquad \text{(A1.8)}$$

The elements in the first column of the third-order determinant are the coefficients of the minors and it should be noted that the signs in front of the coefficients are alternately + and −, beginning with a plus. If the signs are attached to the minors the *cofactors* of the elements are obtained; these are usually denoted by capital letters

$$\Delta=a_1\text{A}_1+a_2\text{A}_2+a_3\text{A}_3$$

where

$$\text{A}_1=\begin{vmatrix} b_2 & c_2 \\ b_3 & c_3 \end{vmatrix},\quad \text{A}_2=-\begin{vmatrix} b_1 & c_1 \\ b_3 & c_3 \end{vmatrix},\quad \text{A}_3=\begin{vmatrix} b_1 & c_1 \\ b_2 & c_2 \end{vmatrix}$$

Fourth and higher order determinants may be reduced in order by the same procedure.

Sets of equations leading to high order determinants may be solved by using expressions similar to those in equations A1.5 and A1.6.

$$x=\frac{\Delta_1}{\Delta},\quad y=\frac{\Delta_2}{\Delta} \text{ etc} \quad \text{(Cramer's Rule)}$$

The following properties are useful in expanding determinants and may lead to a considerable reduction in effort

(i) The value of a determinant is unaltered if the rows and columns are interchanged

$$\begin{vmatrix} a_1 & a_2 & a_3 \\ b_1 & b_2 & b_3 \\ c_1 & c_2 & c_3 \end{vmatrix}=\begin{vmatrix} a_1 & b_1 & c_1 \\ a_2 & b_2 & c_2 \\ a_3 & b_3 & c_3 \end{vmatrix}$$

(ii) If two rows or columns are interchanged the determinant changes sign

$$\begin{vmatrix} a_1 & b_1 & c_1 \\ a_2 & b_2 & c_2 \\ a_3 & b_3 & c_3 \end{vmatrix}=-\begin{vmatrix} a_1 & c_1 & b_1 \\ a_2 & c_2 & b_2 \\ a_3 & c_3 & b_3 \end{vmatrix}$$

(iii) A common factor in any row or column can be taken outside the determinant

$$\begin{vmatrix} la_1 & lb_1 & lc_1 \\ a_2 & b_2 & c_2 \\ a_3 & b_3 & c_3 \end{vmatrix}=l\begin{vmatrix} a_1 & b_1 & c_1 \\ a_2 & b_2 & c_2 \\ a_3 & b_3 & c_3 \end{vmatrix}$$

(iv) The numerical value of a determinant is zero if
  (a) any two rows or columns are identical or
  (b) the elements in any one row or column are all zero.

(v) The value of a determinant is unaltered by adding to the elements of any row, or column, equal multiples of the corresponding elements of another row, or column

$$\begin{vmatrix} (a_1+lb_1+mc_1) & b_1 & c_1 \\ (a_2+lb_2+mc_2) & b_2 & c_2 \\ (a_3+lb_3+mc_3) & b_3 & c_3 \end{vmatrix}=\begin{vmatrix} a_1 & b_1 & c_1 \\ a_2 & b_2 & c_2 \\ a_3 & b_3 & c_3 \end{vmatrix}$$

$$\text{e.g.}\begin{vmatrix} 7 & -3 & 2 \\ 4 & 2 & -1 \\ 6 & 3 & 5 \end{vmatrix}=\begin{vmatrix} 13 & -3 & 2 \\ 0 & 2 & -1 \\ 0 & 3 & 5 \end{vmatrix}$$

(col. 1 minus 2 × col. 2).

$$=13\begin{vmatrix} 2 & -1 \\ 3 & 5 \end{vmatrix}=169$$

This approach is much less tedious than reducing the determinant to three second order determinants.

APPENDIX TWO

An Introduction to Some Electrical Measuring Instruments

A2.1 INTRODUCTION

In most Colleges and Universities a course of lectures on Electric Circuit Theory is accompanied by a programme of laboratory work designed to enable the student to apply a theoretical knowledge of circuits to practical situations.

The student will encounter in the laboratory a range of voltmeters, ammeters and wattmeters, both analogue and digital, as well as oscilloscopes, bridges and miscellaneous other instruments. It is important when making a measurement that one should know

(i) how the instrument disturbs the conditions in the circuit on which the measurement is being made.
(ii) what parameter is actually being measured or indicated, for example is it the mean value, the root mean square value or the peak value of a current or voltage?
(iii) what effects the waveform and frequency of the current or voltage being measured have on the instrument indication.

So that the student can be aware of the limitations of some of the basic measuring instruments likely to be encountered, a brief review of the principles of operation and characteristics of some instruments follows. It is not intended to be an introductory course in Electrical Measurements, but it is hoped that it will encourage the student to ask the questions 'What am I measuring?' and 'Am I using the right instrument?'

A2.2 THE MOVING-COIL INSTRUMENT

The moving-coil instrument measures direct current. It is used, in conjunction with rectifiers for the measurement of alternating current and voltage, as the basis for most multi-range deflectional instruments.

The essential features of a moving coil instrument are shown in figure A1.

A strong U-shaped permanent magnet has soft-iron pole pieces of the shape shown in figure A1a, so that a soft-iron cylindrical core fits into the space between them. This form of construction results in an almost uniform magnetic field in the gap between the pole pieces and the core.

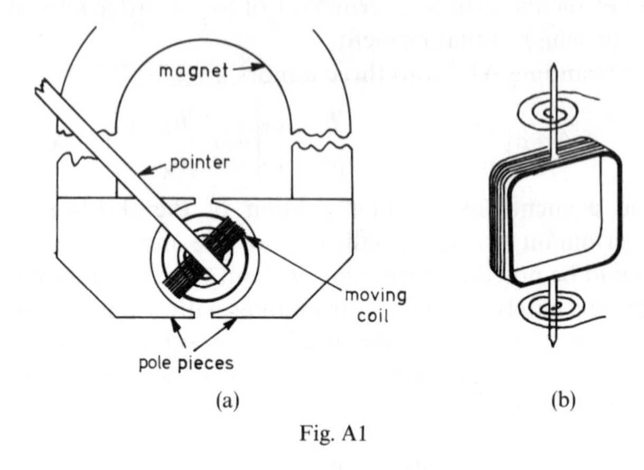

Fig. A1

The moving coil, mounted on a light aluminium frame, moves in the gap, the current being led in and out of the coil by two hair springs as shown in figure A1b which also provide the controlling torque. Damping is provided by eddy currents induced in the aluminium former on which the coil is wound.

The deflecting torque on the coil is given by

$$\text{Torque} = (BIAN)$$

where B = the flux density in the gap, I = the current flowing in the moving coil, A = the effective area of the moving coil, N = the number of turns on the moving coil.

The controlling torque provided by the springs is proportional to the angular deflection θ, so that when the moving coil system is at rest

$$\theta \propto (BAN)I$$

from which it may be seen that the deflection is proportional to the current, giving a linear scale calibration.

A2.2.1 The Moving-Coil Instrument as a Voltmeter

When the instrument is used as a voltmeter it is connected in series with a resistor R_{se} as shown in figure A2a.

The value of the resistor depends on the current sensitivity of the instrument and the voltage range required. For example if the meter gives full scale deflection when passing a current of I_m amperes a total resist-

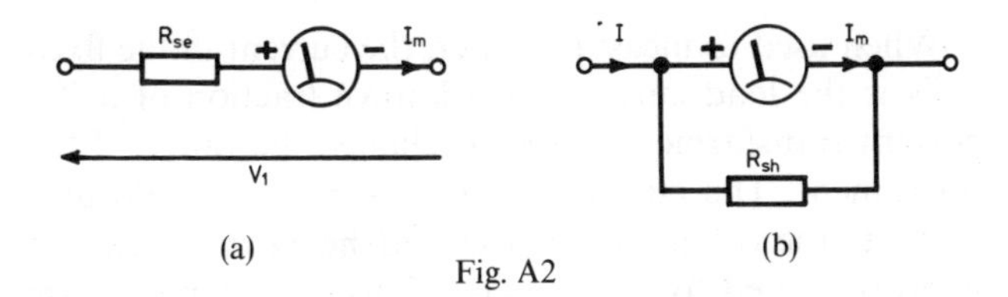

Fig. A2

ance (including the meter resistance) of V_1/I_m ohms will be required to produce full scale deflection for V_1 volts, that is $R_{se} = (V_1/I_m - R_m)$ ohms where R_m is the resistance of the moving coil. The voltage sensitivity of the meter is normally expressed as $1/I_m$ ohms per volt; thus a 50 μA instrument has a voltage sensitivity of 20000 Ω/V and the value of $(R_{se} + R_n)$ for a full scale deflection of 100 V would be 2 MΩ.

The shunting effect, or loading, on the circuit being measured must be considered when selecting an instrument for any particular measurement (see problem 2.6).

A2.2.2 The Moving-Coil Instrument as an Ammeter

When a moving-coil instrument is used as an ammeter it is usually necessary to connect a resistor in parallel with the meter as shown in figure A.2b. If the meter gives full scale deflection for a current I_m amperes and the meter resistance is R_m ohms, the value of the shunt resistor R_{sh}, in parallel with the meter, to produce full scale deflection for a current of I amperes is

$$R_{sh} = \frac{R_m I_m}{I - I_m} \text{ ohms}$$

The resistance of the shunted instrument is

$$\frac{R_{sh} R_m}{R_{sh} + R_m} \text{ ohms}$$

and, before making a measurement, the effect of this resistance on the circuit conditions should be checked (see problem 7.5).

A2.2.3 The Measurement of Alternating Voltage and Current Using a Moving-Coil Instrument

A moving-coil meter may be used in conjunction with a rectifier to measure alternating voltages and currents at power and audio frequencies. An arrangement including a full-wave rectifier is shown in figure A.3.

The instrument will measure the *mean or average* value of the rectified current flowing through it. It is the usual practice for rectifier instruments designed for use with sinusoidal waveforms to have the scale calibrated in terms of the r.m.s. value.

It is important to realize that the application of non-sinusoidal waveforms will lead to erroneous results.

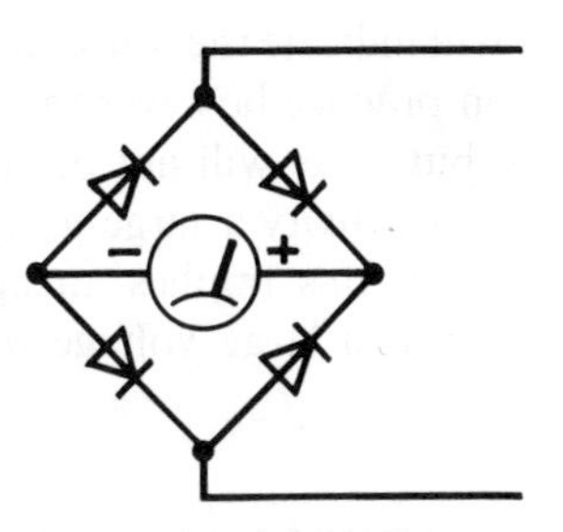

Fig. A3

A2.3 THE MOVING-IRON INSTRUMENT

The moving-iron instrument measures both direct and alternating current. In spite of this advantage it is not as widely used for light-current work as the moving-coil instrument since the latter is capable of greater sensitivity and higher accuracy.

There are several types of moving-iron instrument, but the principles of operation are demonstrated by referring to the repulsion type of instrument shown in figure A.4.

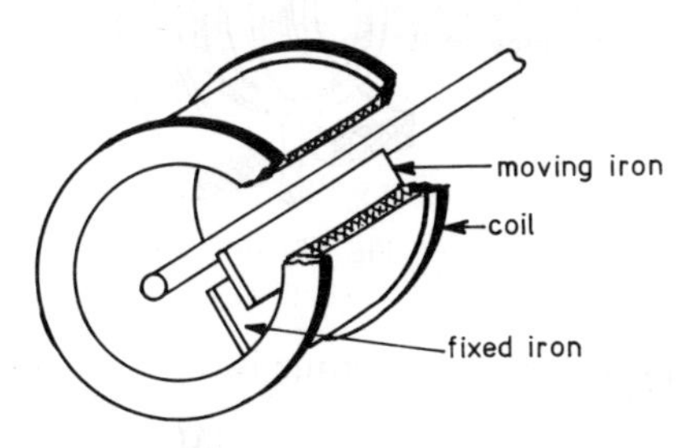

Fig. A4

The current to be measured passes through the coil, along the axis of this coil is a shaft, pivoted at its ends, and carrying a small iron plate. A second plate is fixed inside the coil adjacent to the moving iron plate. When a current flows in the coil the iron plates are magnetized in the same direction, there is a force of repulsion between the plates and the shaft carrying the moving iron plate and the pointer rotates.

The controlling torque is provided by a spring and damping is by means of an air chamber damper since the moving-iron instrument, unlike the moving-coil instrument, has no in-built damping.

The deflecting torque is given by

$$\text{Torque} = \frac{1}{2} I^2 \frac{dL}{d\theta}$$

where $(dL/d\theta)$ is the rate of change of inductance with angular deflection of the moving iron plate. Hence the deflection $\theta \propto I^2(dL/d\theta)$.

The instantaneous torque is proportional to the square of the instantaneous current, so that the average torque is a function of the mean square current and the instrument can be calibrated in terms of the r.m.s. current. In theory the meter will indicate the r.m.s. current regardless of its waveform; in practice however there may be some waveform errors, but these will not be considered here.

To obtain high sensitivity a large number of turns is required on the coil; this implies an appreciable coil resistance resulting in a large voltage drop across the instrument.

A2.4 THE ELECTRODYNAMIC INSTRUMENT

Wattmeters for use at power frequencies are usually of the electro-dynamic air-cored type in which a moving coil is located in the magnetic field of two series-connected fixed coils. The arrangement is shown in figure A.5.

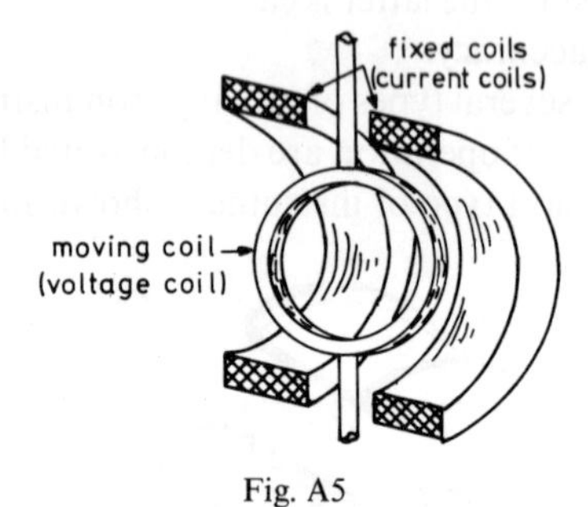

Fig. A5

The expression for the torque is

$$\text{Torque} = I_1 I_2 \frac{\mathrm{d}M}{\mathrm{d}\theta}$$

where I_1 and I_2 are the currents in the fixed and moving coils respectively and $(\mathrm{d}M/\mathrm{d}\theta)$ is the rate of change of mutual inductance between the fixed and moving coils with angular deflection of the moving coil.

If the currents are

$$i_1 = I_{m1} \sin \omega t$$
$$i_2 = I_{m2} \sin (\omega t - \phi)$$

then the instantaneous torque is

$$I_{m1} I_{m2} \sin \omega t . \sin (\omega t - \phi) \frac{\mathrm{d}M}{\mathrm{d}\theta}$$

and the average torque is

$$I_{m1} I_{m2} \cos \phi \frac{\mathrm{d}M}{\mathrm{d}\theta}$$

Since the controlling torque is usually provided by a spring, when the moving coil system is at rest, the deflection is

$$\theta \propto I_1 I_2 \cos \phi \frac{\mathrm{d}M}{\mathrm{d}\theta}$$

where I_1 and I_2 are the r.m.s. values of the currents.

When used to measure power, the current in the fixed coils is the load current, or a known fraction of it if a current transformer is used to change the range of the instrument. The current in the moving coil is proportional to the voltage across the load, hence the deflection is proportional to $I_L V_L \cos \phi = P$ where I_L and V_L are the r.m.s. values of the load current and load voltage respectively and P is the power dissipated in the load.

A high-value non-inductive resistance is connected in series with the moving or voltage coil so that the resistance of the voltage coil circuit is very much greater than its reactance, thus ensuring that the current in the moving coil is very nearly in phase with the voltage across the load. The high resistance also results in a very small current being taken by the voltage coil circuit; the significance of this is apparent in the next paragraph.

There are two ways of connecting a wattmeter to measure power; these are shown in figure A.6.

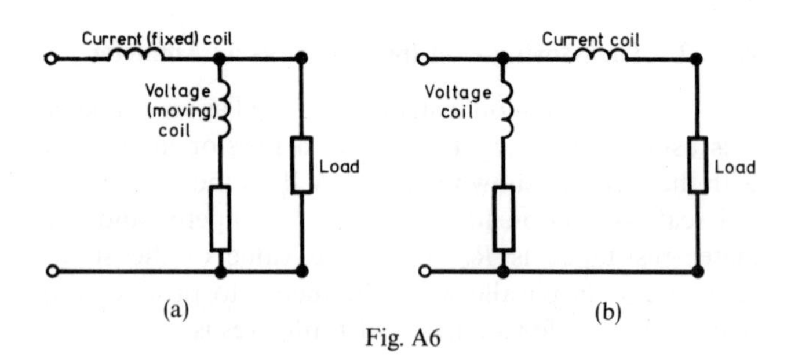

Fig. A6

In the connection of figure A.6a the current in the current coil is not the load current, but is the sum of the load current and the current in the voltage coil; in the connection of figure A.6b the current in the current coil is the load current but the voltage across the voltage coil circuit is the sum of the load voltage and the voltage drop across the current coil.

Both methods of connection therefore result in an error. If the load current is large, the connection shown in figure A.6a is preferable and if the load current is small the connection shown in figure A.6b results in a smaller error.

A2.5 DIGITAL INSTRUMENTS

Instruments incorporating digital electronic systems are now being used in laboratories. The multimeter type of digital instrument is essentially for the measurement of d.c.; sinusoidal voltages can be measured by rectification before being applied to the measuring circuit, so that the average value is measured, but normally the r.m.s. value is presented by the digital read-out. The instrument is therefore subject to the same type of waveform error as was mentioned in section A2.2.3.

APPENDIX THREE

Answers to Numerical Problems

Chapter 1

1.5. 2068 $\mu\Omega$
1.6. (a) $E = 12.000$ V, $R = 0.1\ \Omega$. (b) $I = 0.101$ A, $R = 170\ \text{k}\Omega$
1.7. 1.215 J

Chapter 2

2.1. 5.0 Ω
2.2. 0.59 mA from B to A
2.3. $E = 4.4$ V, $R = 2.2\ \Omega$; $I = 2.00$ A, $R = 2.2\ \Omega$
2.4. $E = 7.1$ V, $R = 178\ \Omega$
2.5. $E = 0.91$ V, $R = 545\ \Omega$; $I = 1.67$ mA, $R = 545\ \Omega$; 0.59 mA from B to A
2.6. (i) 85.71 V (ii) 78.95 V
2.7. 5.0 Ω
2.8. 234.4 V, 38.9 A, 11.1 A
2.9. (a) 237.84 V, 236.83 V, 235.97 V, 234.82 V. (b) 239.14 V, 238.91 V, 239.08 V, 240.00 V

Chapter 3

3.1. 50
3.3. 0.5 A
3.4. 0.58 A, 0.145 A, 0.29 A
3.5. 1 : 1

Chapter 4

4.1. 0.53 s, 170 V/s
4.2. 5.15 s
4.4. 20 H
4.6. 9.8 ms

Chapter 6

6.1. (a) 0.637 V_m, 0.707 V_m (b) V, 1.73 V (c) 0.5 V, 0.577 V
6.2. 0.001 μF, 1987 Ω
6.4. (i) $12.7\ \angle 45°$, (ii) $0.99\ \angle 24.6°$, (iii) $0.78\ \angle 11.3°$
6.5. (i) $(4.3 + j2.5)$, $5\ e^{j30°}$, (ii) $(2.2 + j5.8)$, $6.2\ e^{j69°}$, (iii) $(1.71 - j0.46)$, $1.77\ e^{-j15°}$
6.6. (i) $(-0.46 + j1.31)$, (ii) $(3.4 + j2.2)$
6.8. 48.56 W

Chapter 7

7.1. $\boldsymbol{I}_1 = 0.079\ \angle 121°$ A, $\boldsymbol{I}_2 = 0.135\ \angle 9°$ A, $\boldsymbol{I} = 0.128\ \angle 44°$ A, $\boldsymbol{V}_1 = \boldsymbol{V}_2 = 79\ \angle 68°$ V, $\boldsymbol{V}_c = 102\ \angle -46°$ V
7.2. $R_3 = 2R_4$
7.3. (i) $\boldsymbol{E} = 27.3\ \angle -44\ 7°$ V, $\boldsymbol{Z} = 44.6\ \angle -65°\ \Omega$, (ii) $\boldsymbol{I} = 0.61\ \angle 20.3°$ A, $\boldsymbol{Y} = 0.02\ \angle 65°$ S
7.4. C = 32 pF, $L = 8\ \mu$H
7.5. 4.89 A
7.8. 0.58
7.12. 1/29

Chapter 8

8.1. (i) 0, (ii) 6, (iii) 9.5, (iv) 20, (v) 29.5, (vi) 40, (vii) 60, (viii) -6, (ix) -20, (x) -23.5
8.4. (i) 375 mA, 6.75 mA, (ii) 141.4 V, 1.7 V (r.m.s. values)

Chapter 9

9.3. 56 Ω, 443 Ω, 56 Ω
9.4. $z_i = 2.71\ \Omega$, $z_r = 0.57\ \Omega$, $z_f = 0.57\ \Omega$, $z_o = 2.86\ \Omega$
9.7. 0.997, 252 kΩ, 20.7 Ω
9.8. 1.8 μF, 0.005 μF, 143
9.9. $h_i = (230 - j575)\Omega$, $h_r = (-0.07 + j0.17)10^{-3}$, $h_f = (-47 - j85)$, $h_o = (0.014 + j0.105)$ mS

Chapter 10

10.1. 53.7°
10.2. (i) 21.5 A, $-50°$, (ii) 0.77 lagging, (iii) 2.5 kW
10.3. 107 Hz, 398 Hz, 689 Hz

Chapter 11

11.1. $I_R = 11.5$ A, $I_Y = 21.1$ A, $I_B = 19.8$ A, $V_{RS} = 230$ V, $V_{YS} = 210$ V, $V_{BS} = 397$ V; $P = 12.5$ kW
11.2. $I_R = 40.6$ A, $I_Y = 32.4$ A, $I_B = 66.0$ A, $I_{RY} = 22$ A, $I_{YB} = 44$ A, $I_{BY} = 22$ A, $P = 32$kW
11.3. $I_L = 163$ A
11.4. 132 W, 996 W; 104 Ω; 780 W
11.5. 8.3 kW, 1.7 kW

Chapter 12

12.2. 51.9 mA, 140.6 mW
12.5. 0.148 A

Index